FOREWORD

The Programme centres on road and road transport research, while taking into account the impacts of intermodal aspects on the road transport system as a whole. It is geared towards a technico-economic approach to solving key road transport issues identified by Member countries. The Programme has two main fields of activity:

-- The international co-operation in road and road transport research to provide scientific support for decisions by Member governments and international governmental organisations, and to assess future strategies concerning roads and road transport problems and the priority policy concerns on Member countries;

-- The information and documentation programme (IRRD -- International Road Research Documentation), a co-operative scheme that provides a mechanism for the systematic worldwide exchange of information on scientific literature and current research programmes.

The scientific and technical activities concern:

-- The assessment of urban and inter-urban road transport strategies;

-- The development and management of road traffic control and driver communication systems to enhance network efficiency and quality of services;

-- The formulation and evaluation of integrated road and traffic safety programmes;

-- The construction, preservation and rehabilitation of road infrastructure;

-- The maintenance management of road infrastructure and the evaluation of traffic safety measures and strategies in developing countries.

ABSTRACT

IRRD No. 837329

This report provides a full account of the OECD Full-scale Pavement Test undertaken in 1989 at the Circular Fatigue Test Track in Nantes of the French Central Laboratory of Roads and Bridges (LCPC). The Common Test was financed and implemented by fourteen OECD Member countries and the Commission of the European Communities. Three experimental road pavements -- two flexible and one semi-rigid structure, as well as maintenance overlays applied after significant pavement deterioration -- were tested under 10 and 11.5 tonne truck axle loads. A total of 4.5 million load applications were effected. The objectives of the test are delineated in the Introduction of the report, whereas the test organisation and management are presented in Chapter II. Chapters III and IV describe in detail the pavement structures tested, the measuring systems used, and the conduct of the test and its various phases. Chapters V and VI provide a detailed account of the results obtained, their analysis and interpretation, including the use of pavement models. In addition, Chapter VII presents the few national comparative cross-tests undertaken to date related to the Common Test. The report concludes with a summary and future development needs. Information on important aspects of this international experiment is given in five Annexes. The extensive report is rich in research details and constitutes a substantial contribution to advancing pavement technology and assessing the effects of heavy vehicle axle loads. The detailed research data and documentation of the various investigations undertaken, are available through OECD and will be presented at a special conference in La Baule, France in May 1991.

Subject classification: 22

Field: Pavement design

Keywords: Pavement design; Deformation; Flexible pavement; Semi rigid pavement; Axle load; Experimental road; Evaluation (assessment); Fatigue (mater); Cracking; Rutting (wheel); Deflection; Stress (in material); Strain gauge; Durability; Bearing capacity; Damage; Lorry; Repetitive loading.

ROAD TRANSPORT RESEARCH

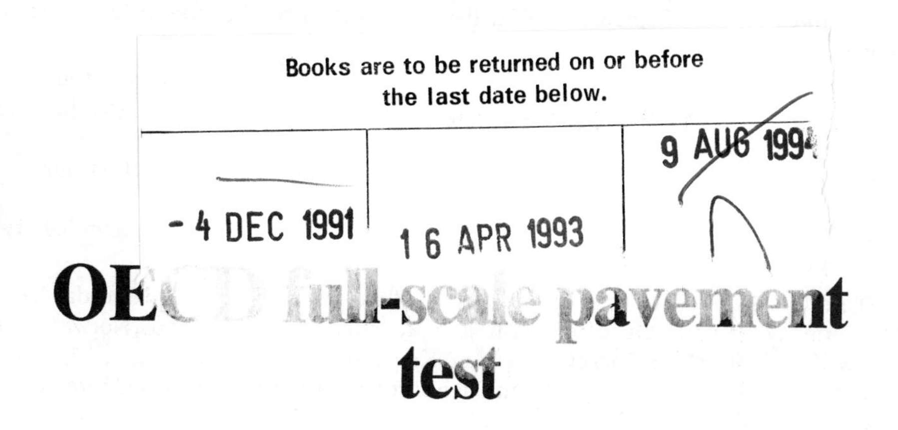

OECD full-scale pavement test

REPORT PREPARED BY
AN OECD SCIENTIFIC EXPERT GROUP

ORGANISATION FOR ECONOMIC CO-OPERATION AND DEVELOPMENT

Pursuant to Article 1 of the Convention signed in Paris on 14th December 1960, and which came into force on 30th September 1961, the Organisation for Economic Co-operation and Development (OECD) shall promote policies designed:

— to achieve the highest sustainable economic growth and employment and a rising standard of living in Member countries, while maintaining financial stability, and thus to contribute to the development of the world economy;
— to contribute to sound economic expansion in Member as well as non-member countries in the process of economic development; and
— to contribute to the expansion of world trade on a multilateral, non-discriminatory basis in accordance with international obligations.

The original Member countries of the OECD are Austria, Belgium, Canada, Denmark, France, Germany, Greece, Iceland, Ireland, Italy, Luxembourg, the Netherlands, Norway, Portugal, Spain, Sweden, Switzerland, Turkey, the United Kingdom and the United States. The following countries became Members subsequently through accession at the dates indicated hereafter: Japan (28th April 1964), Finland (28th January 1969), Australia (7th June 1971) and New Zealand (29th May 1973). The Commission of the European Communities takes part in the work of the OECD (Article 13 of the OECD Convention). Yugoslavia takes part in some of the work of the OECD (agreement of 28th October 1961).

Publié en français sous le titre :

ESSAI OCDE EN VRAIE GRANDEUR
DES SUPERSTRUCTURES ROUTIÈRES

EXECUTIVE SUMMARY

INFRASTRUCTURE NEEDS AND RESEARCH

Predictions that the nineties will be a period of increasing infrastructure needs have become pressing realities. In Europe, the upcoming single market, the missing network links, the deplorable infrastructure in the East and Central European countries, as well as the environmental and traffic safety challenge, underscore these requirements. In the U.S., the new national transportation policy, in Japan the grand scale of the highway improvement and public development plans, and in Australia the enhanced interstate transport policy, confirm the shared interests of OECD countries in this sector.

Strengthening road transport and infrastructure development is a key element in ensuring sustainable economic growth, social development and mobility. The diversification of markets, the specialisation of economic and industrial activities and the expansion of the service sector are the driving forces behind growth, and more growth, of road and freight transport.

Research and new technologies are vital to the continued strength of OECD economies. Research on road infrastructure has assumed international dimensions and this in spite of the widespread belief, in the seventies and eighties, amongst some of the leading public and private policy-makers, that roads and road transport constitute a traditional, mature industrial sector with declining opportunities for scientists and innovators.

PAVEMENT RESEARCH AND FULL-SCALE TESTING

Since the early seventies, OECD's Road Transport Research Programme has conducted research reviews and technology assessments on pavement issues focusing on structural performance under heavy axle loads, road maintenance techniques, and pavement rehabilitation strategies. In the eighties, the OECD Steering Committee decided that international co-ordination and systematic information exchange of pavement research was needed to supplement limited resources and coalesce fragmented research efforts at the OECD's nations' road research centres.

To enhance the technological base of highway systems, facilities and processes in a priority research area for both highway engineers and truck designers, the full-scale pavement testing field was chosen to serve as a testing ground for international co-operation. An international Scientific Expert Group was created. On the basis of the results of the Group's first collaborative project in 1984 at the Pavement and Vehicle Testing Facility in Nardo, Italy, it was decided to embark on an accelerated full-scale pavement test at the French Laboratoire Central des Ponts et Chaussées (LCPC Central Laboratory for Roads and Bridges) circular test track located in Nantes.

This report presents the joint test programme known internationally as the FORCE Project.

POLICY GOAL AND TEST OBJECTIVES

Although over many years, significant efforts have been made in exchanging pavement technology through a number of international fora, these tend to be placed in the more comfortable context of expert meetings and conferences and take the form of disseminating technical documents and drafting synthesis reports. However, a benchmark proof of actual international co-operation exists only in the conduct and completion of substantive joint research work.

The policy goal of this OECD Expert Group study and the Common Accelerated Test was threefold:

-- achieving savings in pavement construction and maintenance costs, and in road transport as a whole;

-- contributing to the international harmonization of heavy freight vehicle regulations, in particular axle load limits;

-- enlarging international scientific co-operation and research interchange.

The scientific and technical objectives were to:

-- enhance the understanding of the performance mechanics of pavements;

-- evaluate the pavement damaging effects of 10 tonne vs. 11.5 tonne (the new European limit) axle loads;

-- verify the validity of key components of presently applied pavement design and strengthening procedures;

-- improve the state-of-the-art in measuring techniques and scientific analysis methods;

-- extend the transferability of test data between participating OECD research institutions and provide a reference basis for future national cross tests.

In accordance with the last objective, the research centres participating in the Common Test were invited to carry out cross-checking tests on their own facilities.

MANAGEMENT AND FINANCING

The implementation of such a complex project involving many countries and research agencies, and requiring unique scientific expertise, must be based on a well-structured organisation and management. To this end, OECD appointed a Project Manager whose responsibilities were to manage the experiment on behalf of the OECD Road Transport Research Programme and to ensure effective communication with the LCPC's operating team as well as Members of the OECD Scientific Expert Group and national researchers mandated to take part in this joint international venture. Because of the complexity of the project and because the costs of the experiment were substantial, an International Management Bureau comprising Members of the OECD Steering Committee was set up to ensure budgetary and financial control, oversee the project and resolve unforeseen problems. In order to ensure the joint evaluation of the test results, an Analysis Sub-group was established, comprising specialists from various countries, to assess the collected data and measurements and to evaluate and interpret the results obtained.

The Test could not be financed out of the normal budget of the OECD Road Transport Research Programme and therefore OECD Member countries and interested international organisations were asked to grant special earmarked financial contributions. The financing was shared by Australia, Austria, Denmark, Finland, France, Germany, Italy, Netherlands, Norway, Spain, Sweden, Switzerland, the United Kingdom, the United States and the Commission of the European Communities. The total budget available was 3.5 million francs or 700 000 dollars (in 1991).

The organisational scheme included on-site participation involving, at times simultaneously, research teams and personnel from various countries and organisations amounting to some 420 man days. Also, much of the laboratory testing was done in the different participating Member countries as was analysis work for the Common Test and the accompanying cross-tests. The working method adopted offered all participants the unique opportunity of obtaining first-hand experience which could not have been gained by any other channel. Thus the international co-operation as practised through the FORCE Project was a good example of effective and practical interchange of ideas, expertise and experience.

THE TEST

In essence, the test consisted of applying 10 and 11.5 tonne twin-wheel (half-axle) loads to three different pavement structures up to failure or such damage that necessitates strengthening in the form of an overlay, with subsequent loading of the strengthened pavements.

Following discussion among Members of the Scientific Expert Group it was decided that the Common Test should be carried out on pavements that are reasonably typical of those used for different traffic categories in a number of participating Member countries. An important consideration was that the pavement should be relatively easily reproducible for the cross-checking tests and that the materials involved should not be very different from those normally used. The pavement structures were as follows:

-- thin flexible structure consisting of a 6 cm bituminous layer on a 28 cm unbound granular layer,

-- a thick flexible structure consisting of a 13 cm bituminous layer on a 28 cm unbound granular layer,

-- a semi rigid structure consisting of a 6 cm bituminous layer on 17 cm cement-treated gravel.

These were constructed in October/November 1988 in sections of 30 m lengths along an inner circle (16 m) and an outer circle (19 m) of the LCPC's Circular Fatigue Test Track. Bituminous overlays of 6 cm thickness were provided on the thin flexible and the semi-rigid pavements when they reached a failure condition in May and July 1989 , respectively.

These structures, the overlays, the materials used as well as the subgrade were in accordance with precise specifications and their as-built conditions and parameters were determined and recorded.

The advantage of the Nantes circular fatigue test machine is that it can use arms of two different radii over the same structures and maintain a sufficient separation of two modes of loading, so that testing with two arms loaded to 10 tonnes on the inner circle and two arms loaded to 11.5 tonnes on the outer circle was possible. Also, to simulate real traffic loading, the twin wheel positions can be automatically shifted transversally, with a total sweep width of 1.6 m. The testing speed was standardized at 10 revolutions per minute, completing one loading cycle over the width of the pavement in 45 minutes.

In all, 4 555 000 loadings were carried out in less than a year: 573 000 10 t loadings with the 16 m arm on the three inner test sections, and 3 982 000 11.5 and 13 t loadings with the 19 m arm on the three outer test sections. The machine made 1 139 000 rotations.

MEASUREMENTS

A large number of parameters were recorded over the whole period of testing in order to provide the data needed to interpret the behaviour of the structures. These parameters may be divided into four categories:

-- environment such as temperature,

-- pavement response: data from the strain, stress and deflection sensors as well as deflection measurements with the Benkelman beam and the FWD deflectometer.

-- performance: rutting (cross-section measurements), cracking on the trafficked sections and evenness (longitudinal profile).

-- materials: characteristics determined through laboratory testing of samples taken before, during and after the test.

THE PROJECT IN BRIEF

The main components of the FORCE Project can be illustrated as follows:

1	Full-scale test
3	Pavement structures
15	Participating institutions
360	Measuring gauges
5000	Welded cable connections
21 000	Metres of cable
700 000	US dollar (budget)
4 500 000	Loadings applied
60 000 000	Measurements

CROSS TESTS

A number of countries had undertaken specific studies on aspects of the Common Test and have used the opportunity to perform tests on particular problem areas in the framework of the FORCE experiment. Several countries expressed their intention to conduct "comparative cross tests", since, as explained in the full report, the implementation of actual "cross-tests" posed too many practical difficulties. At the time of completing this report, the following countries had carried out, operated or were considering such tests: Australia, Austria, Finland, Germany, Italy, the Netherlands, Spain, Switzerland, the United Kingdom and the United States. It is expected that the data and the results from these experiments will become available in the years to come.

HIGHLIGHTS OF FINDINGS

It is difficult to summarise succinctly the multitude of results obtained and conclusions drawn from a joint experiment of this size. Chapters V, VI and VIII discuss in detail these results and develop their analysis and interpretation. The Project advanced significantly the state-of=the-art of measuring instrumentation (in particular strain gauges), confirmed the importance of temperature effects and monitoring, and enhanced data processing and communication methods. Also, several pavement performance models were applied to compare the empirical results obtained with predictions; these studies and further assessments are likely to provide additional evidence to show that full-scale pavement research conducted under controlled test conditions is the best means of further developing and verifying these models.

A comparison of the performance of pavements under 10 and 11.5 tonne axle loads was a principal aim of the experiment. The results show that the 4th power law constitutes only a general description and approximation of the relative pavement damaging power of axle loads. It must be noted that wide variations to this general rule were found to apply changing continuously with powers from 2 to 9 depending on the degree of pavement deterioration, the criterion used for comparison and the condition of the pavement at the time when the comparison was made. This conclusion covers only the flexible pavements investigated.

Discussions on the problem of the road damaging power of heavy trucks are likely to continue for some time and this despite the move to unification of the European (E.C.) regulations regarding axle loads in international traffic. In the context of present highway rehabilitation cycles, one of the inferences of the FORCE Project is that it supports the basic E.C. economic evaluations of infrastructure/heavy truck issues.

CONCLUDING REMARK

The FORCE project demonstrated the value of international co-operation in experiments of this scale and complexity. The success of the work of the Group was due to a large extent to the willingness of Member countries to participate in an active manner. Active international participation in the Project reached a level never attained before in this research sector. Future multilateral collaboration should draw heavily on this experience so as to ensure effective and successful execution of experimental projects.

There is increasing interest in various aspects of vehicle/road interaction and work on these topics is proceeding in a number of countries. It is important that both vehicle engineers and highway engineers work closely together to ensure that national and international standards and legislation contribute to the benefits of both vehicle operators and road authorities.

TABLE OF CONTENTS

ANNEX A

ANNEX B

ANNEX C

ANNEX D

ANNEX E

ANNEX F

Chapter I

INTRODUCTION

I.1. GENERAL

One of the landmarks in developing design procedures for road pavements -- and in understanding their behaviour -- is the AASHO Road Test carried out in the USA between 1958 and 1961. This test is the most comprehensive one ever undertaken and yielded much new information. It provided a basis for the pavement design procedures used in many countries. However, in countries other than the USA, the empirical results that were obtained need to be interpreted carefully because of the difficulty of applying them to soil, climatic, and materials conditions other than those obtained at the site of the test in Illinois.

Partly because of this, a great deal of effort has been devoted to the development of analytical design procedures which use the engineering characteristics of pavement materials with a mathematical model of pavement behaviour to predict or analyse pavement performance. The number of these models now available, and their continued development, is evidence of their promise and a discussion of the general principles of their use is given in (1). Confidence in the usefulness of the models, however, can be established only by verifying their predictions against real pavement behaviour. For this reason, among others, a number of research organisations have built full-scale accelerated test installations for the study of pavement structures under closely controlled conditions. Such facilities are costly to build and maintain, but are vital to the development of sound analytical design procedures.

Recognising the value of full-scale accelerated pavement testing, the Organisation for Economic Cooperation and Development (OECD) established a Group of scientists. The aim was to study the application of full-scale pavement test procedures in establishing a link between (a) the theoretical approach coupled with laboratory tests and (b) the behaviour of roads in practice. The Report of this Group (2) describes the different types of tests and installations in use in 1972 and discusses their advantages and disadvantages.

In subsequent years new accelerated test facilities were built and existing ones replaced. An international colloquium organised in 1982 under the auspices of the OECD at the Swiss Federal Institute of Technology in Zurich, indicated the potential for international co-operation in this field, and OECD established a new Group of specialists in 1983 to review research on the design, construction and maintenance of pavements using results of accelerated load tests (3).

In addition to the benefits of international collaboration through the exchange of information and the transfer of research results, more practical benefits may be obtained by the validation of methods of measurement or techniques of analysis. Steps towards such validation were taken by the OECD Group of experts created in 1983. A pilot test was carried out at Nardo, Italy, in 1984, to compare the strain measurements in bituminous pavement layers under load, involving nine research teams from eight countries (4,5). Each team installed their own sensors in a purpose built pavement structure and made use of their own techniques and equipment to determine the effective strain at the base of the bituminous layer during the passage of a wheel load. From the way in which the values of a number of parameters varied it was found that the procedures employed were reliable and justified the continuation of international collaboration in this field.

In the next phase of work, from 1986 onwards, the Group made preparations for a "common test" to be carried out on a chosen facility, while at the same time encouraging each of the countries concerned to carry out a "cross-checking test" on their own installation, making use of similar pavement structures and loads.

A total of fourteen Member countries, with support from the Commission of the European Communities, collaborated both technically and financially (with a total of FF3 800 000):

-- Australia
-- Austria
-- Denmark
-- Finland
-- France
-- Germany
-- Italy
-- Netherlands
-- Norway
-- Spain
-- Sweden
-- Switzerland
-- United Kingdom
-- United States

and

-- the Commission of the European Communities.

This joint research project was the first of its kind to be undertaken by the Road Transport Research Programme of the OECD involving such a high degree of international co-operation. This experiment came to be known as the First OECD Road Common Experiment.

I.2. OBJECTIVES

I.2.1. General objectives of pavement tests

The principal aim of national research programmes on highway structures is to achieve better value for the money that is invested. At the same time the costs to the user -- in particular the delays brought about by road works and other causes -- must be minimised. The costs of providing and preserving road infrastructure can be reduced by making use of better materials and maintenance procedures. It is therefore essential to achieve a better understanding of the process of pavement deterioration. User costs can be reduced by providing roads that are stronger and that will therefore support higher gross vehicle weights, loads per axle and/or higher tyre pressures and that preserve a good longitudinal profile so as to reduce vehicle wear, ensuring at the same time safe driving conditions.

Improved understanding of the mechanisms involved in the process of pavement deterioration and the performance of new or improved construction materials can be obtained from full-scale pavement tests. These may take the form of an experimental road section built into the road network or an accelerated test conducted in a fixed laboratory installation. In the former type of test, the performance of the pavement is studied over a long period of time, as for example in the case of the Long Term Pavement Performance (LTPP) project of the US Strategic Highway Research Program (SHRP). On the opposite, the accelerated test allows the application of controlled wheel loads and the rapid acquisition of results with the aim of providing a better understanding of the basic physical principles underlying the mechanical behaviour of the pavements. Such tests are generally carried out on relatively short lengths of pavement under strictly controlled conditions of wheel load, pavement construction and sometimes climatic conditions (i.e., in particular, temperature). By contrast, the road experiment is used to establish empirical laws based on statistically representative sampling of data. The two approaches are therefore complementary and, when taken together, lead to a greater understanding of overall pavement behaviour.

I.2.2. Objectives of the OECD full-scale pavement test

The co-ordinated international research programme on full-scale pavement testing set up by OECD had a number of objectives that can be divided into those concerned with national policy and those of a technical and scientific nature. The common accelerated test that is the subject of this report, and the proposed cross-checking tests carried out at other national facilities also have specific objectives, and all of these are described in the following:

a) Policy objectives

The work of the OECD group on full-scale pavement tests is aimed at:

-- Achieving economies in the construction, maintenance and rehabilitation of road infrastructure and in road transport as a whole.

-- Harmonizing those regulations concerned with heavy freight vehicles by conducting tests to study the implication of regulatory changes especially in regard to road structures.

-- Promoting further international co-operation to permit more effective research at a national and individual level. Such co-operation may take the form of:

  * Transfer of technology, e.g. by analysing and interpreting the results of the common test.

  * Pooling of information and resources: experience, knowledge, funds, etc. Establishing research programmes of common interest.

  * Developing means of making more efficient international use of often limited resources devoted to scientific and technical research in individual countries.

b) Scientific and technical objectives of the common test

The general objectives of the OECD Group are as follows:

-- Extend the applicability of the results so far obtained and make them available to those concerned with accelerated tests now in progress or planned. This will facilitate the eventual transfer of results obtained at a particular location for use elsewhere.

-- Improve the understanding of the performance mechanics of pavements.
In detail, the aims are:

  * To improve understanding of the mechanisms of pavement deterioration.

  * To evaluate the performance of mathematical models used to simulate the response or predict the performance of pavements.

  * To test empirical relations between the behaviour and response of a pavement.

* To compare the different methods of measurement used in the laboratory and in the field for determining the characteristics of materials (modulus, fatigue strength, plastic behaviour, etc).

* To attempt to establish a better correlation between the results of laboratory tests and the behaviour of pavements in practice.

* To improve procedures used in making measurements of the behaviour of pavements and the interpretation of such behaviour.

The specific objectives of the common test are:

-- Carry out tests on different pavement structures under repeated loads of 11.5 tonnes -- the proposed new European legal maximum axle load -- and 10 tonnes, typifying axle loads currently used. Examine the pavement damage relationship between the two.

-- To verify the validity of design and maintenance procedures used for particular pavement structures and loads in the different participating countries.

-- To continue with the standardization and harmonization of test equipment, measurement procedures, data processing, analytical procedures and interpretation of results.

-- To use this international collaboration to generate new ideas and identify areas where additional work needs to be carried out.

c) Objectives of the cross tests

Participants in the common test were also invited to carry out a cross-checking test on their own installation. A major objective of the cross tests was to promote more intensive international co-operation in carrying out full-scale tests in order to exploit the advantages stemming from the more effective use of such large and expensive facilities.

The scientific objectives should not be considered simply in relation to the common test. A certain number of variables, mainly those associated with the sub-base layer and climate, give rise to differences between the test pavement structures of the common test and the cross-checking tests. However, given strict compliance with detailed specifications prepared on a common basis (materials, test and measuring procedures, interpretation of results, etc.), it should be possible to correlate the different results that will be obtained. It is therefore essential that the cross-checking tests are carried out on the basis of the specifications and procedures that were used for the common test.

The results of a cross-checking test will enable the verification and/or confirmation of the conclusions of the common test and permit them to be extended to the case of other soil, sub-base and weather conditions. A comparison of the results of a cross checking test with those of the common test will also enable the laboratory concerned to verify and validate its own conclusions and to establish a procedure for interpreting the results obtained elsewhere.

Carrying out the cross-checking tests will also permit an overall comparison of the different techniques concerned since, apart from those few where detailed operating procedures will have been established in common, each laboratory will be able to carry out the cross-checking test using its normal operating procedure.

With the combined analysis of the results of the cross-checking tests and the common test and the use of the full-scale installations involved it will be possible to examine the validity of the pavement design procedures employed in the different countries.

I.3. STRUCTURE OF THE REPORT

The remaining Chapters of this report describe in detail the setting up of the FORCE programme, the conduct of the experiment, the results and their analysis:

-- Chapter II sets out the selected test parameters, the test installation and describes the management of the project and the ways in which international co-operation was conducted.

-- Chapter III describes the construction of the experimental pavements and their instrumentation.

-- Chapter IV gives details of the conduct of the test programme including the trafficking of the pavements and the measurements of pavement response and performance.

-- Chapter V reports the results of the experiment and draws attention to the main features of the performance of the pavements.

-- Chapter VI describes the more important aspects of the analyses of the results in relation to the objectives of the project, and

-- Chapter VII gives a brief presentation on cross checking tests and preliminary results obtained, and

-- Chapter VIII sets out the main conclusions and recommendations of the FORCE experiment.

Chapter II

ORGANISATION OF THE TEST

II.1. MANAGEMENT OF THE PROJECT

It was decided at an early stage that rigorous and formal project management would be necessary in order to respond to the complex nature of the joint test both from the scientific point of view and its international feature. To this end, OECD appointed a Project Manager whose responsibilities were to manage the experiment on behalf of OECD, to ensure good communication with the organisation at which the experiment would be carried out, and with the participating members of the Scientific Expert Group. Because of the complexity of the project, and because the costs of the experiment would be considerable, a Management Bureau comprising members of the OECD Steering Committee for Road Transport Research was set up to ensure budgetary and financial control, oversee the project and resolve unforeseen problems. The organisation chart shown in Figure II.1 illustrates the reporting and communication links between the various individuals and groups involved in the experiment.

Figure II.1

MANAGEMENT OF THE PROJECT

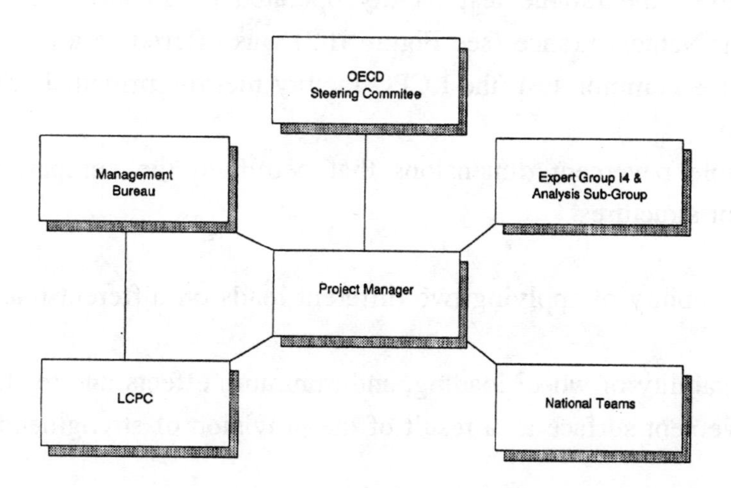

II.2. INTERNATIONAL PARTICIPATION

An important feature of the FORCE project was the fostering of international co-operation on experimental work. In deciding on the means of management and organisation of the project, this aspect was considered very strongly, since much of the success of international interchange depended on effective, well organised communications. It is evident from the organisation outlined in the Figure above that the Project Manager played a leading role in promoting and carrying through this collaboration.

In the formulation of the project, each of the participating Member countries were invited to send technical/scientific teams to carry out experiments on the pavements that were relevant to both the requirements of FORCE and those of the individual country. In this way, participation in the experiment was encouraged, and the Project Manager was able to benefit from the help and assistance offered by those teams. In addition to assisting with experimental work, it was also necessary to make provision for analysis of the results of the experiment. A sub-group was formed from participating teams to assist and advise the Project Manager as necessary, and to carry out the reduction of data and the analysis of results. Over the period of the experiment many of the participating teams took advantage of these opportunities for collaboration. Annex F lists the individuals and organisations who took part.

II.3. TEST FACILITY

Although a number of the participating Member countries have full-scale accelerated test installations, many of these were effectively excluded from consideration as possible test locations because of their commitment to national research programmes or because they were unsuitable for other reasons. However, the fatigue test facility operated by Laboratoire Central des Ponts et Chaussées (LCPC) at Nantes, France (see Figure II.2) was offered as a possible site for the test. For the purposes of the common test, the LCPC facility met the principal criteria, namely:

a) Allowable pavement dimensions that permitted the comparison of at least three different structures.

b) The possibility of applying two different loads on different tracks at the same time.

c) Good stability of wheel loading, and minimum effects due to changes in the level of the pavement surface as a result of the provision of strengthening layers.

Figure II.2

THE LCPC CIRCULAR TEST FACILITY

The facility consists of four single or tandem (half) axles with twin wheels equipped with standard threaded tyres.

Each (half) axle is located at the extremity of an arm and moves along a circular track. The four arms are driven by a motor situated in the centre of the track.

The main characteristics are:
- max. speed: 100 km/h (single axle)
  50 km/h (tandem axle)
- load: single axle up to 80 kN
  tandem axle up to 140 kN
- mean radius of the track: 17.50 m
- transverse displacement: ± 50 cm
- possibility to vary the mean radius
- possibility to driver over an unevenness of ± 10 cm without a change in load

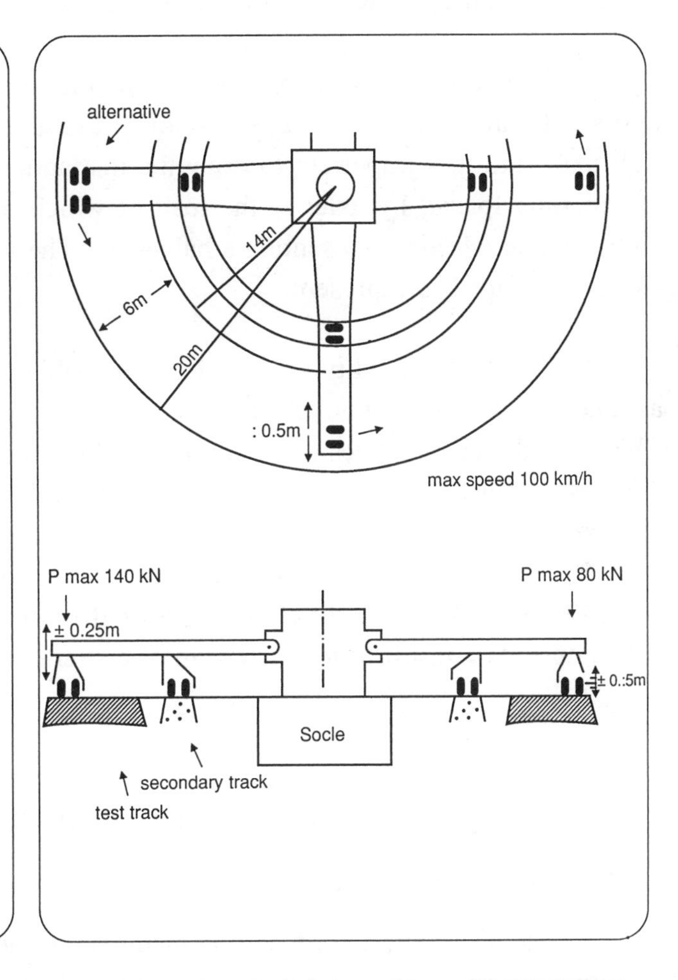

1) Rolling unit
4) Pivot

2) Arm
5) Hydraulic unit

3) Intermediary unit
6) Cooling unit

d) A high rate of application of wheel loads (2400 per hour) and unsupervised operation of the facility.

e) The willingness of LCPC to make available experienced staff to operate the machine and collaborate in the running of the test.

The test facility incorporates four arms driven round the track by 1000 HP hydraulic motors. All current accelerated test facilities use a single wheel to load the pavement, rather than a full axle, and it is important to draw the distinction between the two. Whereas roads in service are generally loaded by axles -- the load of which may be up to, say, 11 tonnes -- test facilities employ single wheels representing a half-axle. The load on this wheel is therefore half that on the axle it is intended to represent.

The LCPC facility -- brief details of which are illustrated in Figure II.2. (see also (4)) -- has dual wheel assembly attached to the extremity of each arm. It allows an equivalent axle load of between 8 and 15 tonnes to be applied to the pavement at speeds of up to 100 km/h. The twin wheel assemblies are continuously displaced to and fro across the track to reproduce the effects of actual traffic. This displacement can be pre-programmed and carried out automatically during a test. The suspension characteristics ensure that the load applied to the pavement remains constant even where the surfaces at different points on the circumference of the track are at different heights, for example, as a result of the provision of a strengthening layer to a section of the test pavement.

II.4. STRUCTURES

Following discussion among members of the Scientific Expert Group, it was decided that the common test should be carried out on three pavement structures, each reasonably typical of those used for different traffic categories in a number of the participating Member countries. An important consideration was that the pavements should be relatively easily reproducible for the cross-checking tests, so that the materials involved should not be very different from those normally used. Although it was appreciated at the outset that these criteria would not be easily met, there was final agreement on the type of pavement structures as depicted in Table II.1.

It was also agreed that in order to satisfy the objectives of the test, a maintenance treatment in the form of a bituminous overlay would be applied to one or more structures as deterioration took place.

Figure II.3 presents details of the experimental pavement sections and the cross sections of each of the intended structures, the thicknesses actually achieved and the overlays as planned.

Figure II.3

TEST SECTIONS AND STRUCTURES

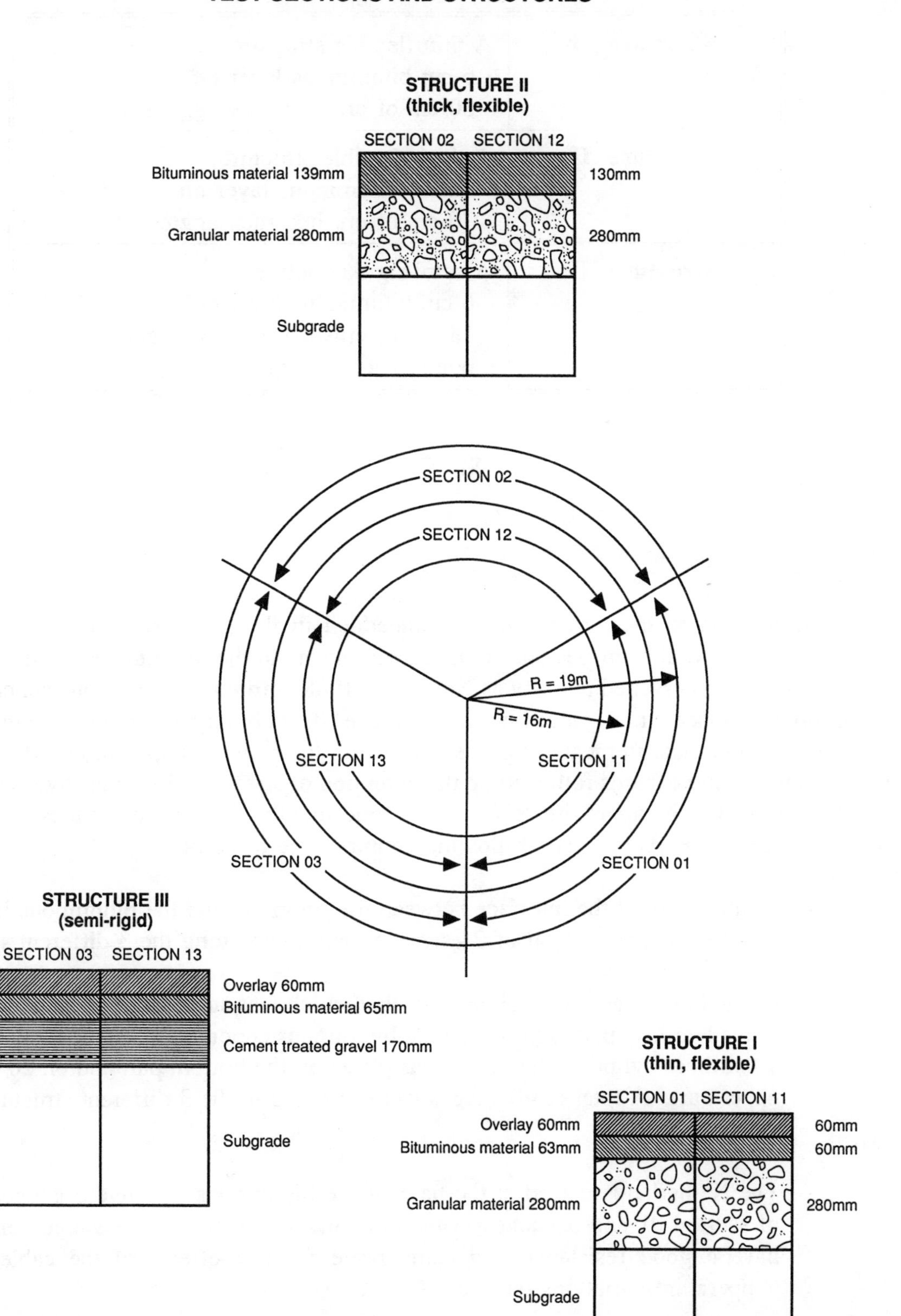
STRUCTURE II
(thick, flexible)
SECTION 02
SECTION 12
Bituminous material 139mm
130mm
Granular material 280mm
280mm
Subgrade
SECTION 02
SECTION 12
R = 19m
R = 16m
SECTION 13
SECTION 11
SECTION 03
SECTION 01
STRUCTURE III
(semi-rigid)
SECTION 03
SECTION 13
60mm
75mm
145mm
170mm
Overlay 60mm
Bituminous material 65mm
Cement treated gravel 170mm
Subgrade
STRUCTURE I
(thin, flexible)
SECTION 01
SECTION 11
Overlay 60mm
Bituminous material 63mm
60mm
60mm
Granular material 280mm
280mm
Subgrade

Table II.1.

TYPES OF PAVEMENT STRUCTURE USED IN THE CROSS TESTS

Structure I	A thin flexible structure 6 cm bituminous layer on 30 cm of crushed rock aggregate
Structure II	A thick flexible structure 12 cm bituminous layer on 30 cm of crushed rock aggregate
Structure III	A semi-rigid structure 6 cm bituminous layer on 18 cm of crushed rock aggregate bound with cement

II.5. SPECIFIC STUDIES

II.5.1. Instrumentation

In addition to the various gauges embedded in the structures for the purpose of the international test, several countries placed their own sensors in the bituminous layers. Hence some teams of specialists intervened as early as November 1988 before the bituminous concrete was laid down, in order to place strain gauges on the subgrade. In February 1989, these teams came back to proceed with the measurements at phase zero using their own equipment and data acquisition systems. Later on some teams followed up the evolution of strains and stresses by proceeding with measurements on the site approximately every second month. The results of these measurements are not included in this report. The following countries are to be mentioned:

-- Spain placed at the interface between the subgrade and the bituminous layer 6 series of 4 sensors, i.e. a total of 24 sensors distributed along the 3 different structures;

-- Finland used the same technique as that which was successfully tested at the occasion of the Nardo experiment by placing bituminous concrete cylinders in cored holes. On 20 of these cylinders the gauge was placed in the bottom part and on 20 others in the upper part. A total of 40 gauges were installed in the 3 different structures (see also Annex E);

-- The Netherlands placed at the base of the bituminous concrete 5 gauges in the axis of section 01 and 5 gauges in the axis of section 02. These gauges of a new type have a good resistance and compensate for side-effects of the cable length and temperature variations (see also Annex E).

II.5.2. Measurements

Apart from the Falling Weight Deflectometer (FWD) measurements conducted by the Italian team, specialist teams came with their own equipment to proceed with measurements and collection of various parameters. FWD from France and the Netherlands were also brought to Nantes to measure the pavement response. Switzerland carried out an opto-electronical determination of the pavement deflection. This measurement, which is considered as accurate, was put on parallel with the data obtained with Type 1 and Type 2 deflection sensors (for description see Chapter III). The German team came strongly equipped to operate stresses on the structures with the help of a vibrator, using another approach to determine the structural condition of the pavement after loading it. Finally, the Austrian team carried out the plate bearing tests at various levels on section 02.

II.5.3. Data analysis

To analyse the data collected several specialists worked in accordance with the programme set out by the Project Manager. The huge amount of data to be processed and its computerization would not have been possible without the help of participating countries. Engineers studied the results obtained as soon as they were available and specialists from Australia, Denmark, Spain and the United States proceeded with the use of pavement performance models. Apart from the co-operation aspects, specialists had the opportunity to become familiar with measurement and deterioration monitoring techniques previously unknown to them.

II.5.4. Laboratory tests

The numerous samples sent to participating countries have been subject to a great deal of laboratory testing, starting from tests for the grading analysis to tests to determine the bituminous concrete characteristics under a large set of different temperatures and frequencies.

The largest range of tests was conducted to establish the best possible knowledge for each material used.

II.5.5. Follow-up

Only some aspects of the specific studies and the cross-checking tests have been incorporated in this text. However, it is envisaged to further report on this research in the framework of the concluding FORCE Conference and/or in national publications.

Chapter III

TEST PAVEMENTS AND INSTRUMENTATION

III.1. CONSTRUCTION AND OVERLAY

The test pavements were constructed in October and November 1988 by a highway construction company in accordance with a contract placed by LCPC, acting on behalf of OECD. The contract detailed the required materials and/or their characteristics. This section of the report gives brief descriptions of the specification for each of the materials used.

III.1.1. Subgrade

In order to ensure that the test would be representative of roads in service, without leading to an excessively long life of the test pavements before reaching a critical condition, it was thought that the subgrade would need to have a CBR of:

6 per cent minimum
1O per cent maximum

To achieve this, it was necessary to import suitable material to supplement the naturally occurring soil. To minimize costs it was envisaged that the imported soil would be obtained from a site relatively close to the LCPC centre at Nantes. The material selected was a micaceous schist similar to that already existing at the test installation.

In practice, the old pavement on the site was removed down to a depth of about O.65 metres (with respect to the concrete surface at the centre of the circuit). The existing subgrade, made up of small slabs of micaceous schist, was worked over to a depth of 1 metre and then compacted to achieve a density of 95 per cent of the Optimum Normal Proctor value (NPO) over the complete depth for 95 per cent of the points where the density was checked. The moisture content of the soil at the site was found to be 7 per cent.

The imported material -- similar to the original subgrade material -- was laid on this support in a thickness of 0.3-0.5 m (depending on the particular circumstances) and compacted in the same way as previously. This was repeated until a total compacted depth of about 1.5 m had been achieved. In this condition, the soil had good load bearing properties which facilitated the construction of the subsequent pavement layers. Details of the results of tests carried out on the subgrade to assess its initial condition are given in Chapter V.1.

III.1.2. Road-base materials

The road-base materials, comprising a plain crushed rock aggregate and a cement treated aggregate were specified as shown in Annexes A.1 and A.2 of this report.

Untreated Crushed Rock

The principal requirement for the untreated material was that it should be representative on average of the untreated rocks used for road base layers of flexible pavements, and without any exceptional characteristics.

The granular material, a O/30 Maraîchères aggregate from a quarry close to the Nantes test centre, was a good quality crushed rock, was placed in mid-September 1988, using a grader and a smooth-wheeled roller with a small amount of vibration for compaction. The moisture content of the material during construction remained acceptable; the average moisture content of 4 samples was 4.85 per cent, with a standard deviation of 0.245 per cent. At a moisture content of 4.6 per cent the theoretical maximum density of the material was 2100 kg/m^3.

The standards for laying the granular material are described in Annex A.3 and details of the results of tests carried out on the laid material, both in-situ and on laboratory samples, are given in Chapter V.

Cement-treated Material

The main requirement of the cement treated material used in Structure III was that it should be a high strength material likely to lead to very much longer pavement lives than were considered likely for Structures I and II, and requiring little maintenance. The selected material comprised a 0/20 mm continuously graded crushed rock aggregate with an intended cement content of 3.5 per cent. The added water content of the material was 6 per cent by weight.

In-situ density measurements made after placing the material were required to give a density of at least 97 per cent of that of the modified Proctor Test over 95 per cent of the points surveyed.

III.1.3. Bituminous materials

The requirements for the bituminous concrete were for a formula resulting in a flexible and impermeable material representative of those formulae used for flexible roads in a number of countries. Clearly, these formulae differ according to the country concerned since the choice of a bituminous coated material depends on a number of factors involving the climate, the statutory vehicle weight limits and the pavement maintenance strategy.

Since it was not possible to arrive at a formula common to all the participating Member countries, it was decided to use a formula currently used for French roads carrying moderate heavy commercial traffic. The chosen material was the continuously graded O/lO, NO 2, Maraîchères quarry formula, a sandy mixture having a 6O/7O penetration grade bitumen content of 6.45 per cent.

An advantage of this mix is that it can be applied in cold weather and achieve good compaction, as much as 95 per cent of the target density obtained with the Gyratory Compaction Test. The bituminous concrete surfacings were laid in 60 mm thick layers, and the binder content of 6.4 per cent and the mixing/laying temperature of 175°C were deliberately selected in order to prevent any compacting difficulties. In fact there was a strong wind on the site on Friday the 25th of November and the ambient temperature was 5 to 7°C in sheltered locations and 8 to 10°C in the supporting soil. The equipment employed in laying the materials comprised a tracked Vogele finisher, a 21 tonne (3 x 7 tonnes) pneumatic tyre compactor and a 16 tonne smooth compactor. Vibration was not employed during the compaction operations in order to avoid any damage to the sensors installed in the pavement.

The standards for laying the bituminous material are described in Annex A.3.

III.2. INSTRUMENTATION

In order to follow the deterioration of the pavements and to analyse fully their performance, it was necessary to measure different pavement response and performance parameters continuously as the tests proceeded. Although many such measurements could be made, each using a variety of techniques, it was decided at an early stage in the design of the experiment that the number and frequency of these measurements should be sufficient to produce the right amount and quality of information without leading to excessive demands on the personnel running the experiment. For these reasons, it was decided that the principal measures of pavement response would be the longitudinal and transverse strains at the under-side of the road-base and within the bound pavement layers (bituminous and cement treated aggregate), the vertical stress and strain in the unbound layers (supporting soil and untreated aggregate) and the surface deflections. A particular type of measurement sensor was selected for each parameter.

III.2.1. Choice of sensors

The results of a questionnaire study of the measuring methods employed in OECD Member countries provided a basis for the choice of sensors. It was also noted that conditions on a construction site are sometimes incompatible with the fragile nature of the sensors; it is thus preferable to increase the number employed in order to ensure that notwithstanding any sensor failures the value of each parameter will be measured in a statistically significant way.

In the case of sensors for the measurement of strain and deflection, two different types were selected and installed in order to guard against the possibility of a general failure, or loss of performance of a particular type and to be able to compare the measurements of each type. The types of sensor chosen for the measurement of parameters of interest are described in the following paragraphs.

III.2.2. Horizontal tensile strain

These sensors are required to measure the horizontal strain within the material in response to the application of a load. They comprise strain gauges based on thin conductors whose electrical resistance varied as a function of the mechanical extension to which they are subjected. The strain is measured in units of 10^{-6} m/m (microstrain).

The tests previously carried out at Nardo confirmed the reliability of the so-called "H" shaped sensors consisting of strain gauges protected by a strip of plastic material. Two aluminium bars attached to the extremities of the plastic strip ensure that the gauge is properly anchored to the material in which it is embedded. More than 120 of these "type 1" strain gauges were installed in the Nantes pavement structures, at a variety of different depths.

A second model, referred to as "type 2", was slightly different in that the gauge was cemented to an aluminium plate and protected by a resin coating. It was important, however, to select a suitable plate thickness, to prevent the gauge acting as a reinforcing element in the pavement layer since the measured values of strain would then be less than the correct values. Figures III.1 and III.2 show examples of each of the two types of strain gauge.

III.2.3. Vertical strain

Vertical strain measured in the subgrade is an important indicator of the load-spreading performance of the pavement. Because two of the pavements studied relied upon thick granular road bases for their strength, it was decided also to attempt to measure vertical strain within this layer. The gauges selected use short inductive displacement transducers to each end of which is secured a perforated metal disc that permits good contact with the surrounding material. The gauge measures the relative displacement of the two metal discs, and this is converted to strain on the basis of a calibration previously carried out using a micrometer rig. Figure III.3 illustrates this type of gauge.

Figure III.1

STRAIN GAUGE - TYPE 1

Figure III.2

STRAIN GAUGE - TYPE 2

III.2.4. Vertical stress

The chosen sensor for the measurement of vertical stress in the subgrade comprised a miniature inductive displacement sensor fixed between two diaphragms secured to a steel annulus. The direct output signal indicates the effective displacement of the diaphragms from which the soil stress is deduced by reference to a calibration curve derived from measurements with the sensor under known pressures in a pressure vessel. This type of gauge is illustrated in Figure III.4.

III.2.5. Surface deflection

As a loaded wheel passes over it, the surface of a flexible pavement is subjected to a transient vertical displacement. This phenomenon has become a widely used indicator of pavement condition, and many methods of pavement maintenance employ it. It was therefore important in the present experiment to make accurate and reliable measurements of surface deflection under moving wheel loads. The in-situ methods already developed for this purpose were therefore used. Generally, these rely on the installation of a metal rod in the pavement to a depth at which it is considered that no vertical displacement occurs. A sensor element secured to the upper pavement layer rests on the road, which is then acting as a datum. As the surface deflects, the sensor element is activated and a direct or indirect measurement can be made.

For this experiment, two types of sensor element were chosen:

-- Type 1 comprising a spring steel plate secured to the pavement surface at one end with its free end resting on the datum rod. Four resistance foil strain gauges mounted on the plate give a measure of the deflection. For these gauges, the datum rod was installed at a depth of about 2m.

-- Type 2 consisting of an inductive transducer, the iron core of which was secured to the datum rod and the winding to the upper pavement layer. The datum rods used for these gauges were installed at a depth of about 6m in the subgrade.

Each of these two types of gauge is illustrated in Figures III.5 and III.6.

III.2.6. Temperatures

In order to be able to interpret and analyse other measurements and to draw conclusions about the overall performance of the pavements, it was essential to monitor carefully the temperatures in the pavement structures throughout the experiment. Copper constant thermocouples were therefore inserted at various levels in the different pavement structures at the time of construction.

Figure III.3

VERTICAL STRAIN GAUGE

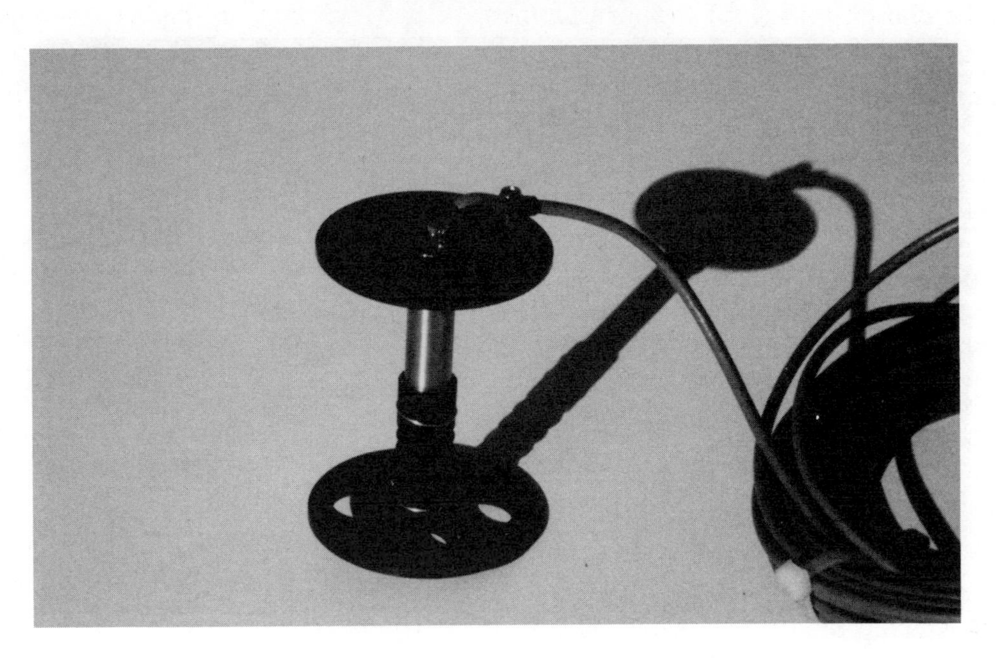

Figure III.4

VERTICAL STRESS GAUGE

Figure III.5

DEFLECTION SENSOR - TYPE 1

Figure III.6

DEFLECTION SENSOR - TYPE 2

III.2.7. Frost level

Because it was known that the region in which the experiment was carried out is sometimes affected by frost, it was decided to monitor whether this took place and to measure the effects. Frost penetration in a pavement structure can be determined using a cryopedometer. This consists of a tube filled with glass balls and fluorescein. This is a compound which changes in colour if affected by frost. The depth of frost penetration can be measured directly by measuring the depth to which the change of colour is observed. These gauges are not referred to later in this report because no frost penetration was recorded.

III.2.8. Hygrometry

The level of the water table was regularly determined by means of a piezometer installed near the surface of the subgrade. A tensiometer was also employed in order to obtain information on the degree of saturation of the soil and on the movements of moisture that could take place within it.

III.3. INSTALLATION OF THE SENSORS

The sensors described above were installed either before or during the construction of the pavements. In the case of those installed at the interfaces between the layers, this was a comparatively straightforward matter, using techniques normally employed. Nevertheless care was necessary to ensure that the sensors were positioned correctly and provided with adequate protection against the possibility of their being damaged during movements of construction equipment on the site.

The installation of sensors within the granular layers (both soil and road base) proved to be more difficult. In some cases it was necessary, following the placing of the materials, to excavate a small hole for installing the gauge, to position the sensor while making sure that it was in the required position and that its "zero setting" was correct. The excavated material was then replaced such that the location was restored to its original condition as far as possible. The nature of the granular materials gave rise to a number of difficulties in this process, and in the case of the cement treated aggregate added difficulties were brought about by the need to avoid any interference with the setting of the cement. Further details of the installation are given later in Chapter IV.

Chapter IV

CONDUCT OF THE TEST

IV.1. TEST PHASES

The test may be placed in the context of the total process of building a pavement and monitoring its evolution over time, the sole reference datum being the age of the structure. In fact, in the course of its life each pavement passes through different phases that correspond to:

- -- changes in its structural set-up
- -- changes due to loading and other stresses
- -- changes in "visible" behaviour
- -- changes due to a new life cycle (rehabilitation or new stress patterns).

The first phase of constitution and consolidation includes construction work and the period before the pavement is subject to stress and under the sole effect of climatic factors. The second phase may be subdivided to allow for the two main sources of stress: mechanical stresses and climatic stresses which may correspond to different periods during which contrasting environmental conditions or special phenomena are present. The latter may be connected with water: rise in the water table, heavy rain (or drought) or unusual temperature variations such as high mean values during testing or unusually high or low daily temperature gradients. During the third phase, pavement behaviour may change following surface irregularities produced by modifications in surface geometry, e.g. deformations in the form of ruts or cracks. Finally, a new cycle may be considered to start with maintenance work, e.g. the strengthening of severely damaged structures.

For the purpose of this study, the experiment is broken down into phases corresponding to construction, measurements and loading.

PHASE 1 (weeks 42 to 7):

Construction of test pavement(s) and installation of measurement systems, i.e. from the start of earthworks (17th October 1988) to the completion of systems' adjustment (15th February 1989).

PHASE 2 (weeks 7 to 11):

Inventory of the "Point Zero" stage covering the measurements by the international teams (15th February 1989) up to the completion of the measurements by the OECD task force (14th March 1989).

PHASE 3 (weeks 11 to 17):

Fatigue loading by rotating the machine -- small radius arm (10 t) and large radius arm (11.5 t) -- at constant speed starting on 21st March 1989 up to the occurrence of generalised failure of the 01 test section (27th April 1989).

PHASE 4 (weeks 18 to 22):

Loading with small radius arm only (10 t), i.e. four 10 tonne arms on the inner circle (3rd May 1989) and ending with the appearance of damage on test section 11 (30th May 1989).

PHASE 5 (weeks 23 to 30)

Loading with large radius arm only (11.5 t) following overlay of test section 01 from the time of overlaying test section 01 (5th June 1989) to the overlaying of section 03 (27th July 1989).

PHASE 6 (weeks 30 to 39):

Loading with large radius arm only (11.5 t) following overlay of test section 03, i.e. 27th July 1989 up to a cumulative application of 4 million loads (28th September 1989).

PHASE 7 (weeks 40 to 44):

Continuation with heavy loading (13 t) from the completion of 4 million loads (5th October 1989) until the end of the testing (5th November 1989).

Annex B presents these seven phases together with the measurement and overlay operations.

IV.2. LOAD APPLICATIONS

The objectives of the test are set out in Section I.2 of this Report. In essence they were to apply loads to three different pavement structures until the damage to the weakest was such as to necessitate overlay work. After strengthening, the behaviour of the test sections would be evaluated under subsequent loading. The comparative effects of 10 and 11.5 tonne axles would also be examined. All these aims necessitated a properly managed project, especially in regard to the application of loads.

It should be pointed out that, for ease of understanding, this Report always refers to load per axle, even though in the actual testing each arm was equipped with a half axle (dual-wheel) and applied only half the load.

One of the advantages of the Nantes test installation is that it can use arms of two different radii (16 and 19 metres) over the same structures and maintain a sufficient separation so that the two modes of loading do not affect each other. This allows testing, as in Phase 3, with 2 arms loaded to 10 tonnes on the inner circle (16 m) and 2 arms loaded to 11.5 tonnes on the outer circle (19 m). The automatic transverse distribution of the load applications is representative of real traffic loading conditions (Figure IV.1). For each of the 11 twin wheel positions, the test track makes a given number of applications according to a predetermined law with a sweep width of 1.6 m. At a standardized speed of 10 revolutions per minute, it completes one loading cycle over the width of the pavement in 45 minutes.

Tyre pressure was set in accordance with axle load. In order to conform as closely as possible to actual traffic conditions, it was decided to follow the recommendations by the manufacturer for Dunlop tubeless tyres SP321, size 12.00R20 (see Table IV.1). At regular intervals during the testing, the dual-wheel loads were checked for weight on a special scale and tyre pressure was checked practically every day.

The area of the tyre in contact with the pavement surface was estimated from two different measurements. The outer contour was obtained by spraying paint onto a piece of paper placed between pavement and tyres, while the inner contour was given by painting a tyre in its raised position and then lowering it onto paper. The true value of the contact area was considered as lying between these two. The difference in contact area between 10 and 11.5 tonne axles is less than 5 per cent if tyre pressures are 6 and 7.1 bars respectively. A twin wheel unit may hence be assimilated to two circular areas having a diameter of 276 mm and an area of 600 cm^2 whose centres are 360 mm apart (Figure IV.2).

The general programme of load applications over the testing period is presented in Figures IV.3 and IV.4 for the inner and outer circles respectively. The loads applied each week are presented cumulatively to show loading over time. In all, 4 555 000 loadings were carried out

Table IV.1.

TYRE PRESSURES AS A FUNCTION OF AXLE LOAD -- DATA SUPPLIED BY MANUFACTURER FOR DUNLOP SP321

Load per axle (tonnes)	Load on tyre (tonnes)	Tyre pressure (bars)
8.2	2.05	6.0
10.0	2.50	6.0
11.5	2.88	7.1
13.0	3.25	8.5

Figure IV.1

TRANSVERSAL DISTRIBUTION OF LOADS AND TWIN WHEEL CONFIGURATION

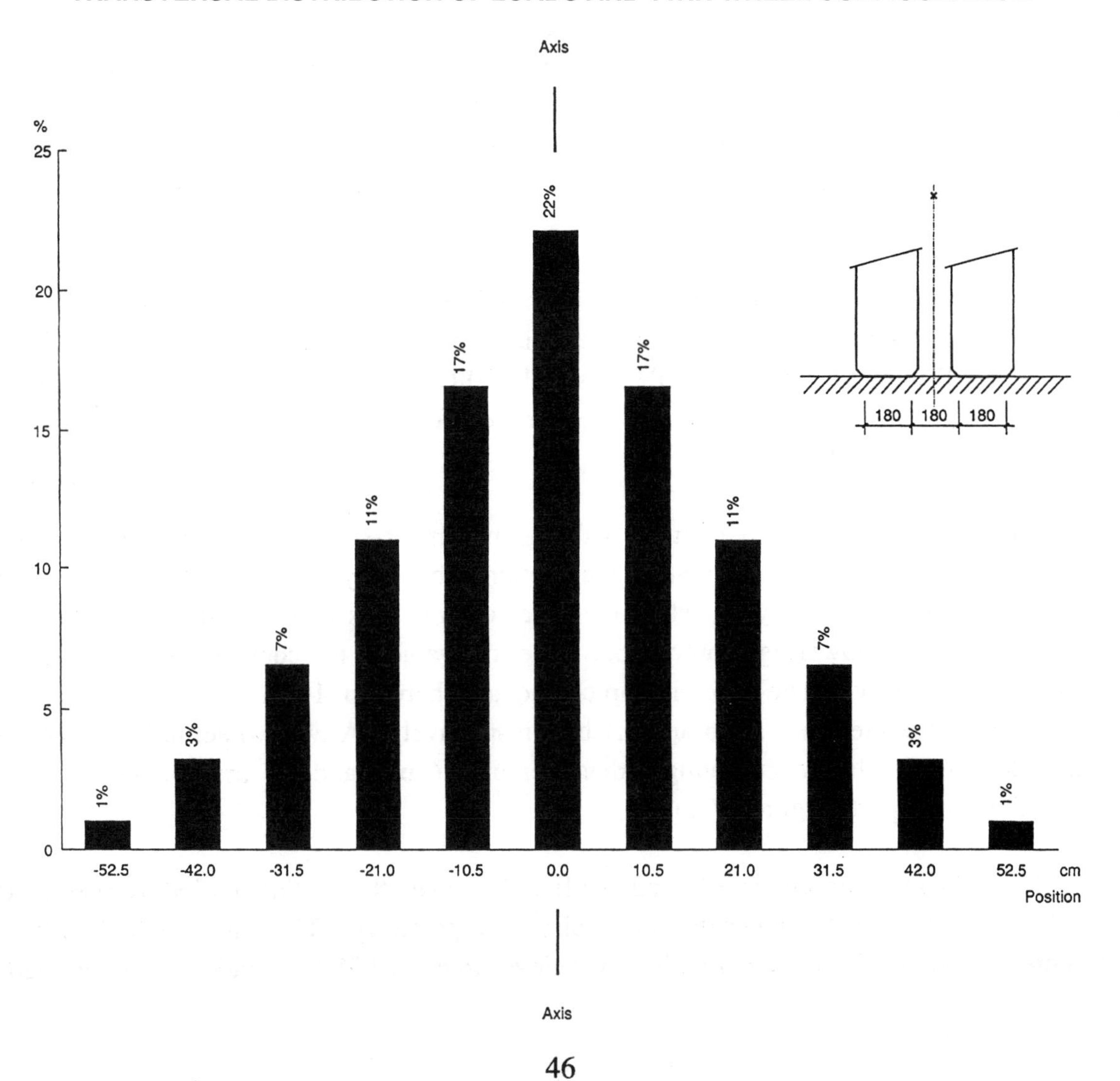

Figure IV.2

SCHEMATIC REPRESENTATION OF THE TYRE CONTACT AREA ON THE PAVEMENT (cm^2)

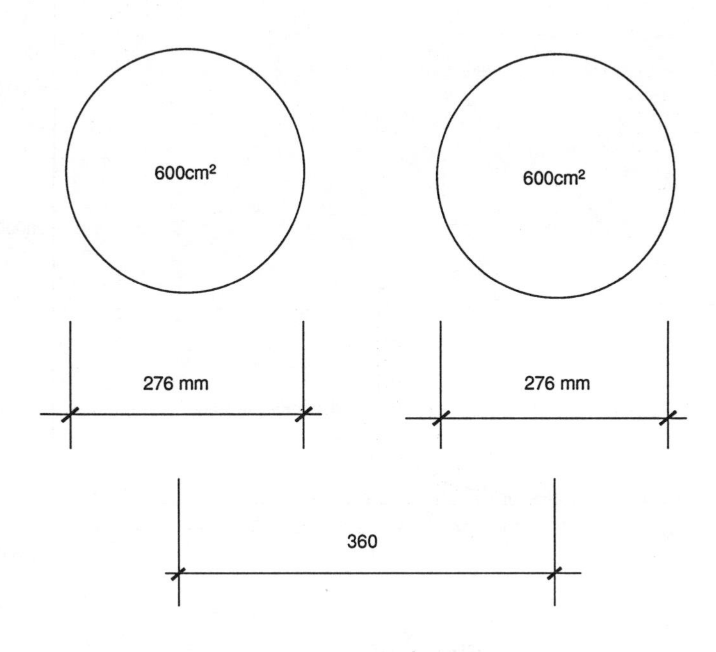

less than a year: 573 000 10 t loadings with the 16 m arm on test sections 11, 12 and 13, and)82 000 11.5 and 13 t loadings with the 19 m arm on test sections 01, 02 and 03. The fatigue ter made 1,139,000 rotations for the most part at a rate of 10 rounds per minute.

The pilot loading (phase 2) which began with measurements for the Point Zero inventory s intended to establish data on the initial properties of each of the three structures. This phase o provided the opportunity to study the response of each structure to different loads applied with ying transverse positions and speeds. Given the large numbers of sensors, it became necessary repeat certain loadings and speed conditions.

In order to explore the range of parameters a limited number of speeds, positions and ids was selected (Tables IV.2. and 3) and, to ensure a realistic set of data, the influence of each rameter was examined by blocking the two others at standard values.

Figure IV.3

LOADINGS ON THE INNER RADIUS — SECTIONS 11, 12, 13

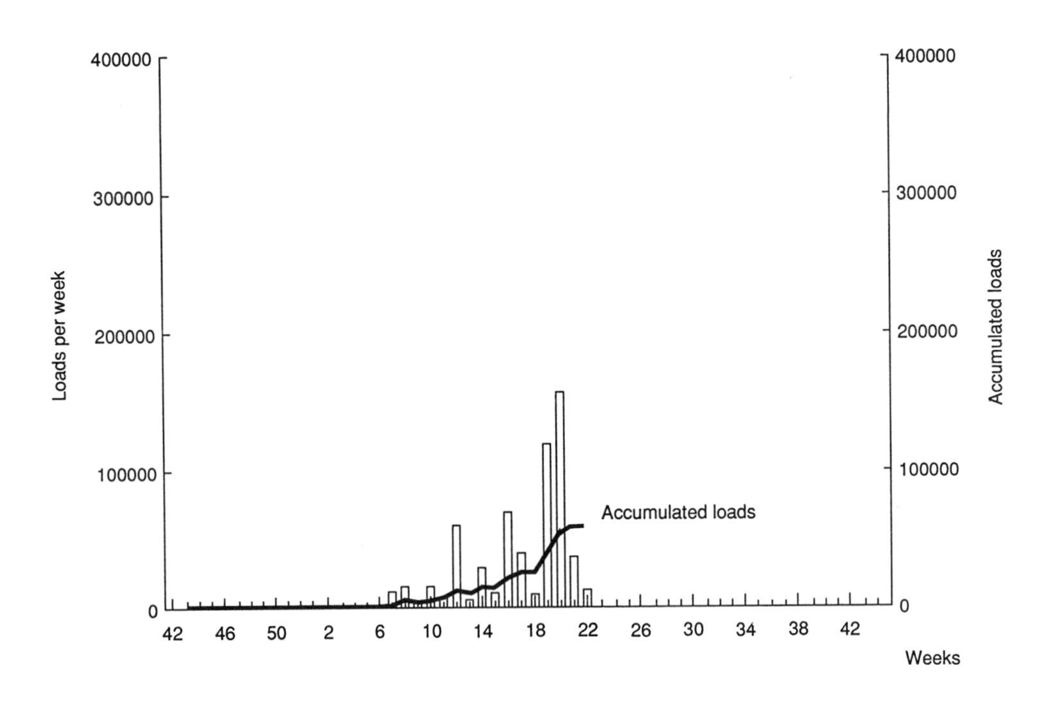

Figure IV.4

LOADINGS ON THE OUTER RADIUS — SECTIONS 01, 02, 03

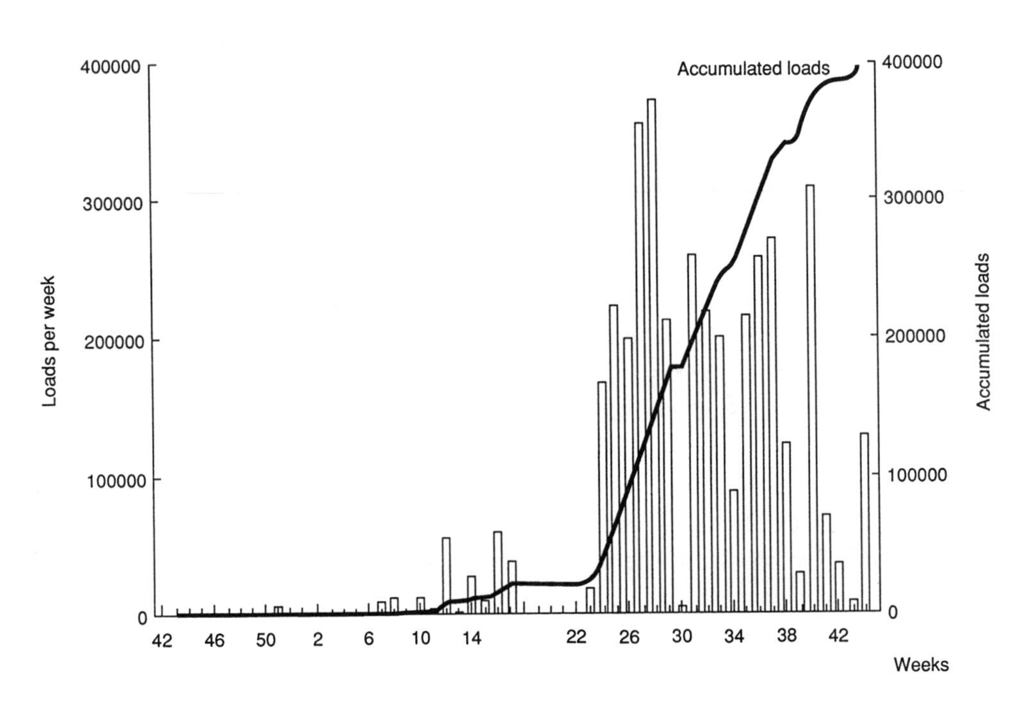

Table IV.2.

RUNNING SPEED OF CIRCULAR TEST MACHINE

Rotations per minute	**S p e e d (km/h)**	
	R (int)* = 16 m L (int)* = 100.5 m	**R (ext) = 19 m L (ext) = 119.4 m**
0.5	3.9	3.6
0.1	6.0	7.2
2.0	12.1	14.3
4.0	24.1	28.7
7.0	42.2	50.1
10.0	**60.3**	**71.6 ****
12.0	72.4	86.0
13.0	78.4	93.1

* R = Radius L = Length** Standard speed

Table IV.3.

LOADS APPLIED

		S p e e d			
		10r/min		**4r/min**	
Load	8.2 t	*	*1*	*	1
	10.0 t	0+3	2	0+3	2
	11.5 t	2	0	2	0
	13.0 t	1	3	1	3
	Radius	16 m	19 m	16 m	19 m

Key * impossible since weight of arm greater than load

** possible to operate only for few minutes (overload on intermediary support)

1 2 3 cases of "Load 1", "Load 2" and "Load 3"

0 case of standard load

In phase 3 -- comparisons of the different loads -- the distress in each of the pavements was observed with a 10 t load on the 16 m arm and an 11.5 t load on the outer 19 m arm. The scale of cracking and rutting on test section 01 after the application of 270,000 loads led to the continuation of the programme into phase 4, with all four arms turning on the 16 m circle, giving a total of 570 000 loadings in the inner sections.

Phases 4, 5 and 6 were carried out under standard conditions with 11.5 t on the four arms turning on the 19 m circle. During this period two test sections (thin and semi-rigid structures) needed to be reinforced with a bituminous overlay described in the next chapter.

After carrying out the 4 million loadings planned in the initial programme, the Expert Group took up a suggestion made by the Analysis Sub-Group and added a new phase 7, applying 550,000 13 t loads on the outer sections. The total loading period hence started on the 8th February 1989 and ended on 5th November of the same year. In all there were 1,139,000 rotations with 4,550,000 load applications.

IV.3. MEASUREMENTS

A large number of parameters were recorded over the whole period of testing, in order to provide the data needed to interpret the behaviour of the structures. These parameters may be divided into four categories:

(i) Environment: temperature, weather and water table level.

(ii) Pavement response: data from the strain, stress and deflection sensors as well as deflection measurements with the Benkelman beam and the FWD deflectometer.

(iii) Performance: rutting (cross-section measurements), evenness (longitudinal profile) and cracking on the trafficked sections.

(iv) Materials: characteristics determined through laboratory testing of samples taken during and after the test.

The frequency of measurements was determined as a function of changes of the structures: occurrence of damage, before and after maintenance work, etc. The complete programme is presented in Annex B.

IV.3.1. Environmental parameters

Temperatures were recorded in two structures at varying intervals from 5 minutes when structural measurements were made to 1 hour during the fatigue loading phases. Thermocouples were placed in test sections 02 and 03 at the surface (-20 mm), in the middle and base of the bituminous concrete layer, and in the subgrade. Their positions are presented schematically in Figure IV.5. Four sensors had ceased to function properly by 13th June and the corresponding data were withdrawn from the study.

The climatic data for the site are those provided by the national meteorological station at Nantes Atlantique airport, a few kilometres from the LCPC. Average, cumulative, minimum and maximum values are given each day, where applicable, for rainfall, evaporation, sunshine, ground and air temperatures, wind speed, atmospheric pressure, evaporation and relative humidity.

These measurements show that:

-- most loadings were carried out when it was dry
-- temperatures were generally high
-- sunny days produced high temperature gradients in the structures
-- there was no frost.

Figure IV.5

SCHEMATIC REPRESENTATION OF TEMPERATURE SENSORS PRIOR TO OVERLAY (LEVEL IN mm)

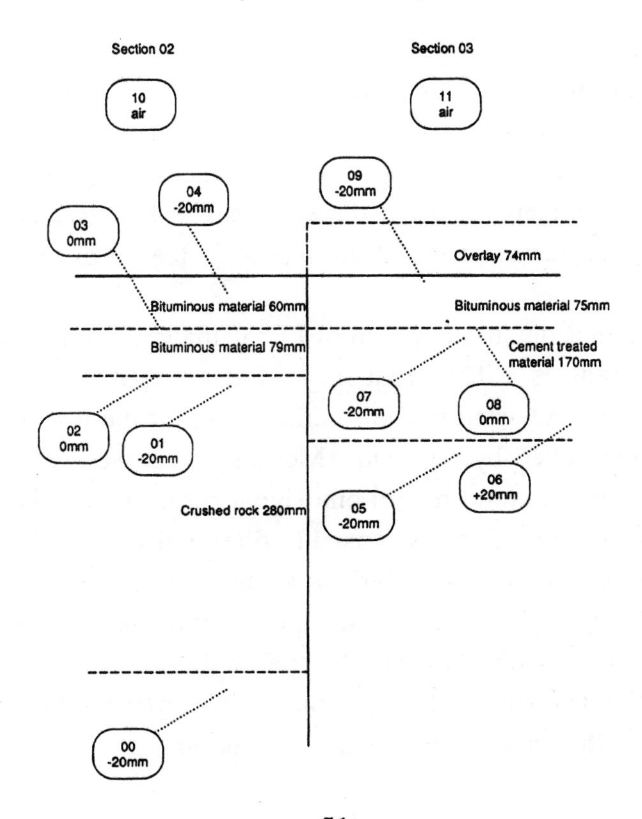

There were slight climatic differences between phase 3 (comparison between the 10 and 11.5 tonne loads) and phase 4 (loading with 16 m arm). In the latter case, the temperatures were higher and the rainfall lower. Weekly data on air temperatures and rainfall over the testing period are presented in Figures IV.6. and IV.7. Annex C gives other climatic data on soil temperatures, sunshine, windspeed, relative humidity and evaporation.

The level of the water table was monitored at the edges of sections 02 and 12 by a piezometric tube, and the water content of the aggregates was measured by a double neutron probe. Measurements showed the water table to be close to the surface (-0.8 m) during phases 2 and 3 (point zero inventory testing, 10 and 11.5 tonne loading); it then fell during phase 4 (16 m radius) to reach -1.4 m at the start of phase 5 (4 x 11.5 tonnes) and -2.4 m at the end of the test.

IV.3.2. Pavement response parameters

The response parameters were recorded at different points distributed uniformly over each test section, in order to assess the homogeneity of the structures. The axes of measurement locations and the points at which the sensors were concentrated are given in Figures IV.8.

The sensors described in Chapter III were installed before or during the construction of the pavements and recorded the following parameters:

- horizontal strains (longitudinal and transverse)
- vertical strains
- vertical stresses
- surface displacements and/or deflection.

The distribution of the sensor locations is presented in Figure IV.9, and the position of each sensor is indicated accurately in three dimensions. When test sections 01 and 03 were overlaid, longitudinal and transverse gauges were placed in the 19 m circle.

The automatic data acquisition system of LCPC made it possible to input simultaneously the measurements of 32 sensors. The frequency of data input and conversion of analogous information into digital data is adjusted to the rotating speed of the test machine so as to obtain a reading for every 20 mm travelled by the load. Measurements were recorded continuously over 1¼ rotations, so that each sensor could record one signal for each arm passing, i.e. four complete signals. An automatic computer program was used to filter and smooth the curves algorithmically: each signal was then analysed and the characteristic values were retained. These values were, first, the relative maxima and minima, the zero reference point being taken when the load was 4 m away from the sensor; second, the distance travelled by the load between the maximum and minimum (distance between peaks) and, finally, for the surface deflections sensors, the radius of curvature of the path of the signal in the range of maximum deflection.

Figure IV.6

WEEKLY AIR TEMPERATURES

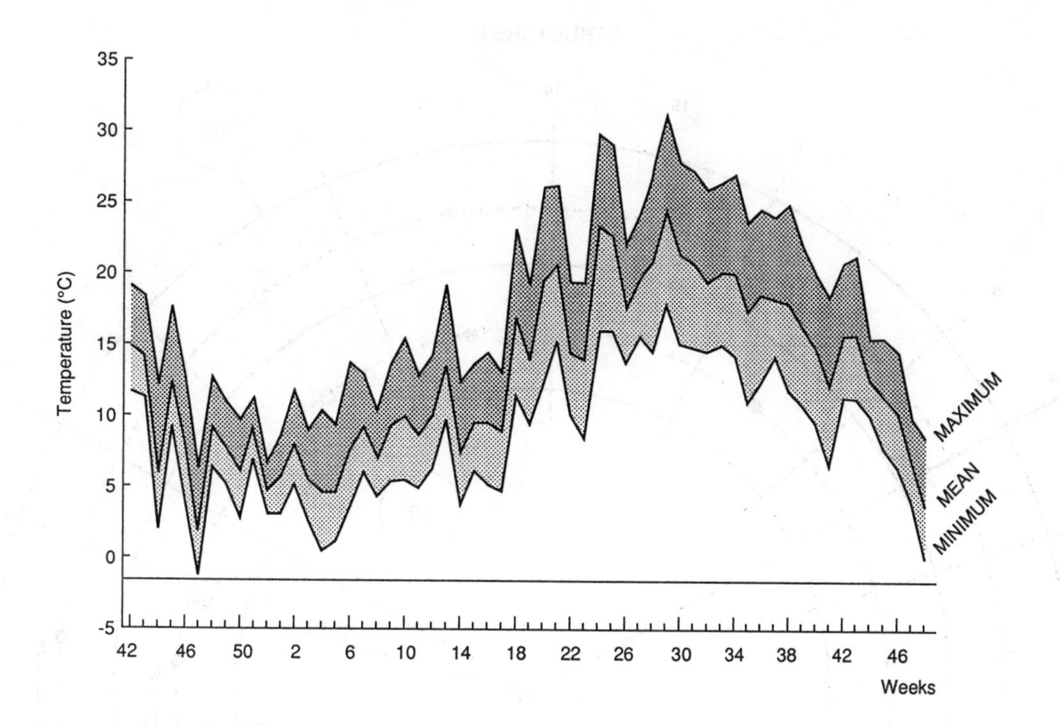

Figure IV.7

WEEKLY RAINFALLS

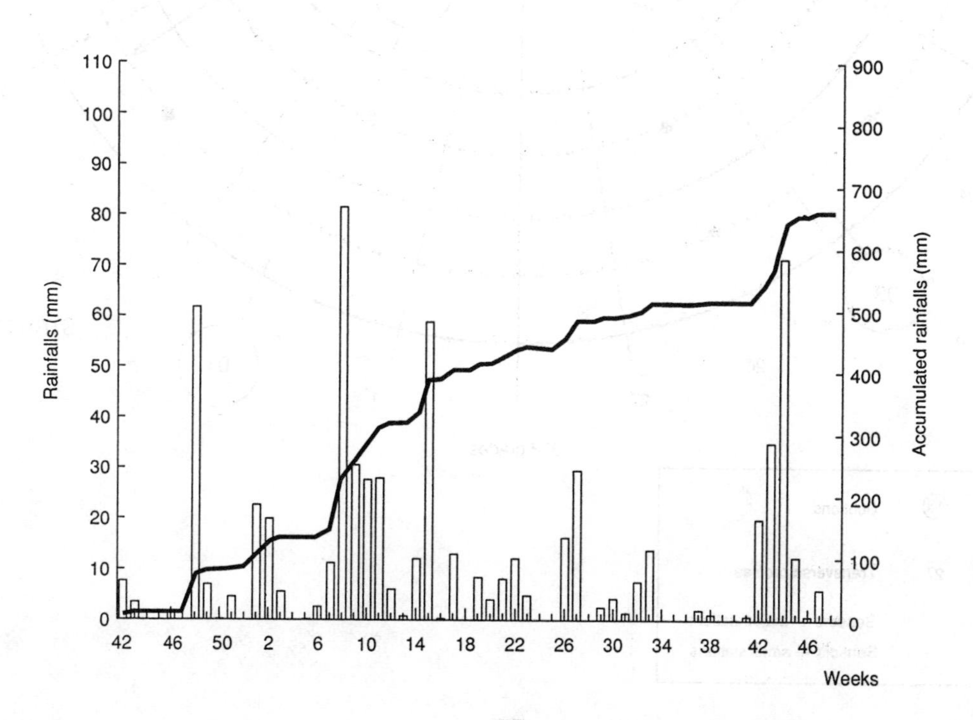

Figure IV.8

POSITIONS OF MEASUREMENT AXES AND GAUGES

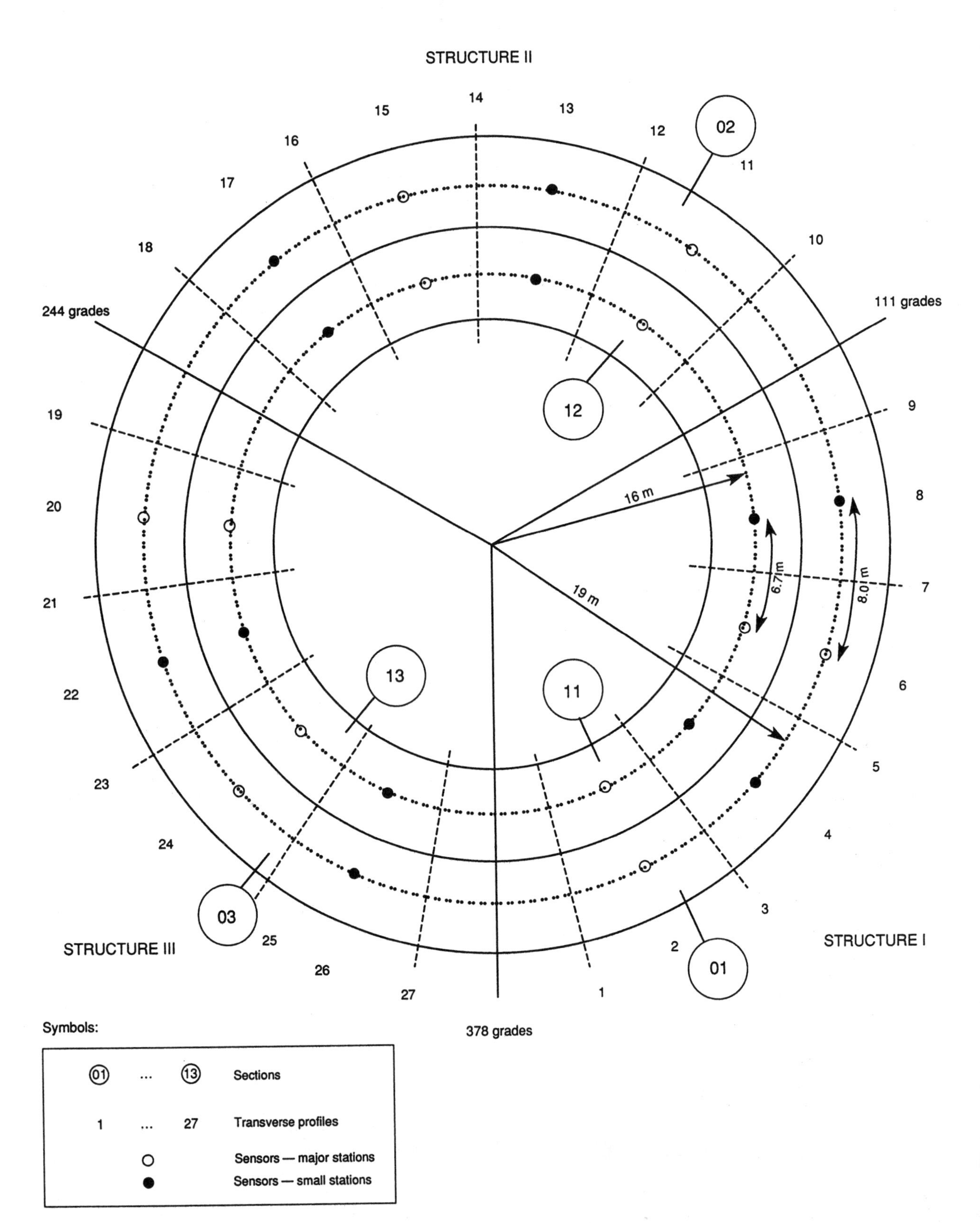

Figure IV.9

SCHEMATIC POSITION OF SENSORS

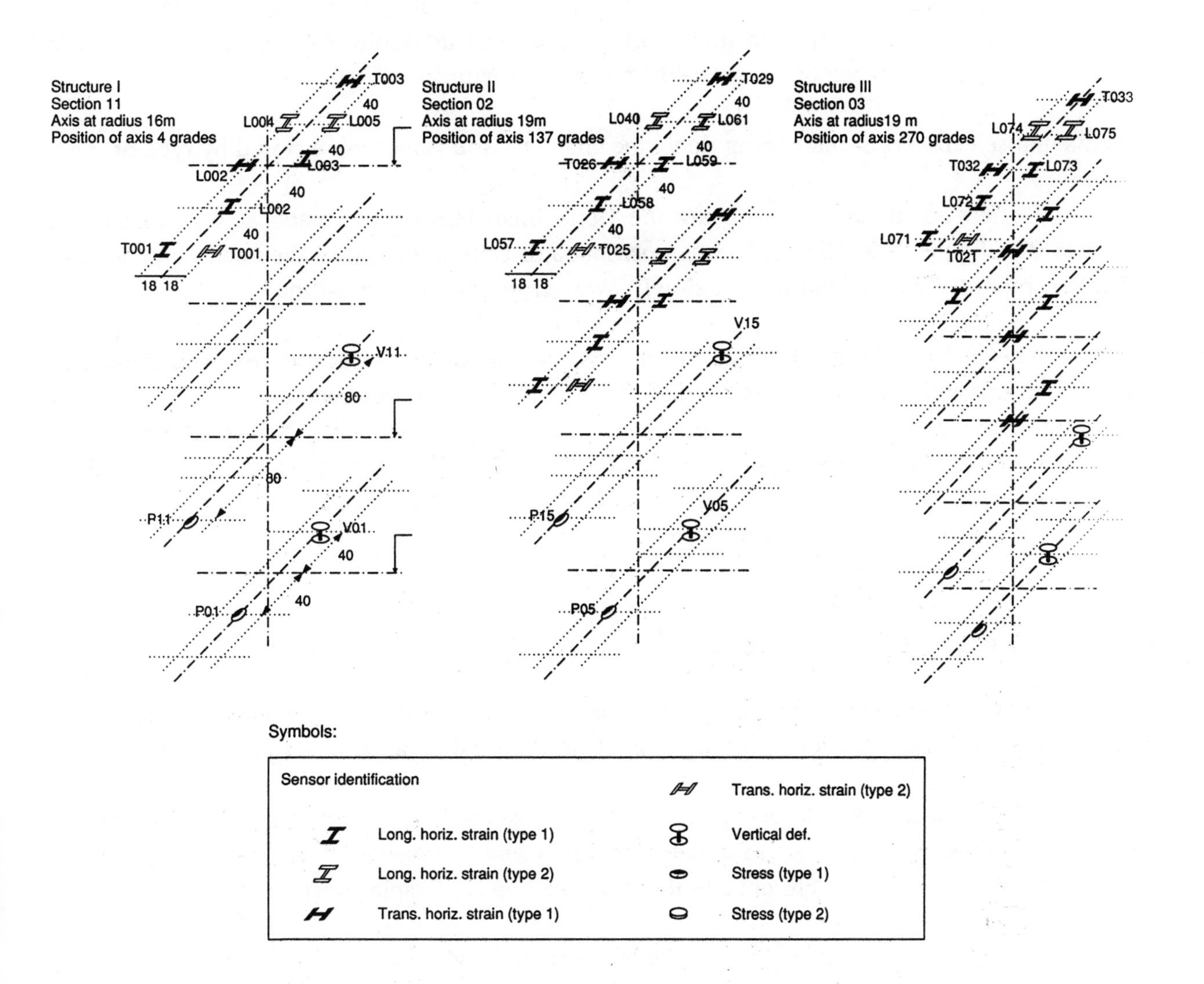

Each signal was then visualized by a specialist using specific software, and assigned a quality rating A,B or C (Figure IV.10):

- A: a signal of good visual quality with correct identification of the characteristic values.
- B: a signal subject to background interference, but with apparently correct analysis.
- C: a signal subject to major interference and unusable; the sensor or its electrical connections being probably broken or disrupted.

This manual selection of signals being done, the characteristic values were stored by type of sensor.

Deflection measurements using the Benkelman beam were made at 4 m intervals on axes 1 to 27 (Figure IV.8). The axle was positioned directly at the tip of the beam and the elastic deflection recorded as the load moved slowly away from the initial position.

The Falling Weight Deflectometer was used to record responses of each structure at regular intervals and especially before and after the Point Zero measurements as well as after laying the strengthening courses. Two Dynatest 8000 deflectometers were used by the Italian company RODECO and by the Saint Brieuc Regional Laboratory in France. It was decided to adopt a measuring step of 1 m along the centre line of the test sections, the load being selected to give a deflection at the centre of about 1 mm.

IV.3.3. Parameters of pavement behaviour

Visible changes in the pavement structures were assessed by measurements of their surface geometry (cross-section and longitudinal profile) and detailed description of each crack.

The cross-section was assessed by a transverse profilograph (five axes per test section). These measurements were used to represent graphically the value of a rut under a 2 m bar (Figure IV.11) whose ends were outside the trafficked area. Graphs were digitalized and stored.

The longitudinal profile was recorded by fixing a wheel to an arm of the testing machine and linking it to an inductive sensor (see Figure IV.12). The arm remains horizontal and moves around the track at it's minimum speed (around 3 km/h), while the sensor records vertical movements in the wheel as it moves over the track. Initially, the longitudinal profile was recorded graphically, and then digitalized and stored; subsequently automatic acquisition of digitalized data was introduced.

As soon as a crack appeared it was marked by hand with a colour paint (Figure IV.13) mapping each cracking stage. Each crack was recorded digitally so as to be able to reconstitute and analyse the surface conditions. A first analysis provided the length of cracking as defined in Figure IV.14. This value is divided by the actual trafficked length of the section to calculate the percentage of section length cracked.

Figure IV.10

**QUALITATIVE CLASSIFICATION OF SENSOR SIGNALS
(EXAMPLE OF LONGITUDINAL GAUGE HAVING AN "A" LEVEL OUTPUT)**

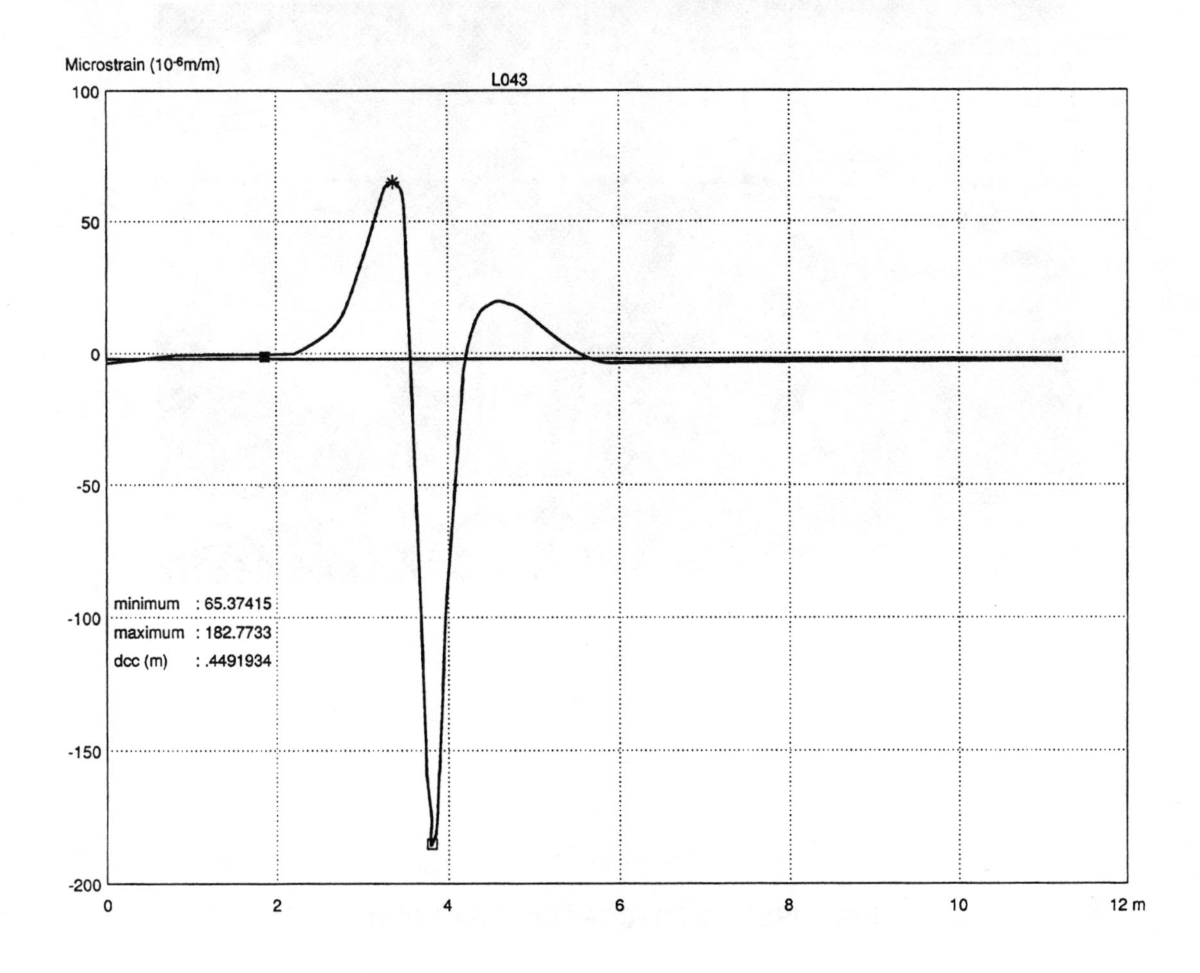

Figure IV.11

RUT DEFINITION

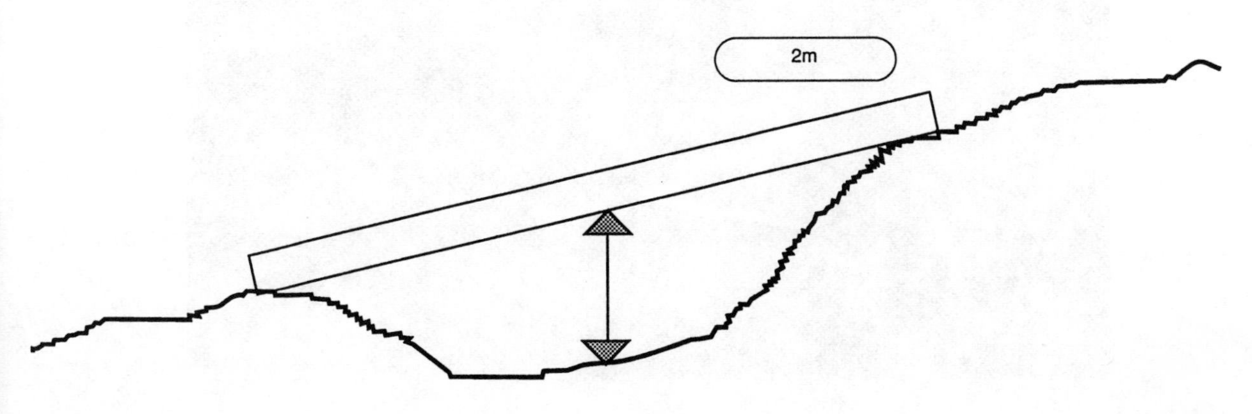

Figure IV.12

RECORDING OF THE LONGITUDINAL PROFILE

Figure IV.13

PRINCIPLE FOR RECORDING CRACKING

IV.3.4. Materials

Apart from taking control core samples, materials for laboratory testing were extracted only once. This took place about half way through the test on 22nd August. To avoid any disruption to the test, samples were taken in section 12 away from the trafficked area, in order to ensure homogeneity in the materials and avoid cracks in the samples. The samples included more than 100 cores (diameter 150 mm) and eight 400 x 600 mm sections (see Figure IV.15). Cores were also taken in section 13 in order to determine the mechanical characteristics of the cement-bound structure. It was not possible to use all the samples as a result of the prevalence of cracking: the modulus test for example, had to be abandoned.

At the end of the test, cores were taken and metre-deep trenches were carried out for each structure to confirm the measurements of layer thickness by PENETRADER (6), developed by the Rouen Regional Laboratory.

Figure IV.14

DEFINITION OF THE EXTENT OF CRACKING

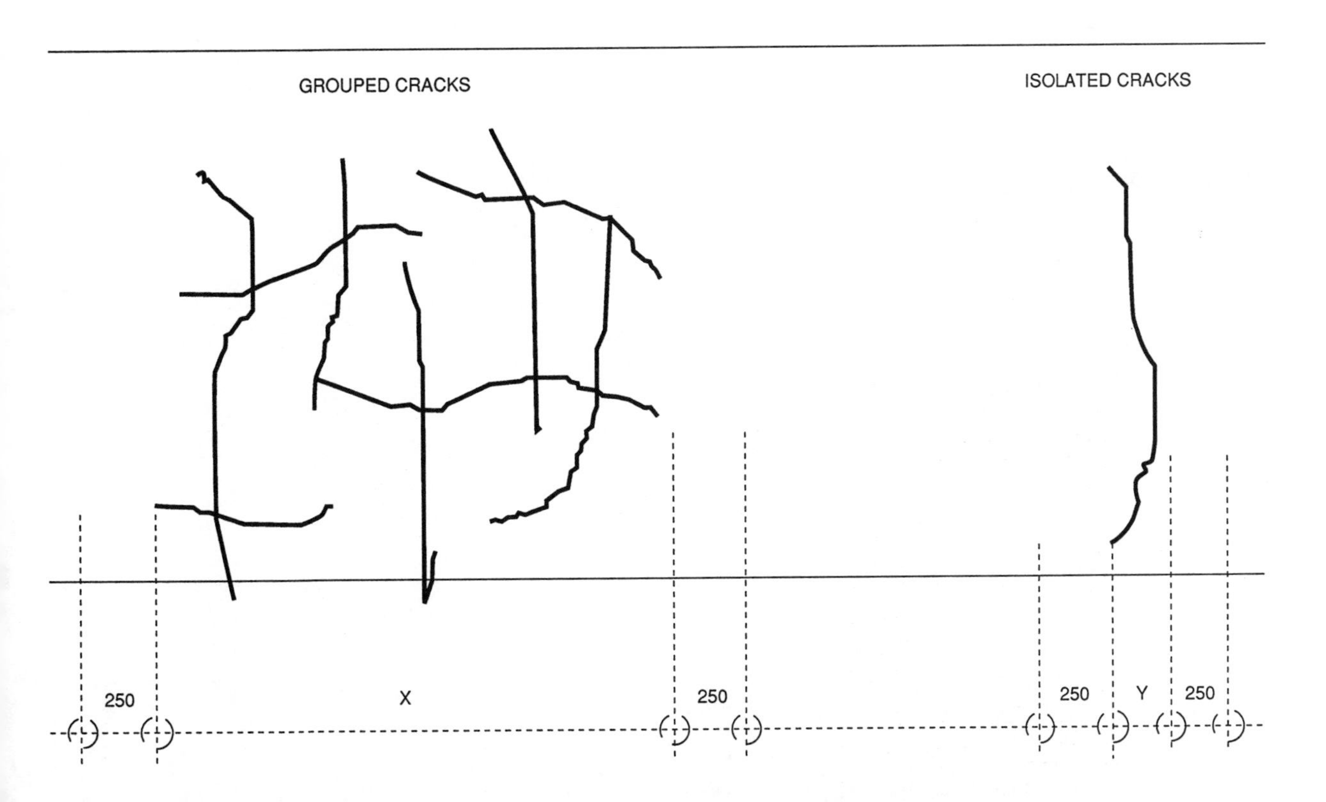

Figure IV.15

CORES TAKEN FROM SECTION 12

Chapter V

RESULTS

The measurements described in Chapters III and IV were carried out and collected in the appropriate form by the Project Manager. In order to assess the mechanical and other properties of the materials, samples were taken during or immediately after construction. The results of the laboratory tests carried out were presented in written reports submitted by the organisations who were contracted to carry out the tests or who offered to do so. Measurements of pavement response and performance were stored in digital form on a main-frame or micro-computer for later analysis.

The purpose of this Chapter is to present the main features of the results in sufficient detail to serve as a background to the analyses developed in Chapter VI. Because the results of the experiment provide assessments of the materials' properties, the overall performance of the pavements as well as their response under the test conditions, these headings are used in the remainder of this Chapter.

V.1. MATERIALS PROPERTIES

V.1.1. Subgrade.

Although the imported soil met the required conditions in that it was available relatively close to the test site and had an adequate strength as measured by CBR, major difficulties were encountered in determining its mechanical characteristics by laboratory testing, and in interpreting the results of in-situ measurements in order to arrive at values of the mechanical properties. In summary, these difficulties were due to:

a) The presence of some very large particles in the mass of material. The material originally comprised a O/100 mm grading which was reduced to O/50 mm after compaction, with nearly 75 per cent of particles smaller than 31.5 mm.

b) The fact that the structure of the soil was made up of small slabs which resulted in anisotropic behaviour when the material was dry. Where tests were attempted with moulded specimens, it was found that these slabs could remain parallel to one another at the base of the mould.

c) The sensitivity of the material to the presence of water because of the large proportion of plastic fines.

Because of the difficulties presented by this subgrade, it has proved extremely difficult to establish the mechanical properties of the material. Although a number of in-situ and laboratory measurements were carried out, the variability of the material simply leads to highly variable results. For this reason, other supporting information and techniques were used in order to arrive at figures for, in particular, the modulus of the material, that could be used in later analyses. In the remainder of this section, the results of tests actually carried out are described, and their variability is discussed; other supporting information is presented, and methods of interpretation are introduced.

The earthwork operations were carried out on 17th October 1988 in good climatic conditions and with no rainfall. Subsequently, the subgrade was protected from direct rainfall to prevent changes in the strength of the material.

Results of Tests Carried out

Deflection measurements. Subgrade deflection (in 10^{-2}mm) was assessed by measurements of transient deflection carried out under a 10 tonne axle load (2 x 5 tonne twin wheel load). The average of the results of the measurements on the 3 zones of the test track on which the experimental pavements would be subsequently constructed were as follows:

Zone Structure	Average Deflection	Number of Measurements
1	279	3
2	213	2
3	186	3

These results suggest that Zone 1 is rather less stiff than zone 3, confirming the indications of the FWD surveys carried out at the time of construction. This may be due to some feature of the laying of the imported subgrade of differing thicknesses; however, subsequent measurements obtained with the FWD suggest a more uniform subgrade strength as the experiment continued. Taking all the results from the Benkelman Beam measurements as a single set, the average deflection under a 10 tonne axle load was

$$d_{av} = 227.75 \times 10^{-2} \text{ mm with a standard deviation of } 54.10^{-2} \text{ mm}$$

CBR measurements. In the course of construction of the subgrade, samples were removed from the top 3000 mm of the subgrade for later measurement of remoulded CBR. The results of these measurements, at the natural moisture content of the extracted sample, W, are shown below:

	Density (kg/m³)	W (%)	CBR (%)
	2120	7.00	31
	2060	7.10	22
	2130	7.00	40
Average	**2100**	**7.03**	**31**

These values are rather widely dispersed and give values for the CBR which are considerably higher than were required by the specification. It could be considered that since they were obtained for the natural water content during the course of the work on the site they are not altogether representative of conditions throughout the course of the experiment, when lifting of the water table would have wetted the soil. The variability of the results also raises the possibility that the use of the CBR test on this type of soil may be inappropriate.

Proctor test results. The results of the Normal Proctor test were as follows:

Density (Dry) kg/m³	Moisture Content at Normal Proctor Optimum (%)
2120	7.0

The densities measured on the site were generally found to be in the range 2020 to 2080, with a moisture content of about 7 per cent. It should be noted that these values were rather less than those for density at the Normal Proctor Optimum moisture content.

Laboratory test results. The samples of soil taken during construction were given to a number of different research organisations who carried out a variety of different tests on them. In particular, those tests carried out by BVFA of Austria and Delft University of Technology are of interest in assessing the soil.

As to the grading analysis undertaken by BVFA of Austria, Figure V.1 shows the results of a grading analysis of a sample of the soil material taken from the quarry site by the BVFA (curve I). It can be seen that:

-- The size of the largest elements was greater than 75 mm.

-- 82 per cent of the elements are smaller than O/31.5.
-- The fines content at 80 µm was 27 per cent.

The nature of this grading, somewhat finer than that suggested by the composition analysis noted earlier, indicates that the behaviour of the material will be governed by that of the fines, and this is confirmed by the water absorption index (ENSLIN) of 94.00 per cent.

The actual density of the aggregate component of the soil alone was measured as 2770 kg/m^3.

Delft University of Technology carried out a triaxial test on the soil in order to establish values for the resilient properties of the material. In order that this could be achieved, however, it was necessary to reduce the particle size in the sample, and the material was therefore passed through a 19 mm sieve to give a sample that could be tested in a 100mm specimen diameter triaxial apparatus. Eleven levels of confining stress, and two levels of cyclic stress were used, on specimens that were prepared as closely as possible to the optimum conditions indicated by the Proctor Test.

Target Values		**Specimen Values**		
W_{opt} (%)	$Density_{max}$ (kg/m^3)	W (%)	Density (kg/m^3)	Density / $Density_{max}$ (%)
7.0	2120	7.7	2079	98

The stiffness modulus, M_r, was expressed, following the K-theta model developed by Hicks and Monismith, as follows:

$$M_r = K_1 \left(\frac{\theta}{\theta_0}\right)^{K_2} \qquad \text{Eq. V.1}$$

where: K_1 = 56.8 MPa
Θ = the sum of the main stresses in kPa
Θ_0 = the reference stress of 1 kPa
K_2 = a coefficient having a value of 0.32.

The correlation coefficient of the regression line through the data points from the tests was O.87.

Figure V.1

GRADING ANALYSIS OF THE SUBGRADE

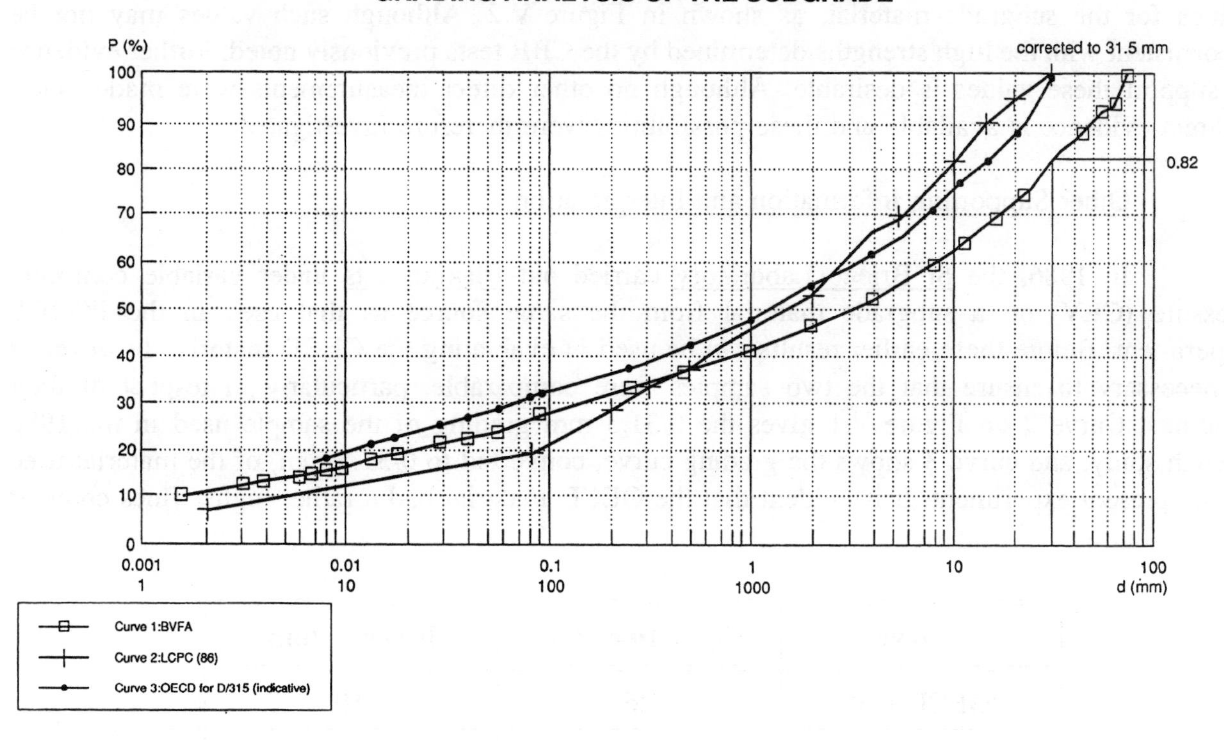

Figure V.2

RESILIENT MODULUS M_r VERSUS SUM OF PRINCIPAL STRESSES θ (SUBGRADE)

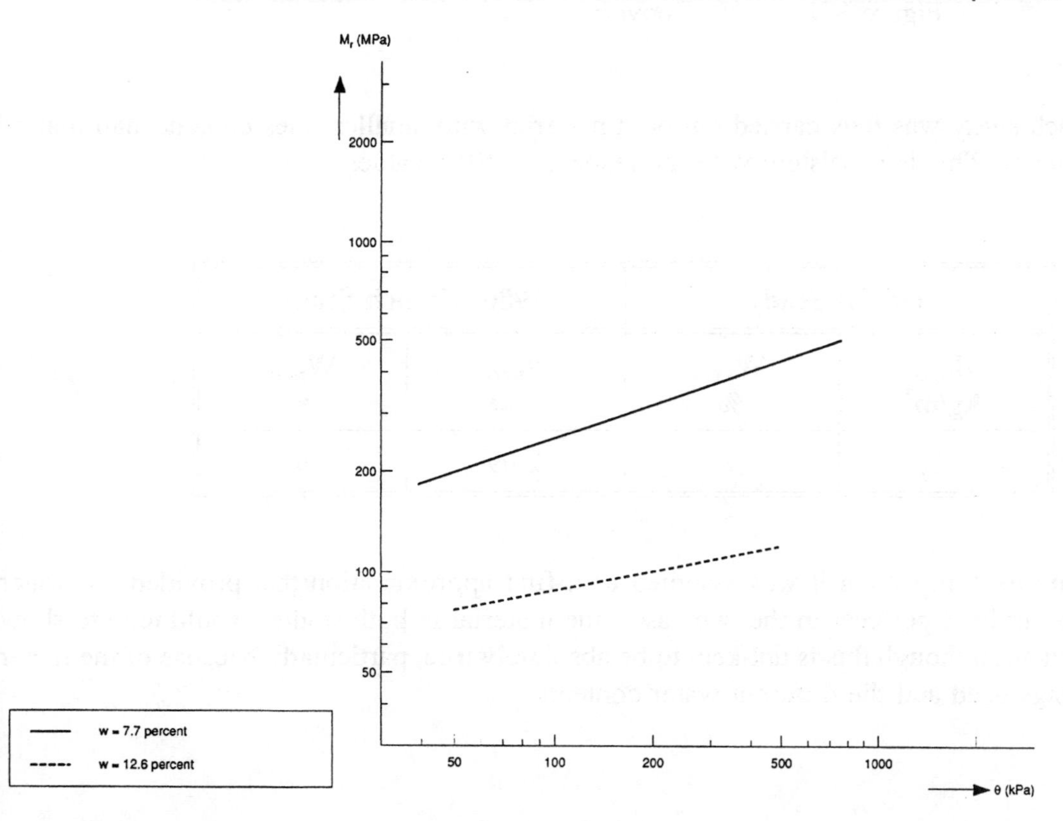

It can be estimated that the average values of Θ, the sum of the main stresses, likely to be encountered in the pavement, will be of the order of 100 kPa; this would lead to high modulus values for the subgrade material, as shown in Figure V.2. Although such values may not be inconsistent with the high strengths determined by the CBR tests previously noted, further evidence to support these values is desirable. Although no other direct measurements were made, other indirect evidence is available and these possibilities were therefore investigated.

Other Supporting Information and Interpretation

In 1986, the St Brieuc Laboratory carried out triaxial tests under variable confining pressure (CLV) on a subgrade material from the same source as that used in the FORCE experiment. Before these earlier results can be used in evaluating the OECD material, however, it is necessary to ensure that the two samples were comparable, particularly in respect of their gradings. Curve 2 on Figure V.1 gives the 0/31.5 mm grading of the sample used in the 1986 French study, and curve 3 shows the grading curve, converted to 0/31.5 mm, of the material used in the present experiment. It is evident that the OECD material had a rather higher fines content:

Curve	80µM fines (%)	Fines < 2µm
OECD (1)*	26	10
86 study	19	7
OECD (3)**	30	12

* See Figure V.1. ** Converted

The 1986 French study was thus carried out on a material with smaller fines content than that of the OECD material. This is consistent with the respective NPO values:

OECD Study		1986 French Study	
d_{NPO} kg/m^3	W_{NPO} %	d_{NPO} kg/m3	W_{NPO} %
2.12	7	2.09	9

From this comparison it was assumed as a first approximation that provided the water content is different by 2 per cent in the two cases, the material in both studies would tend to show the same behaviour, although this is unlikely to be absolutely true, particularly because of the rather different gradings used and the different water contents.

The results of the French study of the subgrade mechanical properties were obtained by interpreting the results of a triaxial test under variable confining pressure according to Boyce's method. Table V.1 shows the results of the study, in which

-- p'_o is the average effective stress before loading
-- p_r is the average of the principal stresses due to external loading corresponding to $\Theta/3$.

In a presentation similar to that employed by Delft University of Technology:

$$\Theta = 3p'_o + 3p_r.$$

The results given in Table V.1 are shown in graphical form in Figure V.3.

It should be noted that both the average effective stress and the sum of the principal stresses play a very important role in the variation of the modulus values, both in the French 1986 study and that of Delft University of Technology.

The variation can be represented by the equation given below:

$$E\ (MPa) = 88.4 \left(\frac{p'_0}{p_r}\right)^{0.52}$$

The French tests were carried out on a sample of material that had somewhat less fine elements in grading than that used in the FORCE experiment, at a moisture content W_{OPN} of 9 per cent at the beginning of test, varying to 10 per cent, and at levels of principal stresses lower than those used by Delft University of Technology. Nevertheless, the measured modulus values are of the same order as those measured by Delft when the same level of stresses is applied with respect to the time significance of p'_0 and p_r. Another study with a higher moisture content W = 12.6 per cent showed that the resilient modulus was decreasing (Figure V.2).

Applications to FORCE Project

Figure V.4 shows how the level of the water table changed during the course of the experiment. It can be seen that there was a period of likely absorption of water, at least into the original re-worked soil that remained on the site, between March and May, 1989, when the water table rose markedly. These changes resulted in changes to the moisture content of the subgrade which are shown in Figure V.5. The estimated variation of water content of the material during the experiment, (6.5 per cent to 10 per cent) may lead to a 3-fold change in the modulus. The changes in strength of the subgrade brought about by the changes in levels of the water table can be estimated if the consequent changes in the effective static pressure are known. These were estimated to be as shown in Figure V.6 for two depths in the subgrade, allowing likely changes in the estimated strength of the material to be calculated.

Table V.1

RESULTS OF ST. BRIEUC ON SUBGRADE MATERIAL, 1986

p'_0 kPa	p_r kPa	E MPa
10	5	127
	10	89
	50	39
	100	27
	150	22
30	5	226
	10	158
	50	59
	100	48
	150	39
60	5	321
	10	225
	50	98
	100	69
	150	56

Figure V.3

POISSON'S MODULUS AND COEFFICIENT

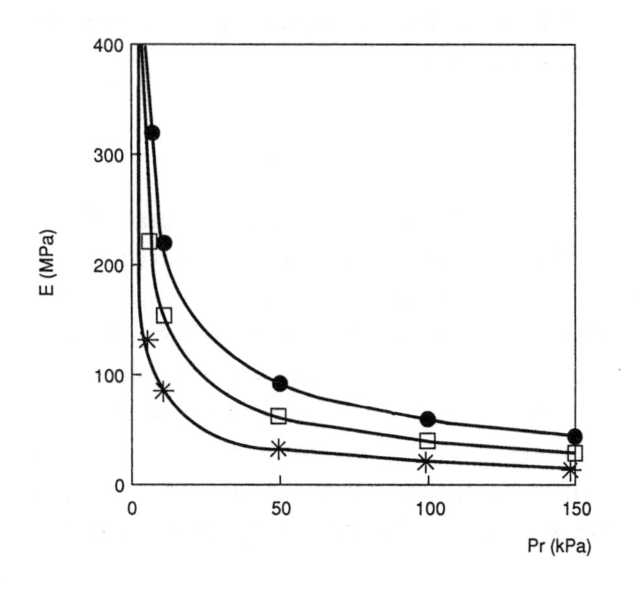

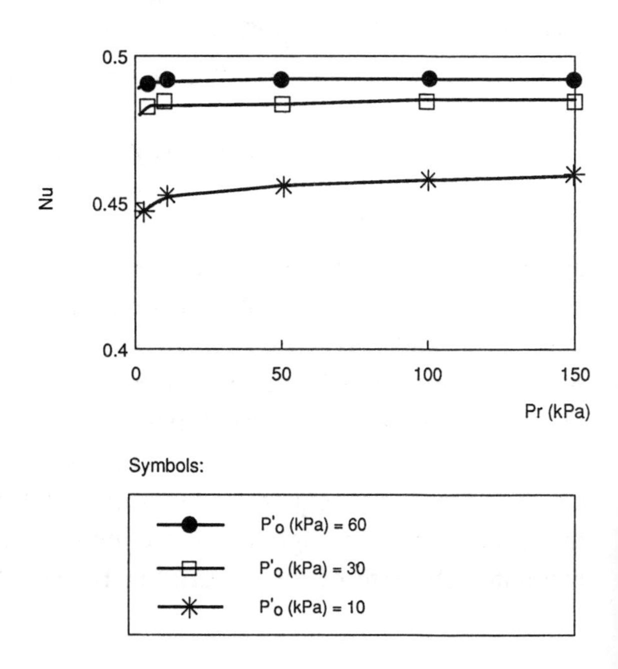

Figure V.4

LEVEL OF THE WATER TABLE

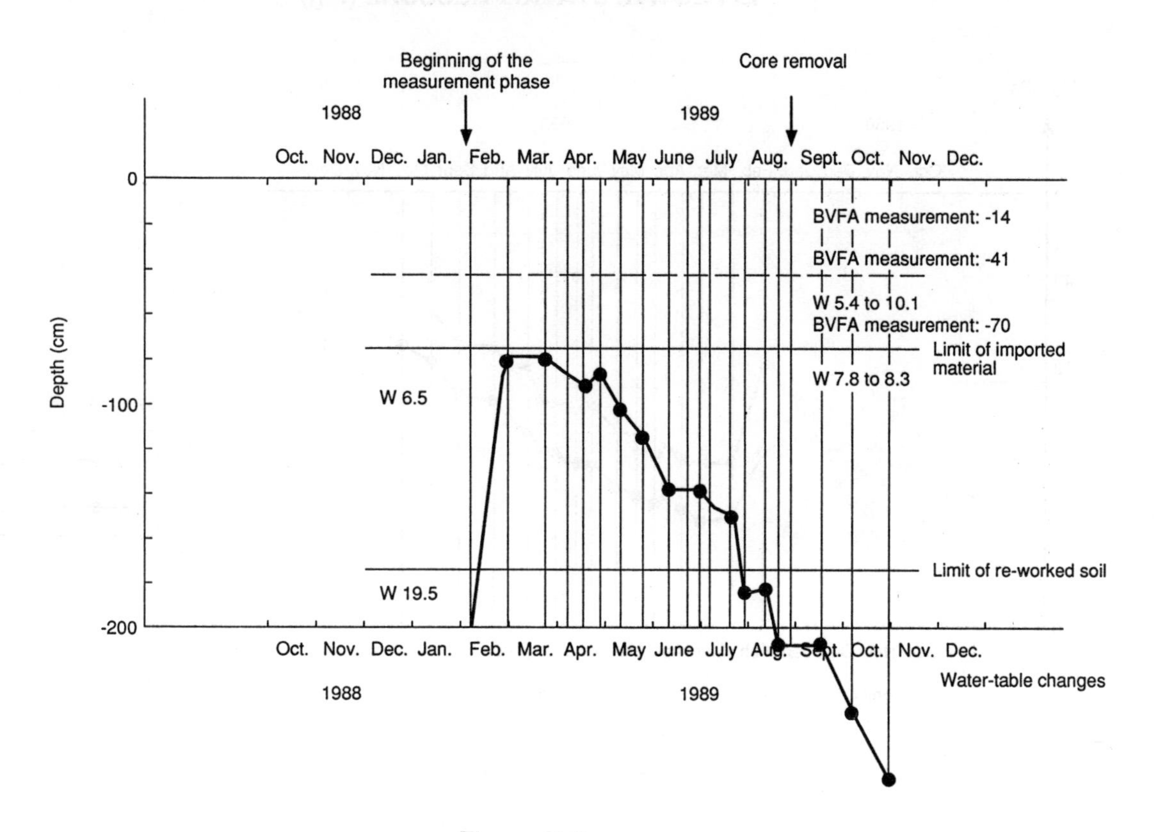

Figure V.5

CHANGES IN THE MOISTURE CONTENT

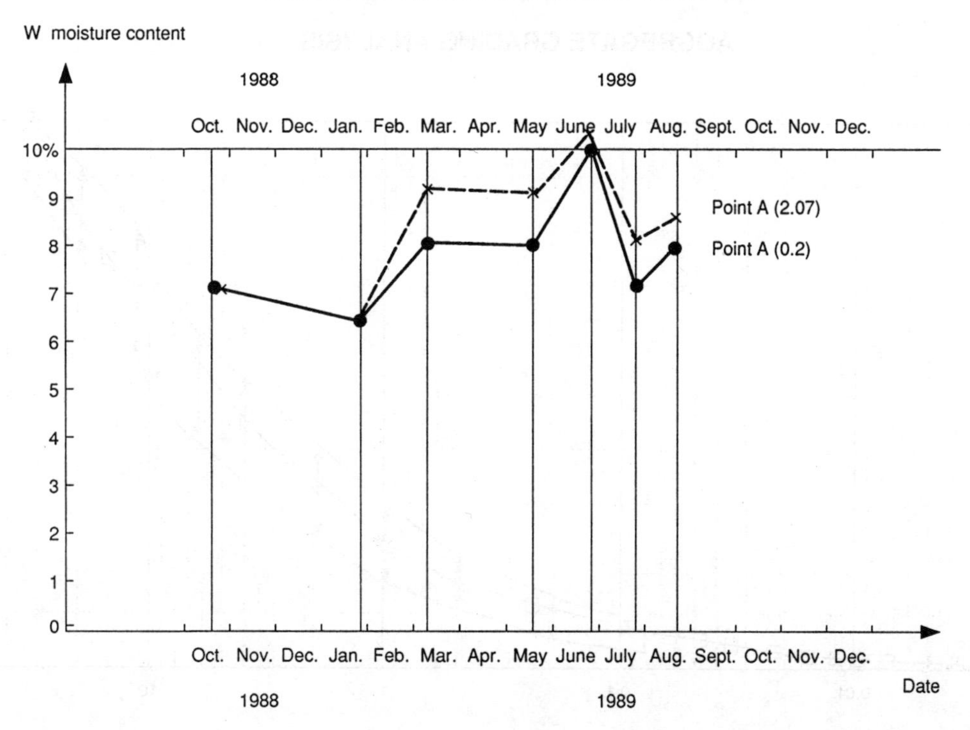

Figure V.6

EFFECTIVE STATIC PRESSURE (P'_o)

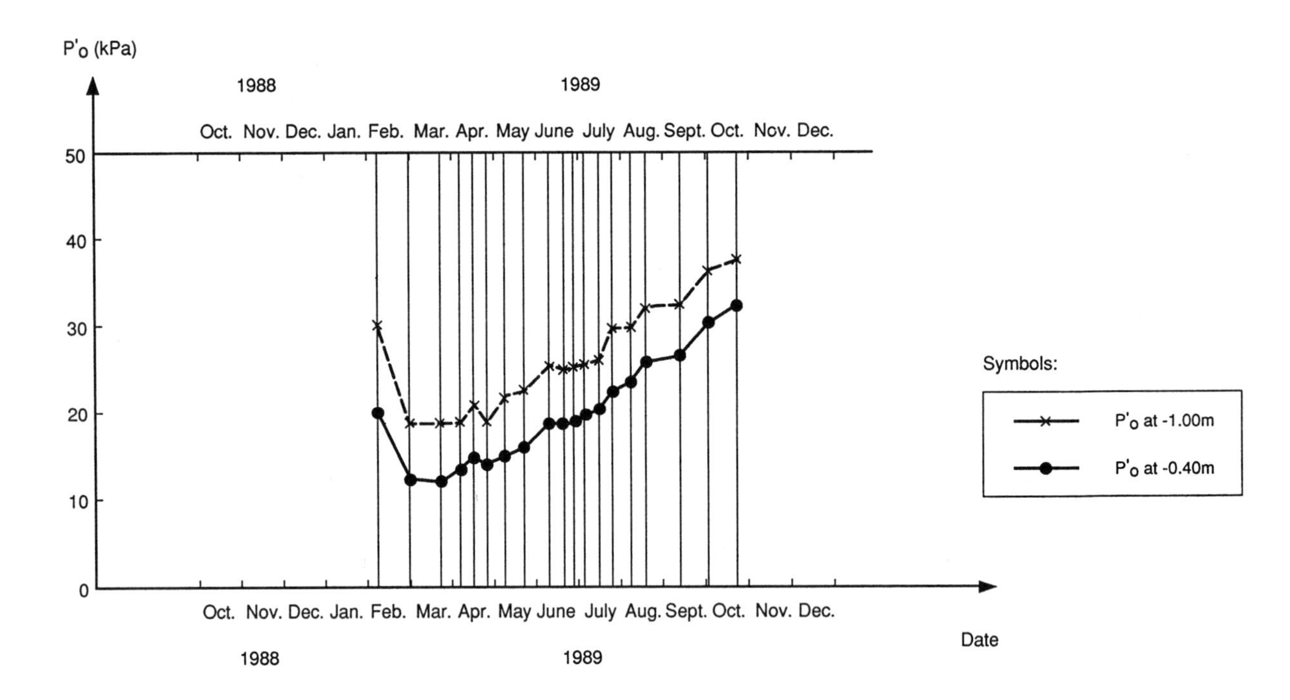

Figure V.7

AGGREGATE GRADING ANALYSIS

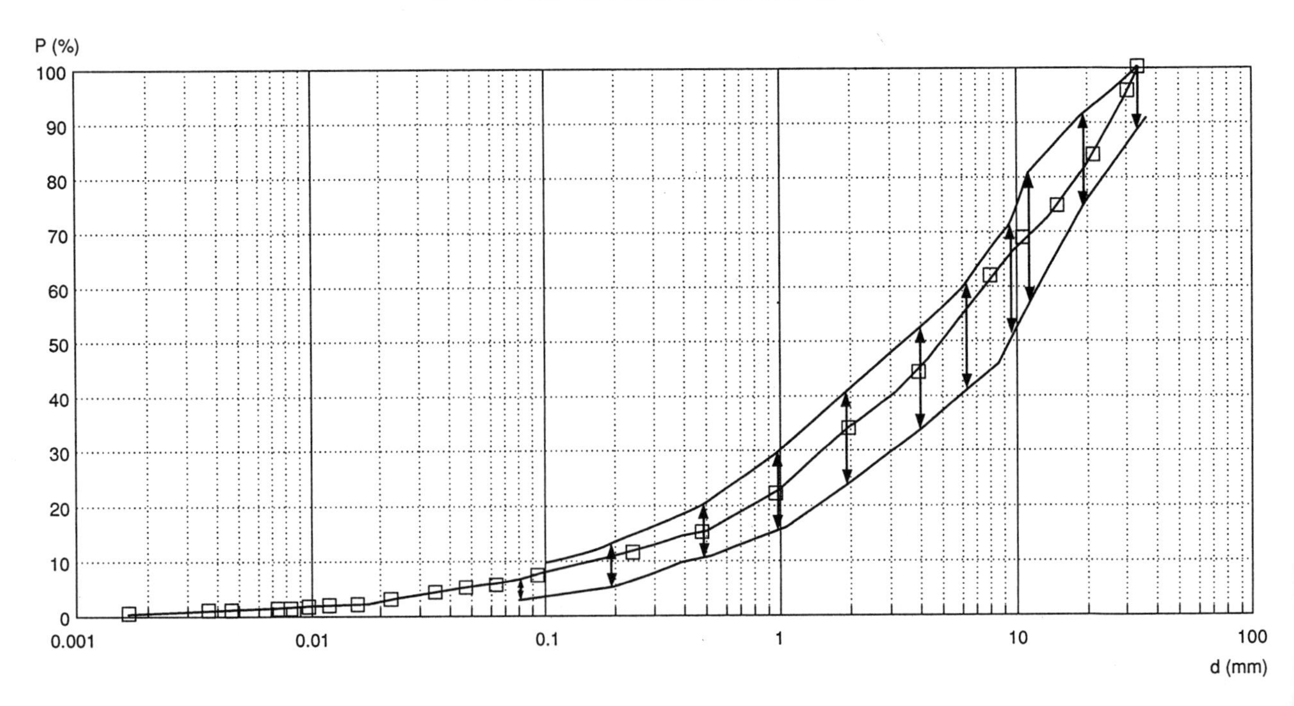

V.1.2. Granular materials

As noted in Chapter III and Annex A, the required general properties of the untreated granular material were that it should be representative of those materials used by participating members for road base layers and should have no exceptional characteristics. In practice, the selected material was a good quality crushed gneiss rock from the Maraîchères quarry near Nantes, having slightly poorer characteristics than that used in France for very heavily trafficked roads.

The 0/30 material selected was laid on 17th October 1988 by grader, and compacted with a smooth wheel tandem roller using partial vibration. During construction, the moisture content of the material was monitored and for four samples was found to average 4.85 per cent with a standard deviation of 0.245. After compaction the density achieved was 2100 kg/m^3 for a moisture of 4.6 per cent.

Samples of material taken during construction were subjected to a series of laboratory tests to establish the mechanical properties of the material; these were carried out at different laboratories, with the following results.

Aggregate Grading

Measurements of aggregate grading were carried out by BVFA, Austria. The results of the tests, together with the specified grading, are shown in Figure V.7. It is clear that the material used not only met the grading limits, but was very close to the centre of the acceptable grading limits.

Cyclic Load Triaxial Test

The Delft University of Technology carried out a large diameter triaxial test on the granular material. A single test specimen 400 mm diameter by 800 mm high was built, and subjected to a confining pressure, σ_3, created by sub-atmospheric pressure within the test piece, and a deviator stress comprising a static and cyclic component. The specimen achieved a moisture content of 5 per cent (against a target optimum of 4.6 per cent) and a density 97 per cent of the maximum density at optimum moisture content. The results of the tests at four different levels of confining pressure are reproduced in Figure V.8.

Using the same terminology as that in Equation V.1 to express the test parameters, the resilient modulus of the granular material can be best expressed as:

$$M_r = K_1 \left(\frac{\theta}{\theta_0} \right)^{K_2}$$

where $K_1 = 37$ MPa
$K_2 = 0.32$

V.1.3. Cement-treated granular material

The cement treated material used as the road base in Structure III was specified as the same grading as that used in the untreated material with the addition of 3.5 per cent by weight of cement. Little testing of the material was carried out at the time of construction. At the completion of the experiment, however, cores and slabs were removed from the structure in order to provide basic information on the material. Seven of the cores taken were investigated by Saint-Brieuc laboratory; the density of the material and its relative compaction were measured and the strength of the material was assessed by the indirect tensile (Brazilian) test. The results of these tests on each of the cores is given in the following Table:

Core No.	Diameter cm	Height cm	Density g/cm^3	Compaction %	Rupture MPa
1	15.75	15.5	2.214	83.2	1.35
2	15.75	15.5	2.188	82.2	1.15
6	15.42	16.5	2.136	80.3	1.25
7	15.75	16.5	2.160	81.2	1.19
8	15.75	16.5	2.171	81.6	-
12	15.73	16.5	2.188	82.2	1.16
13	15.73	16.0	2.188	82.2	-

Note: Modified Optimum Proctor (MOP) reference value $\Gamma d = 2.18$, $w = 6.5\%$. At the time of construction the average value of compaction was 97% of the MOP reference.

It was noted from the appearance of the cores that the material was of a good quality. No direct measurements of the modulus of the material have yet been made. However, the compaction of the material was good. Taking into account the indirect tensile strength compared with that of other similar materials, this suggests that the modulus of the FORCE cement treated base is at least 15 000 MPa.

Tests using the Falling Weight Deflectometer (FWD) were carried out at intervals during the experiment by RO DE CO (Italy). The report on these tests shows that when tests were carried out directly on the as-constructed road base materials, the mean modulus of the material was 10000 MPa with a range of 5000 - 20000 MPa. After the bituminous surfacing had been placed, FWD testing indicated that the mean modulus had risen to 20000 MPa, and this may be due to further curing of the material. These results compare well with those inferred from the indirect tensile tests. It is clear, however, that the FWD results also show that the subgrade exhibits a strong non-linear behaviour and this may affect the interpretation of modulus of the upper layers.

Later, after a period of trafficking during which Structure III became cracked, the modulus of the cement-treated gravel had fallen to approximately its initial value, and still later, when the section had become extensively cracked (30 per cent), the calculated modulus from FWD was only approximately 2000 MPa.

Figure V.8

RESILIENT MODULUS M_r VERSUS SUM OF PRINCIPAL STRESSES θ (GRANULAR MATERIAL)

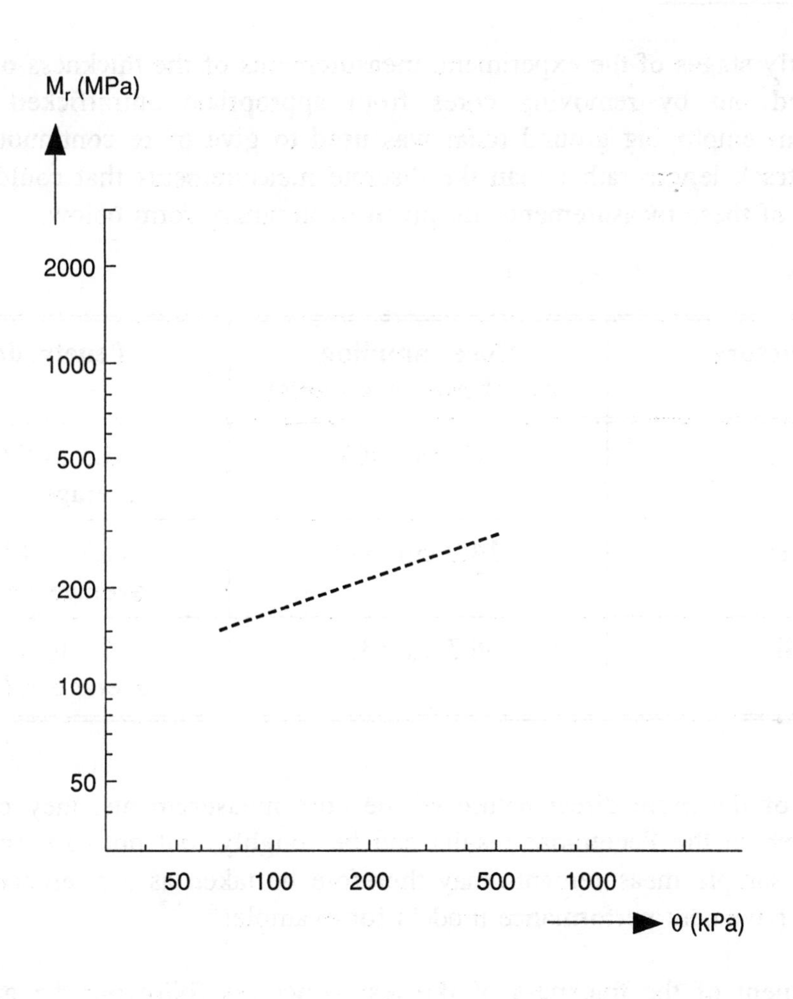

V.1.4. Bituminous material

The bituminous material used both for the initial construction and for the overlay was to the same specification as in Annex A. Many tests were carried out by a number of participating members; although these are not described in detail in the following, they are referred to where necessary.

Initial Observations

In the early stages of the experiment, measurements of the thickness of the constructed layers were carried out by removing cores from appropriate untrafficked areas. Later, a measurement system employing ground radar was used to give more continuous measurements around the whole track length rather than the discrete measurements that could be obtained by coring. The results of these measurements are given in summary form below.

Structure	Core sampling (no. of measurements)	Penetradar
I.	6.7 cm (10)	5.3 to 6.6, average 6 cm
II.	14.0 cm (11)	11.7 to 14.3, average 14 cm
III.	6.3 cm (3)	5.8 to 7.7, average 7.7 cm

Because of the more direct nature of the core measurements, they can be used as a reference against which the Penetradar results can be roughly, but not exactly, calibrated. The results of the core sample measurements may therefore be taken as a reference for use in later analysis, using the pavement performance models for example.

Measurement of the thickness of the test structures following the application of the overlay to test structure 01 yielded the results depicted in the table below which also presents the thicknesses for the non-overlaid structure 02:

Structure	Average thickness	Standard Deviation
01	63 mm	11 mm
02	139 mm	9 mm

It is clear that the average thickness of the overlay applied to Structure I is close to the thickness specified, but with a rather greater variability than is desirable. However, this is probably due to the excessively deteriorated longitudinal and transverse profiles of Structure I after the first phase of testing, which resulted in the need for an overlay of widely varying thickness. The thicknesses noted here were retained as the thicknesses of the bituminous layers for structures 01 and 02.

Grading

Aggregate grading of the bituminous material was examined by BVFA in Austria and by EPFZ in Switzerland. The results of these measurements showed good agreement in spite of the difficulties presented by the choice of different size sieves for sizes greater than 2 mm.

The average aggregate grading curve meets the contract requirements. However, the grading curves resulting from both tests, Figures V.9 and V.10, show a slight discontinuity in the 2mm to 6 mm range, which should favour compaction of the material.

Density and Binder Content

A number of laboratories carried out measurements of density and recovered binder content of the as-laid material.

The recovered bitumen content determined by BVFA, and confirmed by the tests carried out by EPFZ was between 5.9 and 6.2 per cent (average 6.0 per cent). Compared with the specified binder content of 6.45 per cent, this is rather low and could have had an effect on the fatigue characteristics and mechanical properties of the material. The recovered binder tested by BVFA gave a penetration index of between 36 and 39. This shows considerable hardening over the specified 60/70 penetration grade, and should again contribute to changes in the expected performance of the material.

The density of the samples tested by both BVFA and EPFZ gave values within the range 94.6 to 96.8 per cent of the theoretical maximum.

The void content measured by both laboratories, and expressed as percentage by volume, were

- BVFA: 5.3 per cent (Structure I) and 3.2 and 3.7 per cent (Structure II)
- EPFZ: 3.8, 3.6, 3.2 and 3.5 per cent on 4 samples from various locations

The state of compaction of the material was found to be very high. Values between 99.3 per cent and 100.5 per cent of the refusal density were recorded by BVFA on three samples.

Figure V.9

BITUMINOUS MATERIAL GRADING ANALYSIS CARRIED OUT BY AUSTRIA

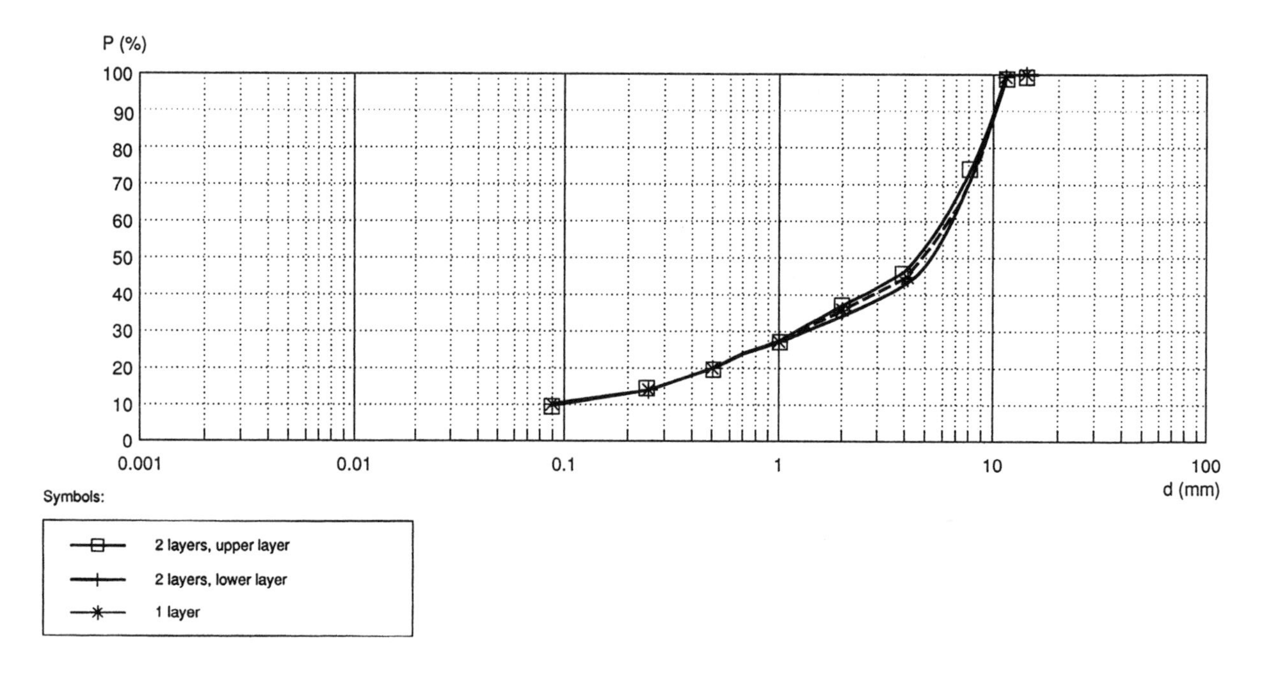

Figure V.10

BITUMINOUS MATERIAL GRADING ANALYSIS CARRIED OUT BY SWITZERLAND

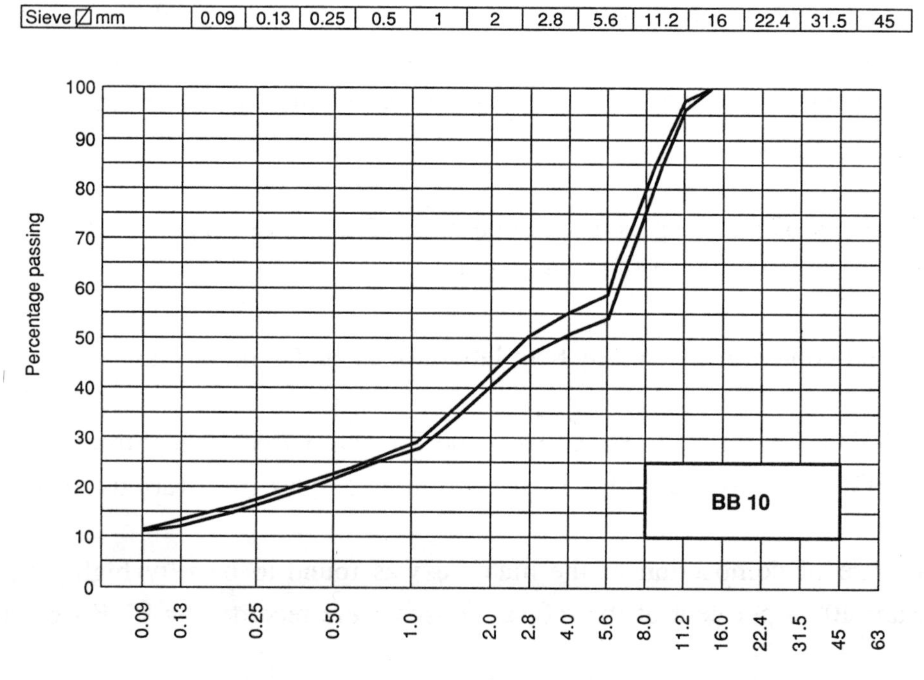

Mechanical Properties of the Material

Stiffness moduli. These were measured by three different organisations:

- Delft University of Technology
- The Bundesanstalt für Strassenwesen, Germany
- The ESSO company, France (for use with the MOEBIUS programme)

Different procedures were employed in each of these tests:

- Delft: dynamic 4-point bending test
- BASt : dynamic 2-point bending test
- ESSO : tension-compression test.

They are described in full elsewhere, but a brief comparison of their results shows interesting differences. Thus the ESSO compression type tests carried out at relatively low temperatures (2O°C and 10°C) result in values that are appreciably greater than those resulting from the Delft tests:

- 25 per cent to 30 per cent greater at a temperature of 10°C
- 15 per cent to 20 per cent greater at a temperature of 2O°C.

By comparison, the results obtained by BASt are still lower than those of Delft at temperatures of 0°C and below, although the differences are not as great, and approximately equal to those of Delft at temperatures of 20°C and above.

The results obtained by the three organisations are extensive, and a summary of the results is given in Table V.2 in order to illustrate the differences observed. Because the same conditions were not used by each of the laboratories, some of the results in the Table have been interpolated.

It appears that the bending tests give lower values for the modulus, particularly at temperatures below about 20°C, than the tension-compression test. Although it is difficult to assess the true value of the modulus, the ESSO tests were carried out in order to investigate creep of the material, and it is likely, therefore, that the Delft and/or BASt values are more appropriate for temperatures up to 30°C. Since the three tests give closer results at 30°C, the ESSO values can be considered to be representative of the modulus at temperatures of 40°C and 50°C.

Fatigue characteristics. Although fatigue tests were carried out by Delft University of Technology and by LCPC in France, only the results from Delft have been considered so far. These were obtained using a 4 point fatigue bending test rig designed to maintain a constant moment over a fairly long section of the test piece. The test was carried out at a frequency of 30 Hz, at a variety of temperatures and strain amplitudes. The test is deemed to have ended when the applied force decreases to half its original value. At that point the number of applications of the load is defined as the fatigue life.

Table V.2

STIFFNESS MODULUS OF BITUMINOUS MATERIAL

Temperature °C	Frequency Hz	Stiffness modulus MPa		
		ESSO	Delft	BaSt
-10	10		23700	20827
0	10		16700	15549
10	10	12350	8830	9997
20	10	6565	5100	5111
30	10	2579	2130	1966
40	10	920		613
50	10	358		

The fatigue relationships established by Delft University of Technology are as follows:

$$N = K \varepsilon^{-n}$$

where:

N =number of load applications to fatigue life
ε =initial strain amplitude
K =material constant
n =material constant.

On the basis of the results obtained on the OECD bituminous material, the coefficients in the above equation have been calculated for each of the test temperatures, using linear regression. The results of this calculation are shown in the following table.

Temperature °C	Factor K	Factor n	r^2
0	$9.583\ 10^{18}$	6.130	0.933
10	$3.607\ 10^{16}$	5.034	0.976
20	$4.015\ 10^{20}$	6.427	0.926

Using these values, the fatigue life of the OECD material can be expressed as:

At 0°C: $N = 9.583 \times 10^{18} \times \varepsilon^{-6.13}$

10°C: $N = 3.607 \times 10^{16} \times \varepsilon^{-5.034}$

20°C: $N = 4.015 \times 10^{20} \times \varepsilon^{-6.427}$

where ε is expressed in micro-strain.

These equations now allow fatigue lives of the material to be estimated for given levels of strain applied to it at given temperatures, or the calculation of strain required to bring about failure of the material in a given number of cycles. For example the strains required ($\varepsilon.10^{-6}$) to give "lives" of 10^4, 10^5 and 10^6 cycles at different temperatures were calculated to be as shown in Table V.3.

Table V.3

CALCULATED MICROSTRAINS FOR GIVEN "LIVES"

	Cycles to failure		
Temp.	**10^4**	**10^5**	**10^6**
0°C	277	190	130
10°C	312	197	125
20°C	383	268	187

The values at 10°C and 30 Hz at 10^6 cycles are fairly close to those reported elsewhere for similar materials. Temperature clearly plays an important role in determining the levels of strain required but the effect appears to be non-linear in spite of the very different stiffness modulus values found for the fatigue test condition of 30 Hz at the lower temperatures.

Because during the trafficking of the pavements, temperatures in the bituminous pavements were likely to rise to greater than 20°C, it is desirable to know the fatigue behaviour of the material at these temperatures so that estimates of pavement life can be made, using models of pavement performance, etc. However, extrapolation of the Delft results beyond the test temperature range is difficult, since the type of equation often used for this purpose

$$(\varepsilon_{\Theta N}) \times (E_{\Theta})^{\alpha} = \text{constant}$$

where Θ = temperature
N = number of cycles
E = stiffness modulus of the material
α = material constant,

does not appear to be directly applicable. In spite of the uncertainties surrounding the use of this equation, it is proposed that it be applied for taking account of temperatures above 20°C. The value of the material constant, α, was estimated from the geometric means of the values of strain given in Table V.3 to be between 0.3 and 0.5 , rather lower than have been reported elsewhere.

V.1.5. Summary

For the purpose of the various analyses of the results of the experiment it is necessary to use the same values of material for the material parameters. There will, of course, be a need to examine the effects of possible variations in materials properties, and for those purposes, the degree of change can be specified.

The results described in the earlier sections of this Chapter show some variability, and consideration has been given to recommended values, or recommended methods for extracting values, to allow analyses of the performance of the experiment to proceed. These considerations may be summarised as follows.

Soil

The question of soil modulus values must be treated with caution since there are few results on which to base a recommendation. Only Delft University of Technology succeeded in carrying out tests, and these were on material whose grading had been altered in order to make the test possible. These tests yielded an equation describing the soil modulus, as follows:

$$M_r = 56.8 \left(\frac{\theta}{\theta_0}\right)^{0.32} MPa$$

In the supporting analysis of soil modulus described in earlier tests carried out on rather different material, it was suggested that the use of the equation

$$M_r = 88.4 \left(\frac{p'_0}{p_r} \right)^{0.5} \quad MPa$$

would give adequate values for the modulus. It is likely that the average effective stress applied to the subgrade is about 25-30 kPa, leading to the prediction of high modulus values.

Although both equations give high modulus values, consistent with the very high CBR values found, experience in United Kingdom suggests an (invalidated) relationship between CBR and modulus (E) as follows:

$$E(MPa) = 17.6\ (CBR)^{0.64}$$

Using a value of 31 per cent (see Section V.1.1.) for the CBR in this formula gives a modulus value of 158 MPa., similar to that predicted by the Delft University of Technology equation above, whereas the FWD testing carried out on the pavements suggests modulus values for the soil in the range 50 - 100 MPa (and the Austrian Plate Bearing Test on the subgrade giving about 55 MPa). For these reasons, it is considered that Equation V.1 be used for the estimation of soil modulus.

Untreated Gravel Road Base

The expression describing the modulus of the gravel material, on the basis of the earlier analysis, was:

$$M_r = 37.0 \left(\frac{\theta}{\theta_0} \right)^{0.32} \quad MPa$$

This suggests a slightly weaker material than an earlier French study indicated, but the difference is small compared to probable variations in overall strength due to thickness of the layer, especially when the stress level applied to the gravel layer was relatively high. It is therefore proposed that this be used for the estimation of modulus of the untreated gravel material.

Cement-treated Gravel Material

Only basic tests have been carried out so far on the cement treated material. These indicate that the material met the specification and that it was laid and compacted satisfactorily. In the absence of the results of more specific tests on the material, which it is expected will be available later, it is proposed that values derived from FWD testing on the pavement be adopted where necessary. These should be compared with and supported by the results of specific testing on similar materials.

FWD testing on the pavement suggested a value for the elastic modulus shortly after construction in the range 5000 - 20000 MPa, with a mean of 10000 MPa. It is very similar to that reported by tests on similar cement-bound materials. The back-calculated modulus of the material rose after the application of the bituminous layer to about 20000 MPa, indicating further curing of the layer, or a strong effect due to the subgrade non-linearity. After a period of trafficking which resulted in 30 per cent cracking, the calculated modulus had fallen to about 20 per cent of this initial value, i.e. approximately 2000 MPa. It is proposed, therefore to assume a value for the initial modulus of the material of 20000 MPa, which decreases linearly with the number of applications of the wheel load (to the point at which it was overlaid) to about 2000 MPa.

Bituminous Material

Modulus. For temperatures up to 30°C it is proposed that the values found by Delft University of Technology or BASt should be used for further analyses. The equation describing the Delft results should be used for any further interpolation.

For temperatures above 30°C, values found by ESSO in their tests and reported by them should be used.

Fatigue. The fatigue tests carried out by Delft University of Technology appear to give satisfactory results for the purposes of analysis of the performance of the pavements. The relationship between fatigue life and strain described earlier in this report should be used, and where interpolations to take account of different temperatures are necessary, the modifying relationship should be used, taking $\alpha = 0.4$.

V.2. GENERAL BEHAVIOUR OF THE PAVEMENTS

In the course of the experiment, a number of measurements were made, as described earlier. Of these, some were widely recognised parameters of pavement performance, namely cracking, rutting, longitudinal profile and transient deflection. These were used to indicate how each of the structures tested had behaved, as discussed hereunder.

V.2.1 Responses as recorded by the measuring system

During the experiment, test track measurements and observations were made and each measurement was identified geometrically (x = longitudinal displacement of the wheel, y = location along the radius, z = depth) and date (t).

In representing the behaviour of a pavement structure in terms of an analytical or empirical model the result R (x, y, z, t) depends on:

-- the nature of loading and stress
-- the geometry of the structure

-- the characteristics of the pavement courses, and
-- the integrity of these courses.

All these data depend on time t.

V.2.2. Effect of temperature during sensor measurements

In the case of bituminous concrete, temperature is a major factor; the methods and problems of measuring and recording temperatures are dealt with in Chapter VI.

At the time of the Point Zero inventory, temperatures tended to be relatively low and although temperatures on subsequent days were higher, they remained generally moderate during test measurements since these were often taken early in the day.

The TRRL has worked out a set of formulae for correcting the results for temperature by means of a regression analysis of all the sensor readings obtained at the time of the Point Zero inventory, for which different temperatures were recorded (see also Chapter VI).

The rules adopted for comparing the results are the following:

(1) $\frac{\sigma_T}{\sigma_{20}} = 0{,}70 + 0{,}015\ T$ for structures I/11 et I/01 before overlay

(2) $\frac{\sigma_T}{\sigma_{20}} = 0{,}52 + 0{,}024\ T$ for structures II/12 et II/02

(3) $\frac{\sigma_T}{\sigma_{20}} = 0{,}76 + 0{,}012\ T$ for structures III/13 and III/03 before overlay

where σ_T is the value for T°C; σ_{20} the value for 20°C.

The variation selected after overlaying sections 01 and 03 was that of section 02 as this variation is related to the thickness of the bituminous layer. The temperature values selected are given in Table V.4.

V.2.3. Overall structural behaviour

The overall behaviour of the pavement structures was examined by studying the impact of two different loads (10 and 11.5 tonnes) on three new structures:

-- A thin, flexible structure corresponding to sections 11 and 01 before overlay;
-- A thick, flexible structure corresponding to sections 12 and 02;
-- A semi-rigid structure corresponding to sections 13 and 03 before overlay.

After the damaged structures had been overlaid, an analysis was made of the behaviour under the impact of the 11.5 tonne load on a damaged thin, flexible structure strengthened by a thin bituminous overlay (section 01 after strengthening) and a damaged semi-rigid structure strengthened by a thin bituminous overlay (section 03 after strengthening).

The criteria adopted for the overall analysis of the pavement were visible changes to the initial geometric and physical state of the test sections and changes in a global bearing capacity factor of the structures.

Changes include cracking, corresponding to the ruptures in the surface course, permanent deformation in the cross section with the appearance of ruts in the bituminous layers, and deterioration in the longitudinal profile -- though in this case any changes observed may not be considered significant since dynamic effects were as far as possible avoided -- as well as changes in deflection under different loadings.

The results considered here are deflections measured with the Benkelman beam under the loads applied by the circular test machine, and Falling Weight Deflectometer measurements. In the latter case tests were made in 1 metre steps showing the more or less heterogeneous nature of the bearing capacity along the longitudinal profile.

V.2.4. Cracking of the various structures

During trafficking of the different pavements, a significant degree of cracking was attained on sections 11 and 01 (70-90 per cent before overlay), having an untreated crushed rock base and a thin bituminous layer, and sections 13 and 03 with a cement treated base (25-30 per cent before overlay). Some very slight indications of cracking on sections 02 and 12 appeared after the application of 400 000 13T axle loads as the last phase of the experiment. Figure V.11 shows the development of cracking as a function of the number of applications of wheel load for each of the sections. Where sections were overlaid, no further cracking was observed as a result of additional trafficking.

The development of surface cracking for five structures is depicted in Annex D. A comparison of the behaviour of each of the sections is most easily made from the semi-logarithmic presentations of Figure V.11. In general, on those sections where cracking took place, its development proceeds in two phases. In the first phase, little or no changes take place until cracking is well-established. Following this phase, cracking develops at a much faster rate, and, for the fully flexible pavements, according to a semi-logarithmic law. For the cement treated structure, the semi-logarithmic law is less well-defined.

It is useful also to consider when cracking was first observed in each of the sections. An examination of Figure V.11 gives the results depicted in the table below (see page 88). There are some inconsistencies in these results, but this is not unexpected, since the onset of cracking in any pavement cannot be predicted with any confidence.

Table V.4.

AVERAGE TEMPERATURES OF THE BITUMINOUS CONCRETE DURING THE VARIOUS MEASUREMENT PHASES

	6/03	7/03	8/03	9/03	13/03	14/03	30/03	14/04	21/04	26/04	12/05
8:00									6.3		
9:00					9.5	7			7 8		
10:00	10.5 11.5	11 11	9	10	9.5 10	7.5 8.2		8 9.5	9 11	8 9	13.5
11:00	12.7 13.8	11 10.5	10 10.5	11.3 12.5	11 14	9 10	14 15	11.3 12.5	12 13.5	11.5 13.5	13.7 14
12:00		10.5	11.5 12.5	14 15	16 17.5	12 14	16.5 18	14 15		14.5 16	15 16
13:00	17		14	16.5 17.5	19 20			18			
14:00	18 20	10.5 11	16	18 18.5	21 21.5		25	17.5 17.5		21	
15:00	20.5 21.5	11.2 11.5	16 16	18.7 18	22 22		25 25	17.5 18			
16:00	21.7 22	12 12.5		17.5 17	21.5 20			19 20			
17:00		13		16.7 16.5				20 20			
18:00											
	13/06	14/6	20/06	4/07	25/07	4/08	10/08	15/09	18/09	28/09	
8:00					16					15	
9:00		21.5		20.5	17 19	17.5 18	17	17		15.5 16.5	
10:00		22.5 23.5	26.5 27	21 22	19.5	18.5 19	17.5 19	17.5 19	20	17.5 18	
11.00		24 25	29 29	23 24					20.5 21	19.5 21	
12:00										22 23.5	
13.00	32										
14:00	34 35										
15:00											

V.2.5. Rutting of the various structures

At regular intervals throughout the test, the transverse profile of the pavements, at 5 positions on each section, were measured. From these measurements, the maximum rut depth was calculated. Figures V.12 - V.13 show the development of rutting (as represented by the maximum rut depth) plotted on a semi-logarithmic scale against the number of wheel loads.

It appears that the development of rutting follows, in general, a logarithmic law. However, in the case of the thin bituminous structure with a granular base, a change of slope after a period of trafficking was noted. In order to examine whether there is any relationship between this change of slope and the development of cracking, Figures V.12 and V.13 also show the moment when the first crack was observed on a particular section. There is no clear correlation and it must be concluded that the onset of cracking does not of itself explain the rapid development of rutting in sections 01 and 11. On the other hand, it would appear to be a factor in accelerating the development of rutting in the semi-rigid structure of section 03.

V.2.6. Longitudinal profile and functional quality of structures.

Present Serviceability Index P.S.I. and Slope Variance SV

The longitudinal profiles of the test sections were measured at intervals during the experiment to give a further measure of the overall performance of the pavements. For roads in service, such information can be used directly, or in combination with other parameters, rutting for example, to indicate pavement condition in terms of Present Serviceability Index (*P.S.I.*). If this, or a similar parameter, can be developed for the FORCE test pavements, the behaviour of the inner sections (10t axle loads) can be compared with that of the outer sections (11t axle loads), and correlations between it and structural behaviour can also be examined for example in terms of deflection and strain of the bituminous concrete.

The *P.S.I.* is a number between 0 (very bad) and 5 (very good), expressing the functional quality of a pavement structure. The general equation for the calculation of *P.S.I.* for pavement structures with a bituminous surface layer is:

$$P.S.I. = 5{,}03 - 1{,}91 \log(1+SV) - 0{,}01\sqrt{(C+P)} - 0{,}00214 RD \qquad \text{Eq. V.2}$$

where

P.S.I. = present serviceability index, expressing the functional quality of the pavement structure

SV = the mean slope variance of the two wheel tracks of a section

C = the surface with severe cracking, expressed in $m^2/1000\ m^2$

P = the surface that has been maintained, expressed in $m^2/1000\ m^2$

RD = the mean rut depth (mm) in both wheel tracks (rut depth measured every 7,5 m)

The length of the FORCE test sections is limited: 40 m for sections 01, 02 and 03 and 33 m for sections 11, 12 and 13. Furthermore, the limited length of the test sections does not allow a satisfactory definition of the variables C, P and RD in the equation noted above. For these reasons, Eq.V.2 may not be applicable and some other parameter describing the deterioration of longitudinal profile may be necessary.

From experience in the Netherlands, taking account of longitudinal evenness in the definition of slope variance, wavelengths of 0,3 - 40 m are important for the definition of *P.S.I.*. These wavelengths determine the comfort of the road users and the magnitude of dynamic axle loads. The parameter developed takes account only of the slope variance of each test section, and is referred to as SV_{25} defined as follows:

$$SV_{25} = 5{,}03 - 1{,}91\log(1 + SV^{*}) \qquad \text{Eq. V.3}$$

* SV is defined as the variance of the slopes measured between points spaced 25 cm.

Interpretation of Measuring Results

Longitudinal evenness of the different FORCE test sections was measured several times during the test. These measurements were carried out using the equipment developed by LCPC and mounted on the moving wheels of the test facility. Measurement of longitudinal profile was carried out by turning the circular test machine at low speed, so that dynamic vertical displacements of the moving wheels can be neglected. Longitudinal evenness was recorded as the (relative) height of the surface of a test section as a function of the longitudinal position around the wheel track. Table V.5 indicates when longitudinal profile measurements were performed during the test, including date and number of wheel loads applied.

Calculation of SV_{25} involves first the calculation of the slope variance, using the results of the longitudinal profile measurements. Slope variance SV is defined as follows:

$$SV = \frac{\sum_{i=1}^{n} (x_i - x_m)^2}{n-1} \qquad \text{Eq. V.4}$$

where x_i is the slope, x_m is the mean slope and n the number of measured slopes.

As stated earlier, slope variance is defined arbitrarily as the variance of the slopes between points 25 cm apart. However, in the FORCE experiment, the distance between the measuring points was not 25 cm., and the measured data were therefore adjusted to take account of this. For the first two measurements, executed on 27 February and 14 March 1989 for all sections, the distance between the measuring points was greater than 25 cm. It was unwise to adjust this data to a smaller distance between the data points, because larger errors occur when doing so. For the very early phase of the test, therefore, SV_{25} cannot be reasonably calculated. For the remaining measurements the distance between measuring points was much smaller than 25 cm, so that the adjustment can be made.

Figure V.11

CRACKING OF THE VARIOUS SECTIONS

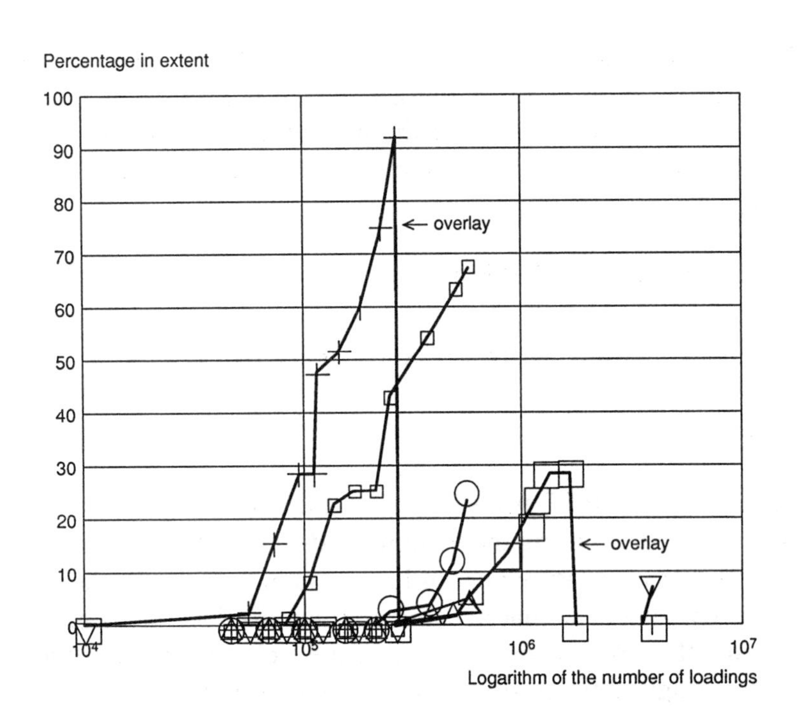

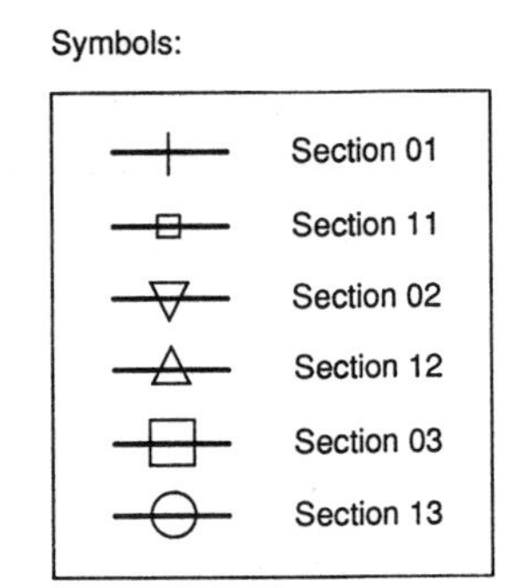

Section No.	Appearance of the first crack	
	Tonnes	No. of cycles
01	11.5	72 600
11	10	103 000
02	11.5	3 800 000
12	10	370 000
03	11.5	550 000
13	10	240 000

Figure V.12

RUT DEPTH ON THE OUTER RADIUS
(11.5 tonnes)

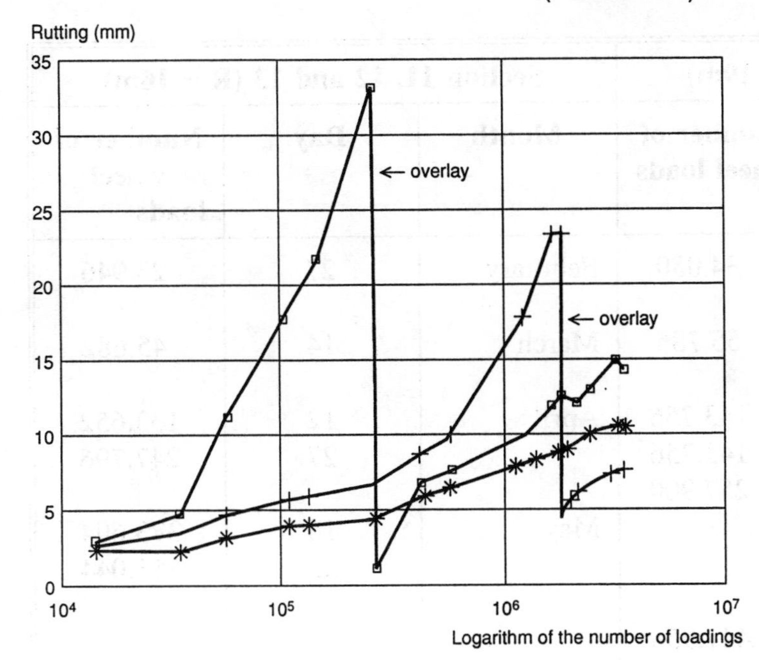

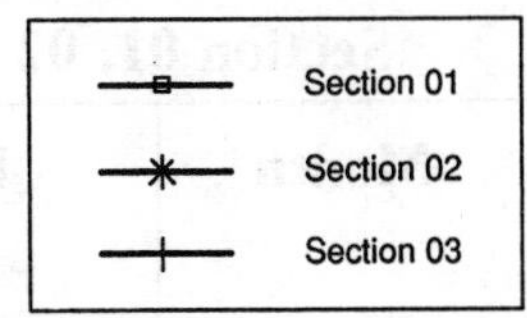

Figure V.13

RUT DEPTH ON THE INNER RADIUS
(10 tonnes)

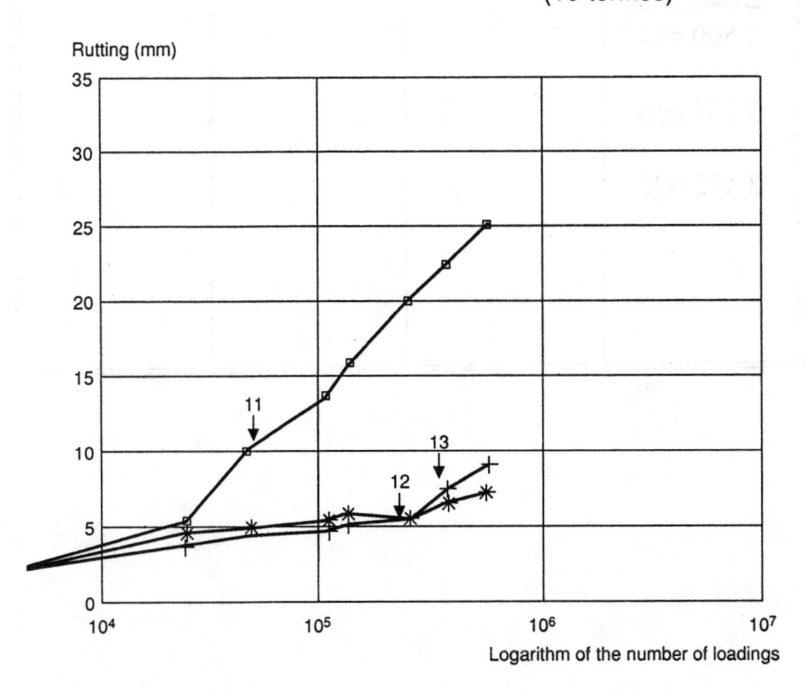

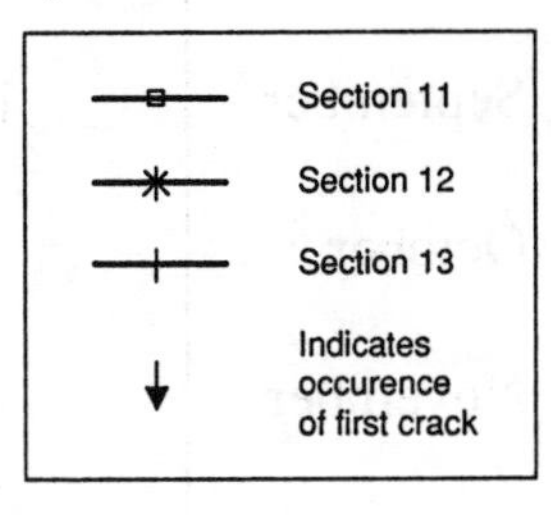

Table V.5.

OVERVIEW OF LONGITUDINAL PROFILE MEASUREMENTS (YEAR 1989)

Section 01, 02 and 03 (R = 19m)			Section 11, 12 and 13 (R = 16m)		
Month	**Day**	**Number of wheel loads**	**Month**	**Day**	**Number of wheel loads**
February	27	34.050	February	27	23.946
March	14	55.786	March	14	45.682
April	11	143.756	April	12	133.652
	12	143.756		27	247.796
	27	257.900			
May			May	16	373.604
				22	561.044
June	19	441.958			
	29	680.906			
July	7	1.067.546			
	20	1.668.022			
	25	1.790.574			
	28	1.790.574			
August	7	2.046.358			
	22	2.500.482			
September	14	3.164.866			
October	4	3.432.902			
November					
December					

The following data were considered for further interpretation:

-- Sections 11, 12 and 13: measurements of 27 April, 29 June, 7 July, 20 July, 7 August, 22 August, 14 September and 4 October

-- Sections 01, 02 and 03: measurements of 12 April, 27 April, 16 May and 22 May

A second problem arises from the joints between different sections on the test track. In these areas large differences in height of the sections occurred within a relatively short distance. In comparison with the rather short length of the test sections it may be that these local extreme unevennesses strongly affect the result of the SV_{25} calculation. An example of this phenomenon is given in Figure V.14, which shows the development of the longitudinal profile of section 12 at four different points of time during the test.

Because these extreme differences in height between two sections disturb the description of the development of the longitudinal profile in an undesirable way, the extremities of the sections have not been taken into account for the calculation of SV_{25}. The results of the calculation of SV_{25} are given in Figure V.15 (inner sections R=16 m) and Figure V.16 (outer sections R=19 m).

Discussion

Because it was not possible to calculate reliable values of SV_{25} at the very beginning of the test (see Figures V.15 and V.16), there is no accurate reference for the calculated results.

Generally it can be stated that the calculated SV_{25}-levels are rather low. When these calculated results are translated to practice, maintenance works would have been executed near the beginning of the test. However, the low SV_{25}-levels could possibly be explained by the fact that it is rather difficult to obtain a good longitudinal profile when building circular test sections with a radius of 16 or 19 m.

Figure V.15 shows the lowest SV_{25}-level for section 11 before overlay. This is what would have been anticipated since section 11 had the thinnest bituminous layer of 6 cm. Sections 12 and 13 show a comparable behaviour with respect to longitudinal evenness.

For section 01 (Figure V.16) SV_{25} is shown only after the overlay. (Just before the overlay, SV_{25} for section 01 was 1.05; this point is not shown in the figure). The behaviour in terms of SV_{25} for sections 01 (after overlay) and 02 is very comparable. It is not clear what happens to section 03 at about 2 million applications of the wheel load. Furthermore it can be seen that all three sections 01, 02 and 03 seem to break down after about 3,2 million applications of the wheel load.

Because of lack of measurements for sections 11, 12 and 13, comparison with sections 01, 02 and 03 is not possible.

The following conclusions can be drawn:

1. The limited length of the FORCE test sections does not allow a satisfactory definition of functional quality in terms of *PSI*.
2. Although the limited amount of data available prevents reliable correlations between loss of longitudinal evenness and number of wheel loads applied, it is clear that considerable deterioration took place, and the calculation of SV_{25} shows how this developed.

V.2.7. Pavement bearing capacity

The bearing capacity was assessed by measurements of the deflection of each pavement section.

Measurements with the Benkelman Beam

The load used in these tests was the one used normally by the test machine. Figure V.17 presents deflection measurements along the profiles under the 10-tonne axle (sections 11, 12 and 13) and the 11.5-tonne axle (sections 01, 02 and 03) at the start of the testing. Measurements were made at a low frequency (in the region of 0.5 to 1 Hertz) and the results highlight the great difference between the thin flexible structure and the thick flexible structure. The mean deflection for the thin course (approximately 150.10^{-2} mm) is twice that of the thick flexible structure. At this stage, the thin structure was not cracked and the difference in thickness of the bituminous overlays (140 mm as against 63 mm) is not enough to explain the difference in deflection, which should probably be attributed to non-linear characteristics of the untreated materials (soil and gravel) as explained in section V.1.

The graph also shows that the flexible structures' longitudinal profile is more or less homogeneous and that no differences in deflection are observed between measurements made under a 10-tonne load (sections 11 and 12) and those under an 11.5-tonne load (sections 01 and 02).

Deflections in the semi-rigid pavement are more heterogenous. There are two main zones: one in the central third of the section's length where the deflection is high (around 75.10^{-2} mm) and where behaviour is similar to that of a flexible pavement; and a zone corresponding to the remaining two thirds, where deflection is low (around $30\text{-}50.10^{-2}$) and similar to what may be expected of a semi-rigid structure.

Under the combined action of traffic and weathering, deflection increases, particular in the early stages and quite markedly on the semi-rigid structures of sections 13 and 03 before overlaying (25th July). There are two reasons for this: a rise in temperature and, more significantly, failure of the treated base (see Figure V.18).

Figure V.14

CHANGE OF LONGITUDINAL PROFILE — SECTION 12 (YEAR 1989)

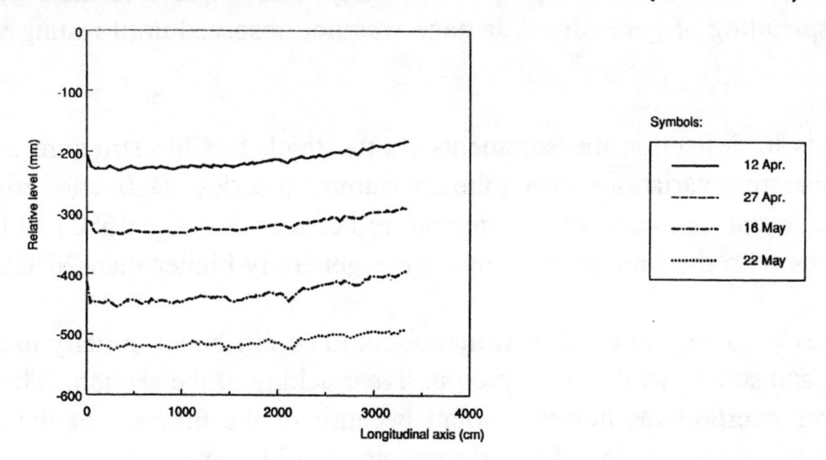

Figure V.15

CHANGE OF SV_{25} FOR SECTIONS 11, 12, 13 (RADIUS 16m)

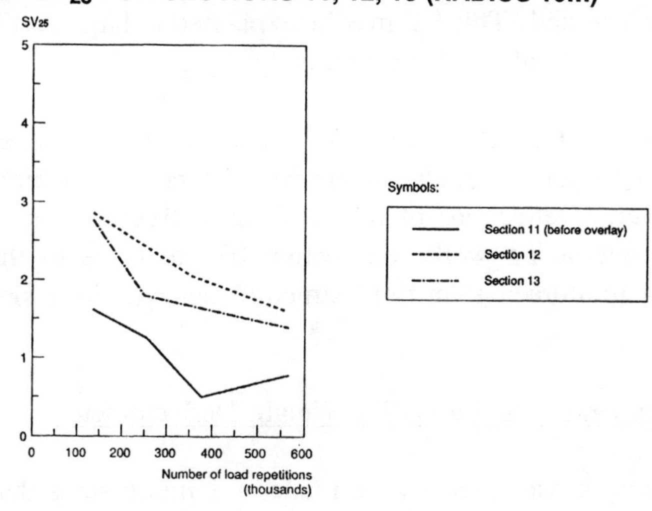

Figure V.16

CHANGE OF SV_{25} FOR SECTIONS 01, 02, 03 (RADIUS 19m)

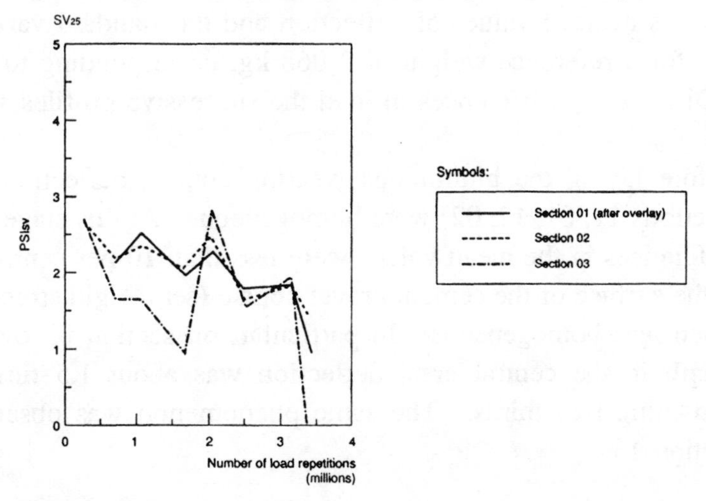

If the global changes occurring in the sections are analysed in more detail it is observed that damage spreads from the weak and partly damaged central area to the whole of the section. On section 03, spreading of generalised damage was not observed until testing was resumed with four arms.

Changes in deflection measurements on the thick flexible structure could be attributed primarily to temperature variations during the measurement series. Deflection rose by some 20 per cent between the initial measurements (temperature between 10° and 15°C) and those made after resuming rotations with the four arms (temperature generally higher than 20°C).

Changes occurring in the thin structure could be attributed initially to the characteristics of the sub-grade and subsequently to the progressive cracking of the section. The relative variation in deflection after overlay was however small because of the thinness of the section (less than 15 per cent after the second series of measurements on 27th February).

Following the overlay of the damaged sections (01 and 03) and at the end of the test, the deflection slightly lessened. This fall may be explained in large part by the lower temperatures and the fall in the water table after a long, relatively dry period.

Numerically, the effectiveness of the overlay may be expressed as a factor of 1.5; deflection is about 10 per cent higher than that for section 02 which had the same total thickness of bituminous layer. Deflections of the semi-rigid structures were reduced by a factor of 1.7. Deflections after overlaying works on section 03 are close to those observed on section 02, confirming that a reinforced semi-rigid structure behaves in a similar way to a thick flexible pavement.

Measurements with the Falling Weight Deflectometer

Deflection measurements were made at 1 metre steps during the seven main series of measurements (the eighth measuring the effectiveness of the overlay works on section 03).

Given the specific operating conditions of the FWD, not all the tests used the same load. The Table V.6 gives average values of deflection and the standard variations for each of the test sections adjusted for a reference weight of 7 068 kg, corresponding to an average plate pressure of 1 000 kPa. Discounting differences in load the successive profiles show that:

-- Before laying the bituminous wearing course, deflections on the granular courses (sections 11, 01, 12, 02) were homogeneous. At this stage of pavement construction, differences in the mean values were less than 10 per cent. Deflection measurements at the surface of the cement gravel course (semi-rigid structure, sections 13, 03) were much less homogeneous. In particular, on section 03 over around one third of its length in the central area, deflection was about 1.5 times as high than over the remaining two thirds. The same phenomenon was observed to a lesser extent on section 13.

Figure V.17

LONGITUDINAL PROFILES ACCORDING TO BENKELMAN BEAM DEFLECTIONS AT THE BEGINNING OF THE TEST (27th February 1989)

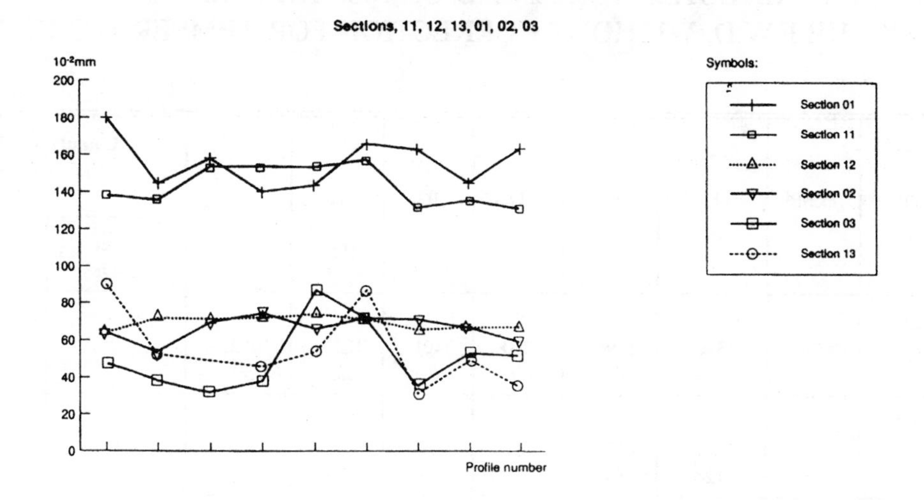

Figure V.18

CHANGES IN MEAN BENKELMAN BEAM DEFLECTIONS AS A FUNCTION OF TEST PROGRESS

(values not modified in temperature)

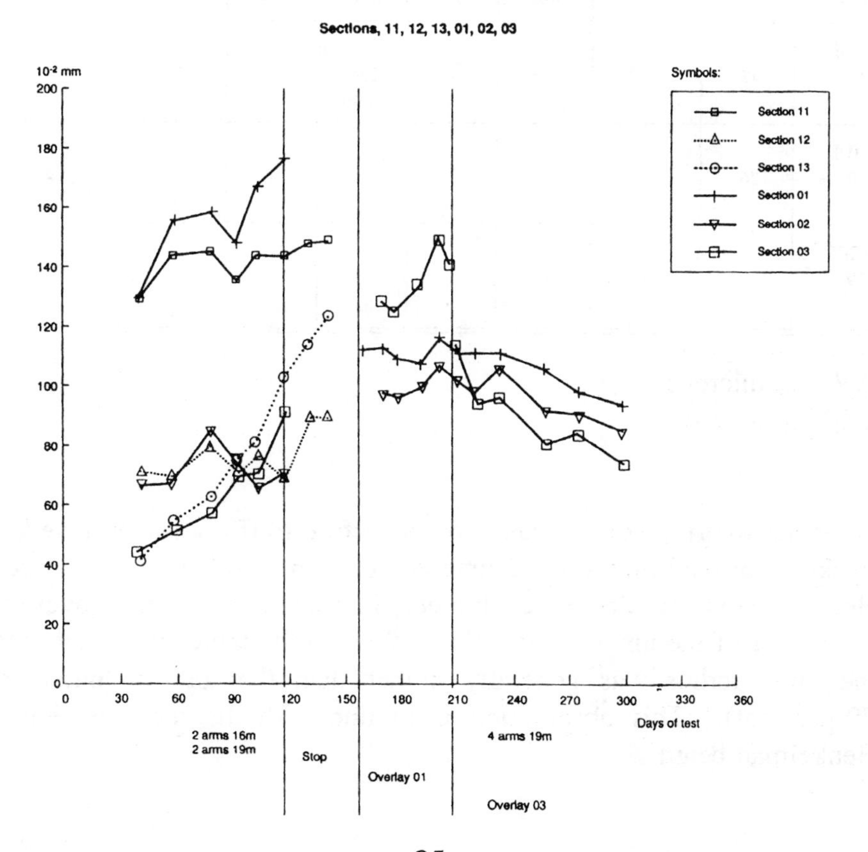

Table V.6.

AVERAGE VALUES AND STANDARD DEVIATIONS OF DEFLECTIONS ADJUSTED TO A LOAD OF 7068 KG AND MEASURED BY THE F.W.D. WITHOUT CORRECTION FOR TEMPERATURE EFFECTS

JOUR	DATE	TEMP	11	01	12	02	13	03	Cumulative No. of load applications	
									inner cycle	outer cycle
325 326	20.21 NOV 88		3320* 308**	3496 375	3200 256	3401 338	1227 222	1092 259	0	0
334 336	29 NOV -1 DEC 88	9°	1281* 124	1129 91	621 51	550 118	477 76	388 69	0	0
61 62	2-3 MAR 89	8°	169 178	1638 235	648 35	592 194	624 173	486 144	27144	37248
144 145	24-25 MAY 89	24°	1767 129	1881 182	1052 83	963 188	1399 264	853 263	561044	258536
158 159	7-8 JUN 89	19°	1614 94	1137 69	813 55	672 118	1347 196	831 273	573258	271554
205	25 JUL 89	42°	-	1353 231	-	1254 169	-	1426 216	-	1790574
208	24 JUL 89	26°	-	-	-	-	-	875 138	-	1700574
271	18 SEP 89	19°	-	853 73		788 65		695 70		3432902

* AVG in microns
** SDV in microns

-- After the wearing course was laid and before traffic wear occurred, the effect of the thickness of the bituminous course was quite marked on the structures 11, 01, 12, 02. Heterogeneous results were obtained in regard to the thin overlay, especially on section 11 of the inner radius. The values in the table show that mean deflection on the inner radius was generally higher than that on the outer radius (by some 20 per cent). This observation is in line with the measurements made with the Benkelman beam.

The wearing course laid on the untrafficked sections had as a consequence that the profile was evened out and that the differences in deflection measurements were smoothed, bringing them down to around 25 per cent:

-- After the passage of 30 000 loads and before the sections were visibly damaged, the mean values for deflection on the thin structure (sections 11 and 01) had significantly increased while those relating to the thick structure (sections 12 and 02) had changed only slightly. Examination of the profiles showed the consequences of an increasing heterogeneity in deflection along the profile. This is seen clearly on section 01 which quickly exhibited signs of cracking (after the passage of 55 000 loads). With trafficking and loading the lack of homogeneity in the roadbase of the semi-rigid structure (sections 13 and 03) became more and more apparent. However, mean deflection values were not significantly greater on these structures after exposure to loading than before.

-- After trafficking on both tracks and before overlaying section 11, the general deterioration in the thin structure (sections 01 and 11) led to a homogeneous deflection profile at high levels. Similar results were given by the Benkelman beam. The thick section tended to remain more homogeneous with a more or less constant deflection. On sections 13 and 03 the average deflection rose markedly, doubling for both sections. The explanations are probably the same as those suggested in connection with the Benkelman beam. (See Figure V.19).

-- The effect of overlaying section 01 was to reduce deflection by a factor of 0.65. Thus strengthened, section 01 became comparable, in terms of deflection, to the thick sections 12 and 02.

In the final stage, the behaviour -- in terms of deflection -- of the three types of structure is comparable. After strengthening, the specific role of cement treated gravel was no longer apparent on section 03 and mean deflections were similar for the three structures, though some 10 per cent higher for section 01 after strengthening. Section 02 tended to show more heterogeneous deflections as compared to the starting point and about double its original level.

V.3. PAVEMENT RESPONSES

V.3.1. Presentation of sensor readings

The results presented in the following figures are adjusted for an 11.5 tonne axle and corrected for temperature (Reference: 24°C). Deformation readings are expressed in micro-strains (10^{-6}), pressures in Pascal (Pa) and deflections in 10^{-2} mm. The following measurements are successively examined:

1. Dynamic deflection
   . in flexible structures

. in semi-rigid structures

2. Vertical pressures in untreated materials
   . under the thin flexible structure
   . under the thick flexible structure
   . under the semi-rigid structure

3. Vertical deformations in the untreated materials
   . under the thin flexible structure
   . under the thick flexible structure
   . under the semi-rigid structure

4. Longitudinal deformations at the interface of the subgrade and the untreated gravel

Figure V.19

CENTRAL FWD DEFLECTIONS AT 1MPa PLATE PRESSURE ON 24TH-25TH MAY 1989

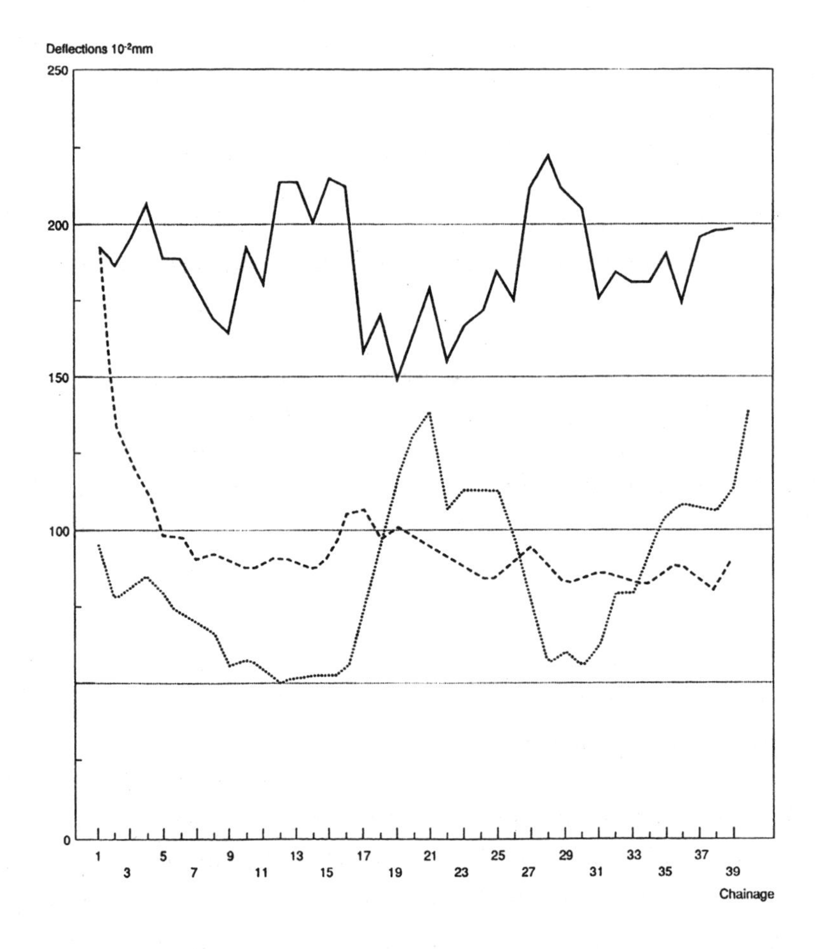

5. Longitudinal deformations at the base of the bituminous courses of the flexible pavements
   . thin structure
   . thick structure

6. Transverse deformations at the base of the bituminous course of the flexible pavements
   . thin structures
   . thick structures

7. Deformations in the cement-treated gravel of the semi-rigid structure
   . at the base of the cement-treated gravel course
   . in the upper part

8. Deformations in the bituminous courses of the semi-rigid structure

9. Deformations in the middle of the bituminous courses of the thick flexible structure

10. Deformations at the base of overlays.

The results are for the most part grouped into pre- and post-overlay. They also relate in general to a speed of 10 rotations per minute in the axis of the wheels and for 19 m and 16 m radii.

V.3.2. Dynamic deflections

Flexible Structures (Sections 01, 11, 02, 12)

Figures V.20 and V.21 present readings for the different sections; a high level of dispersion will be noted:

-- Sections 01 and 11: mean 160.10^{-2} mm (between 50 and 250.10^{-2} mm)

-- Sections 02 and 12: mean 70.10^{-2} mm (between 30 and 100.10^{-2} mm)

Despite the dispersion, the trends noted earlier remain apparent and are accentuated by the parameter of loading speed. The ratio of mean deflections between the thin and thick structures is here 2.5 compared with 2 for the Benkelman beam readings. On the thick structure the deflection was higher on the inner section (12) than on the outer section (02). It should be noted that there is no clear evaluation of changes in deflection with traffic in either of the two phases.

Semi-rigid Structure (Sections 03 and 13)

Figure V.22 presents representative deflection readings for the semi-rigid structure.

During the first period the mean deflection was 40.10^{-2} mm (20 to 50.10^{-2} mm) for both sections. Deflection then rose steadily with traffic, almost reaching the levels measured on the thick flexible structure. Those changes reflect a deterioration in the cement-treated gravel.

V.3.3. Measurements of vertical pressure in the untreated materials

Thin Flexible Structure (Sections 01 and 11)

Figure V.23 illustrates the type of response recorded by the pressure sensors.

In the first period, before any damage occurred to the section, the following values were recorded:

- 440 mm: mean pressure = 40 kPa
- 640 mm: mean pressure = 15 kPa

For section 01, similar magnitudes were recorded: 50 kPa and 10 kPa respectively.

The appearance of cracking in these sections led, in some cases, to significantly increased values (by a factor of 1.5 to 2).

The overlay work on section 01 tended to lower pressure values by a factor of around 2.

Thick Flexible Structure (Sections 02 and 12)

Results are illustrated by the reading presented in Figure V.24. They are relatively coherent compared with those obtained above. At a depth of 500 mm, the pressure is around two thirds of that obtained at the same level on the thin structure. At deeper levels, the values for both structures tend to become much the same as would be expected.

Semi-rigid Structure (Sections 03 and 13)

At the start of testing, the mean vertical pressure was 10kPa (5 to 12,5kPa) as illustrated in Figure V.25. The pressure sensors subsequently recorded the progressive distress in the cement-treated gravel and vertical pressures doubled.

Figure V.20

RESULTS OF DYNAMIC DEFLECTION IN THE THIN FLEXIBLE PAVEMENT STRUCTURE
(SECTION 01 & 11)

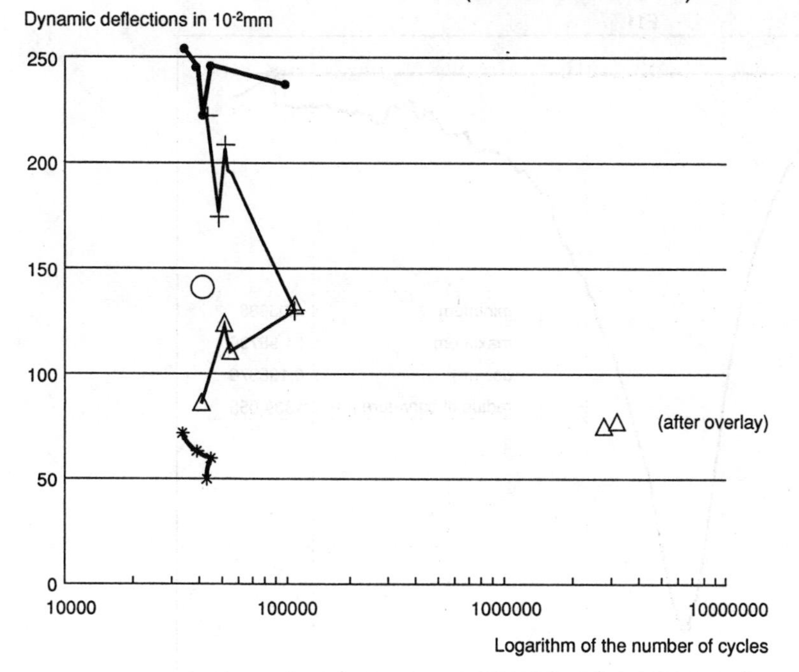

Symbols:

Section 01
- Sensor A 11
- Sensor BB2

Section 11
- Sensor AA2
- Sensor AA3
- Sensor BB3

Figure V.21

RESULTS OF DYNAMIC DEFLECTION IN THE THICK FLEXIBLE PAVEMENT STRUCTURE
(SECTION 02 & 12)

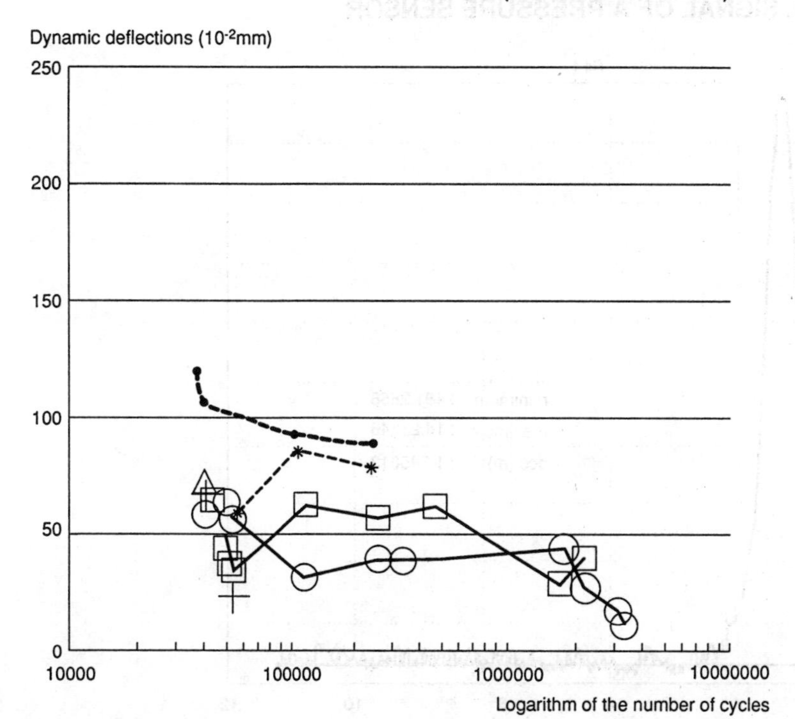

Symbols:

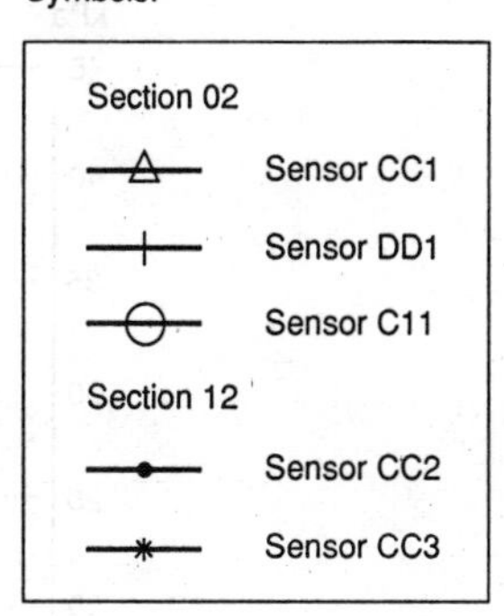

Figure V.22

TYPICAL SIGNAL OF A DYNAMIC DEFLECTION SENSOR IN THE SEMI-RIGID PAVEMENT STRUCTURE

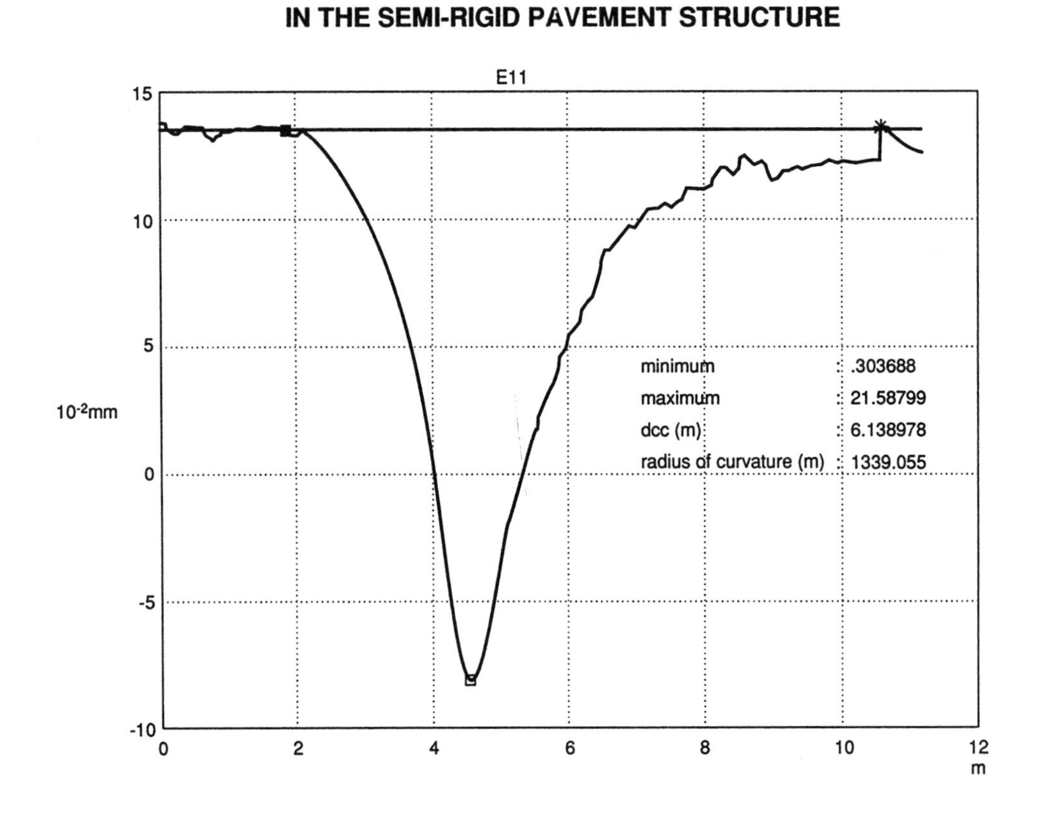

Figure V.23

TYPICAL SIGNAL OF A PRESSURE SENSOR

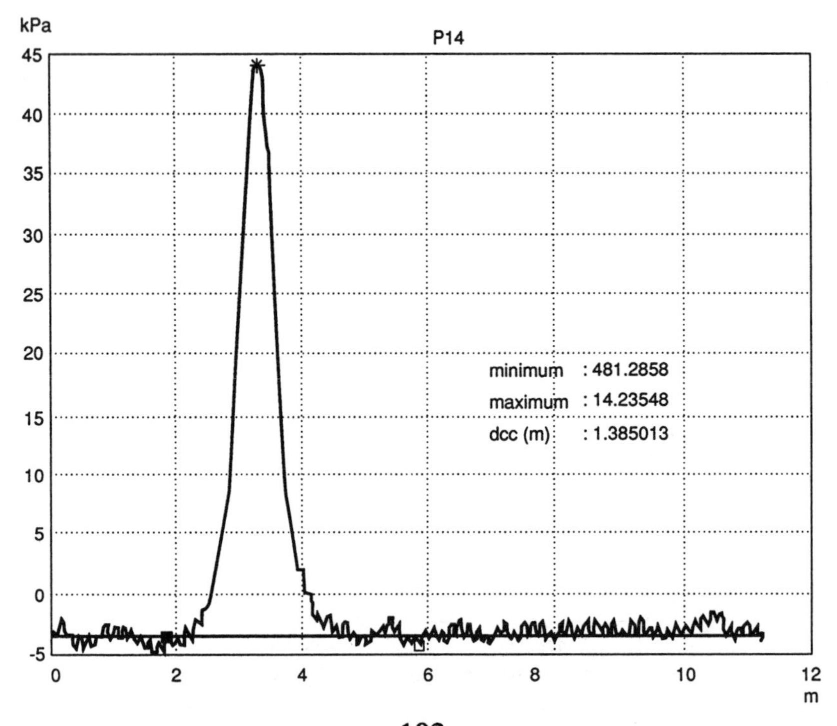

Figure V.24

PRESSURE RESULTS UNDER THE THICK FLEXIBLE PAVEMENT STRUCTURE
(SECTION 02)

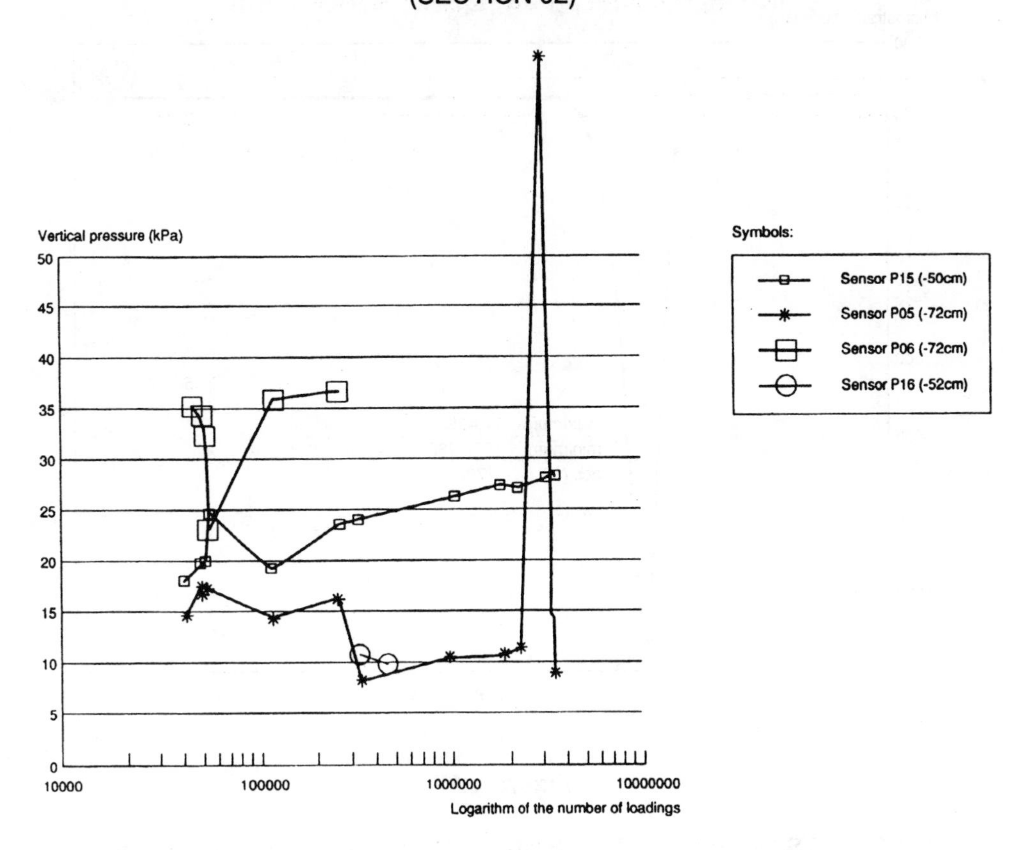

Figure V.25

PRESSURE RESULTS UNDER THE SEMI-RIGID PAVEMENT STRUCTURE
(SECTION 03)

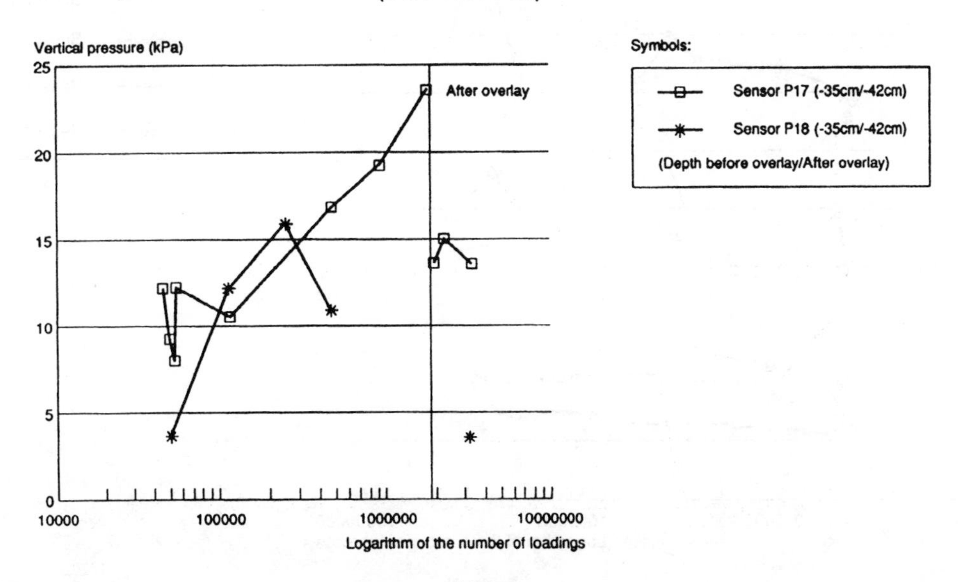

Figure V.26

TYPICAL SIGNAL OF A VERTICAL STRAIN GAUGE

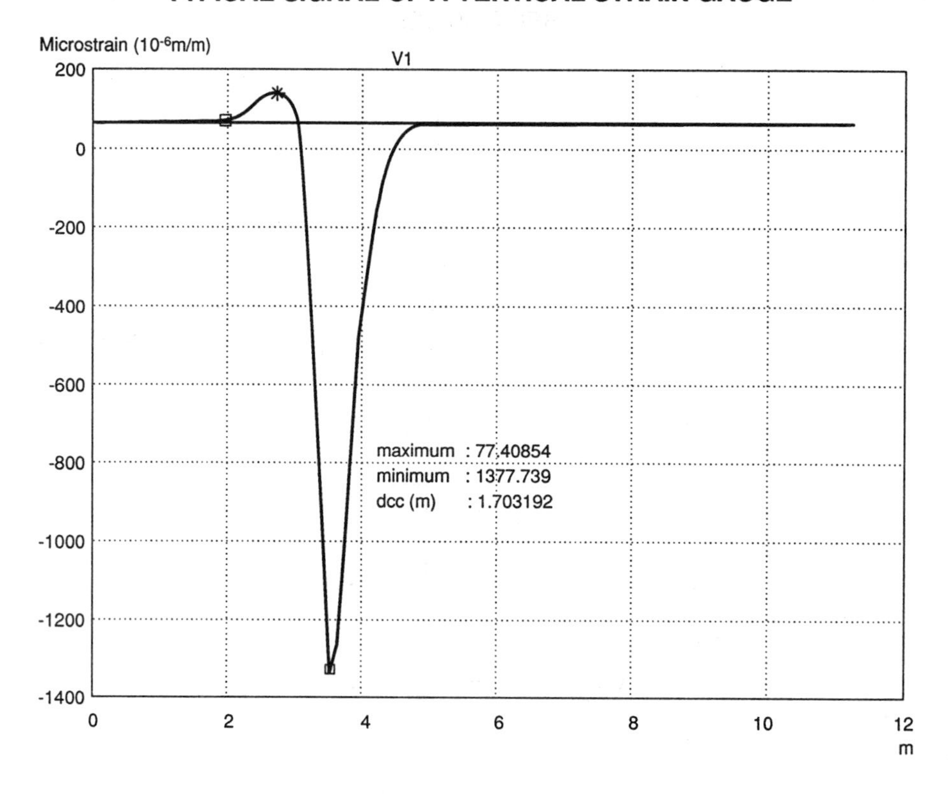

Figure V.27

RESULTS OF RELATIVE VERTICAL STRAIN AT THE UNDERSIDE OF THE THICK FLEXIBLE PAVEMENT STRUCTURE

(SECTION 02)

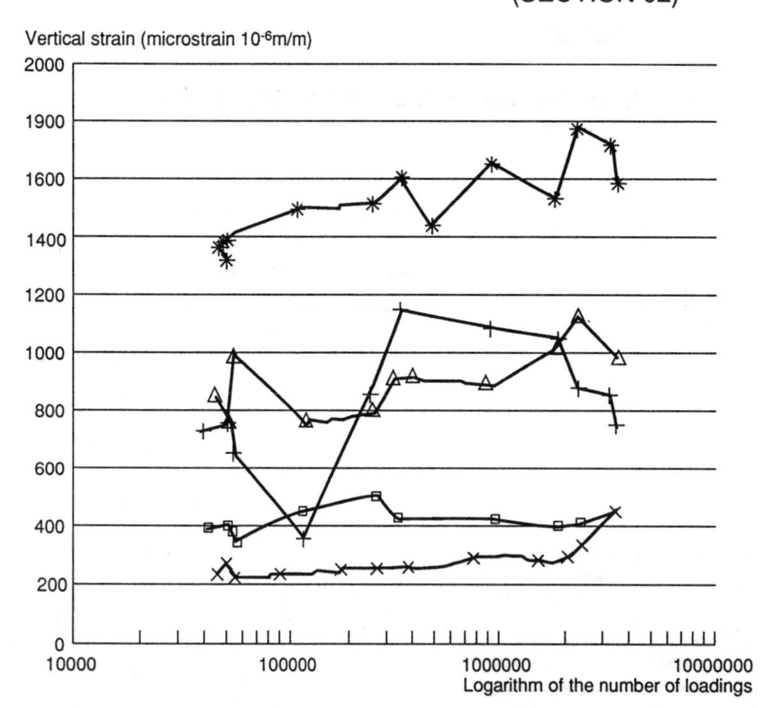

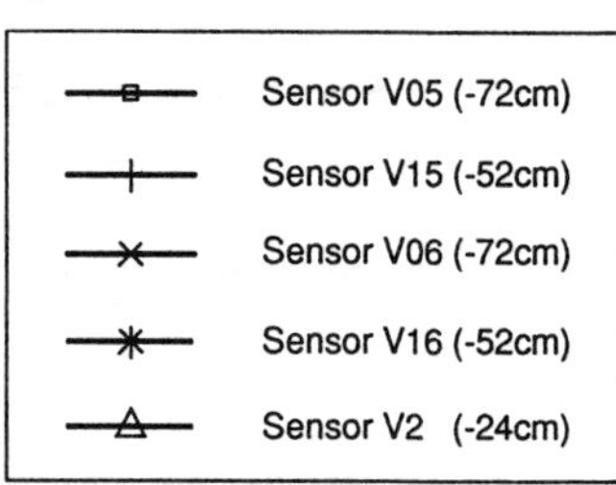

V.3.4. Vertical deformations in the untreated material

Thin Flexible Structure

Figure V.26 illustrates the type of result obtained. The most significant values ε_z for the subgrade are:

-44 mm: 1700 10^{-6}
-- Section 11
-64 mm: 1300 10^{-6}

-44 mm: 1900 10^{-6}
-- Section 01
-64 mm: 500 10^{-6}

In the untreated gravel, an ε_z of 1800 10^{-6} was maintained at 100 mm below the bituminous layer.

The laying of the strengthening course led to reductions in vertical deformations measured at subgrade level of around 30 per cent while at the level of the untreated gravel variations of deformations were not significant.

Thick Flexible Structure

In the subgrade, the readings for section 02 are the following (Figure V.27):

- 440 mm ε_z = 1100 10^{-6} (between 700 and 1 400),

- 640 mm ε_z = 300 10^{-6} (between 200 and 400), and in the gravel:

- 250 mm ε_z = 800 10^{-6}

The ratio between the thin and the thick flexible structure is thus around 2 : 1.

Semi-rigid structure

Figure V.28 presents an example of a reading for the semi-rigid structure. For section 03 the initial state for the subgrade was:

- 410 mm ε_z = 500 10^{-6}

- 610 mm ε_z = 350 10^{-6}

As a result of the progressive deterioration of the cement treated gravel, the values of ε_z increase steadily to reach 2.5 to 3 times the initial levels. As in the case of dynamic deflection, the values of vertical deformation approach those of the thick flexible structure prior to overlay. After overlay, vertical deformation fell by around 30 per cent.

V.3.5. Longitudinal deformations at the interface of subgrade and untreated gravel

These measurements are quite difficult to make.

On section 01 elongations of the order of 200.10^{-6} were recorded. These tend to increase with pavement wear and decrease, as it should be, after the overlay has been provided. The measurements were made using only two sensors that were still functioning after the pavement had been constructed.

In the thick flexible structure, elongations at the interface of the subgrade and untreated gravel tended to be lower (25 to 100 10^{-6}).

V.3.6. Longitudinal deformations at the base of the bituminous courses of flexible structures

Thin Structure

These were the most frequent of the measurements made in the course of testing (Figure V.29 and V.30). The characteristic figures obtained are typical as is seen in Figure V.29.

The mean values obtained initially for sections 01 and 11 were 160.10^{-6} with a marked standard deviation (s = 50.10^{-6}; range 140 - 240.10^{-6}). Following overlay work on section 02 there was a significant decrease in the elongations to an average of 80.10^{-6} with a standard deviation of 20.10^{-6}).

Thick Structure

The findings illustrated in Figure V.31 show a lower dispersion and slightly lower values than above. Mean elongations were respectively 140 and 125.10^{-6} on sections 12 and 02 with standard deviations of 15 and 20.10^{-6} (after eliminating an unusually high reading).

In the course of testing there was little change in these values though there was a progressively higher level of dispersion which may have reflected changes occurring in section 02 as a result of cracking or movement between the two bituminous courses.

V.3.7. Transverse deformations at the base of the bituminous courses of flexible structures

Thin Structure

Figure V.32 shows the characteristic figure representing transverse deformation on the passage of a load.

The initial values recorded for transverse elongation are high, reaching 300.10^{-6} or 1½ times the corresponding longitudinal values. On application of the overlay to section 01, the values fell to about 110.10^{-6} (Figure V.33).

Thick Structure

The same values are obtained (Figure V.34) as on section 01 with overlay, i.e. a mean of 100.10^{-6} with a standard deviation of 26. This is not surprising since in both cases there is the same bituminous thickness.

Here the transverse elongations are smaller than the longitudinal, which is typical of thick bituminous courses.

V.3.8. Deformations in the cement-treated gravel of the semi-rigid structure

Deformations at the Base of the Cement-treated Gravel

The rapid changes occurring in the material destroyed many of the gauges, making interpretation somewhat difficult. There would, however, appear to be two distinct types of behaviour corresponding to undamaged and damaged material. As a function of these stages the values for longitudinal and transverse elongations are as follows:

Longitudinal elongations (Figure V.35)

25.10^{-6} at level -240 mm and 10.10^{-6} at level -180 mm for sections 13 and 03

Transverse elongations (Figure V.36)

On section 03 values for undamaged and damaged material are:

Undamaged material:

-240 mm 65.10^{-6}
-180 mm 20.10^{-6}

Damaged material:

up to 270.10^{-6} before overlay and 500.10^{-6} at the end of testing, a sign that the cement treated gravel had continued to deteriorate after overlay work.

Deformations in Upper Part of the Cement-treated Gravel

This part of the structure showed pronounced deformations following contraction stresses, with longitudinal values of 40 to 100.10^{-6} (Figure V.37) and transverse values of 60 to 200.10^{-6} (Figure V.38) before actual damage occurred.

The greater magnitude of transverse deformations may be explained by the proximity to the pavement surface, the cement gravel being covered only by a thin and relatively flexible bituminous layer. Elongations in the upper part of the cement gravel course were limited to around 30.10^{-6}.

Figure V.28

RESULTS OF RELATIVE VERTICAL STRAIN AT THE UNDERSIDE OF THE SEMI-RIGID PAVEMENT STRUCTURE
(SECTION 03)

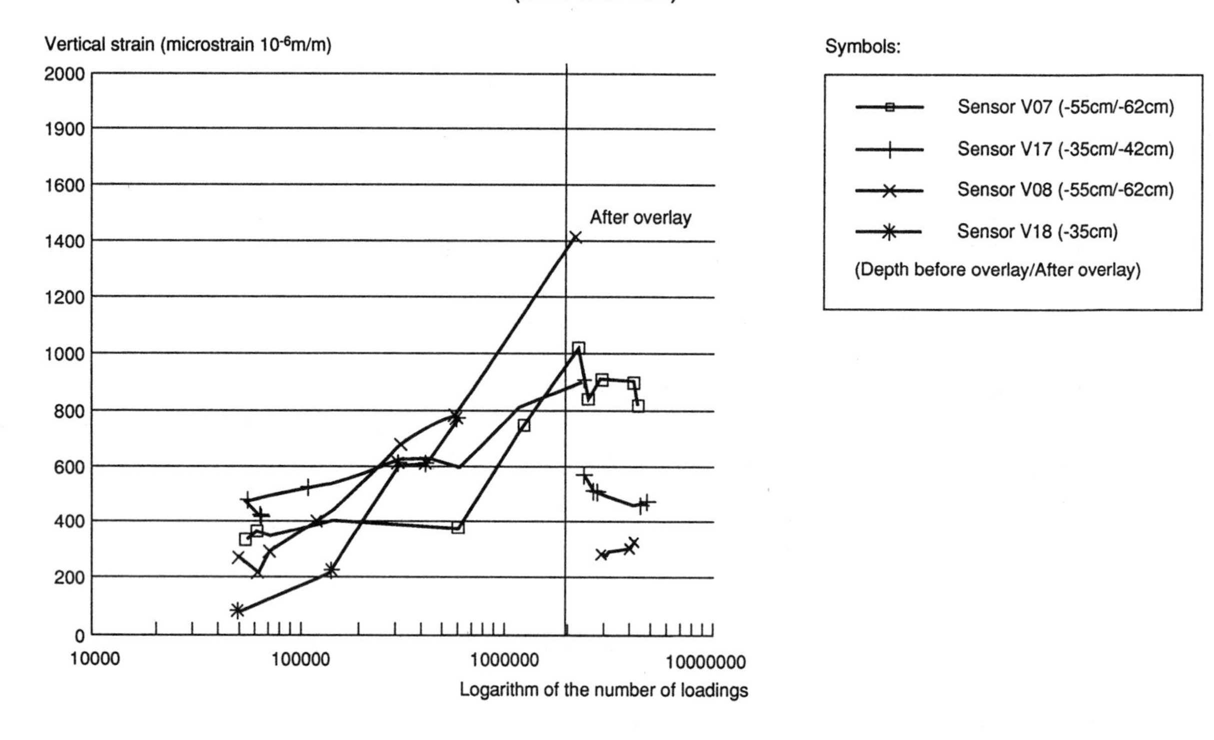

Figure V.29

TYPICAL RESPONSE OF A LONGITUDINAL GAUGE IN THE LOWER PART OF THE LAYER

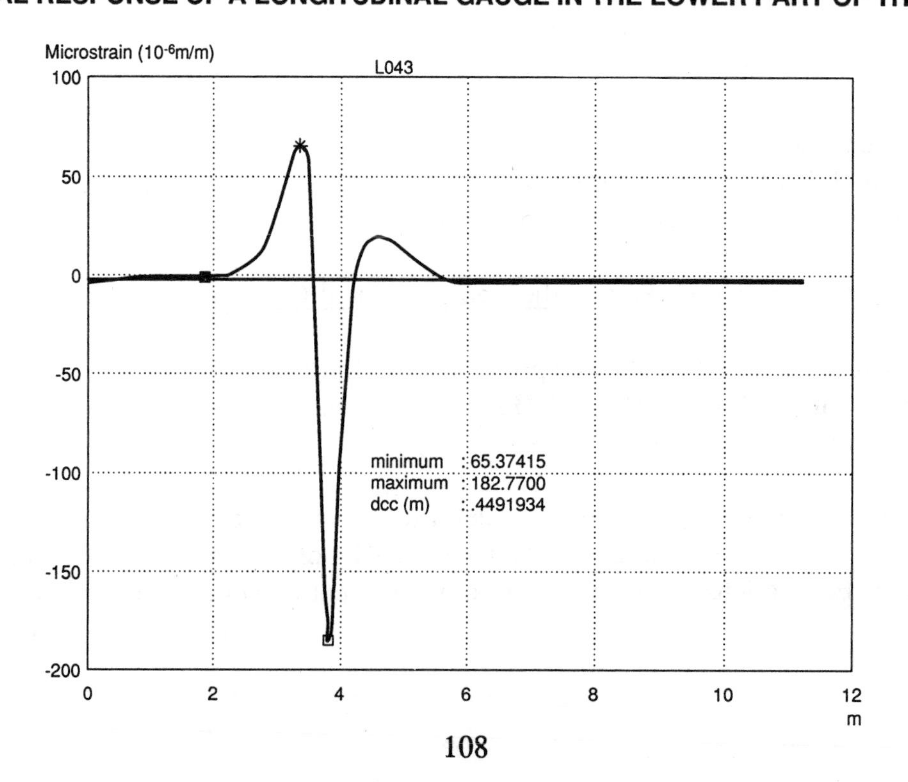

Figure V.30

STRAINS AT THE BASE OF THE THIN FLEXIBLE PAVEMENT STRUCTURE
(SECTION 01)

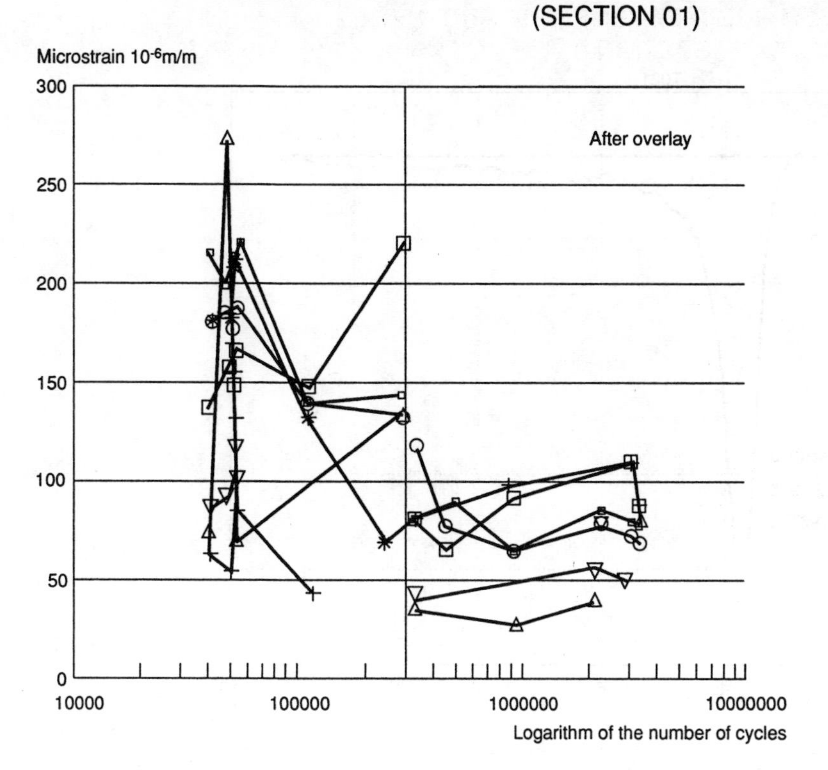

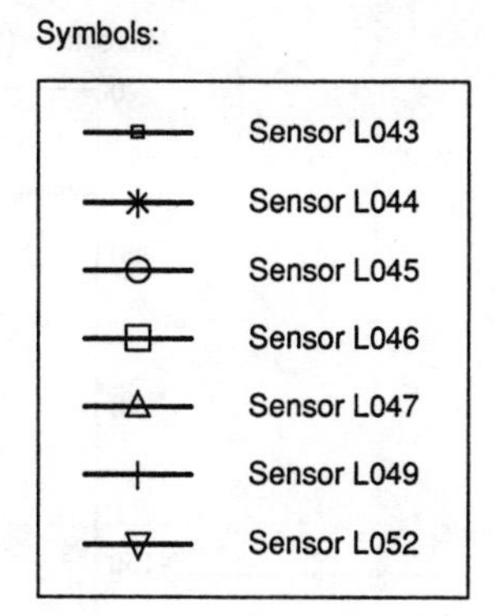

Figure V.31

LONGITUDINAL STRAINS IN THE LOWER PART OF THE THICK FLEXIBLE PAVEMENT STRUCTURE
(SECTION 02)

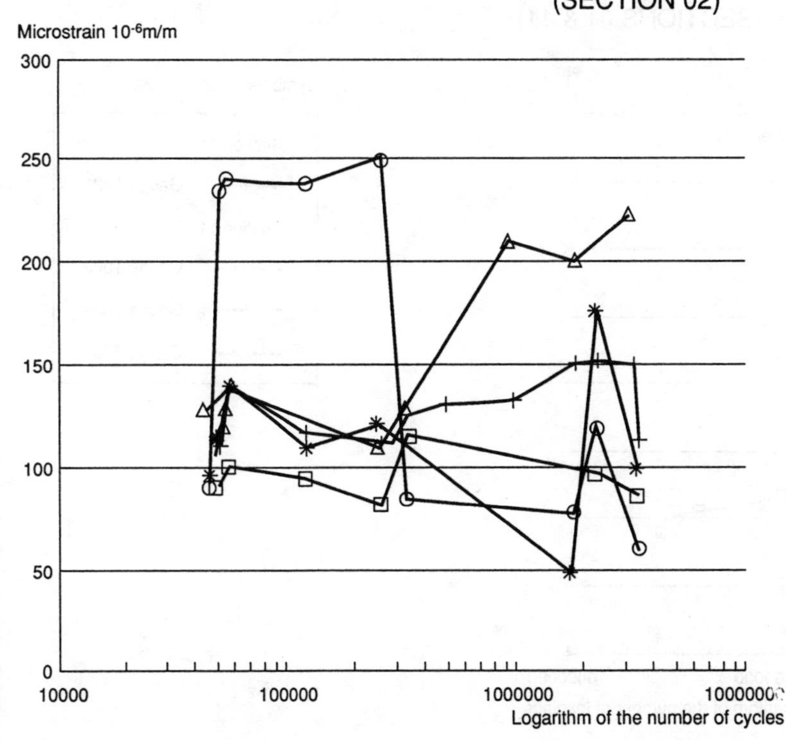

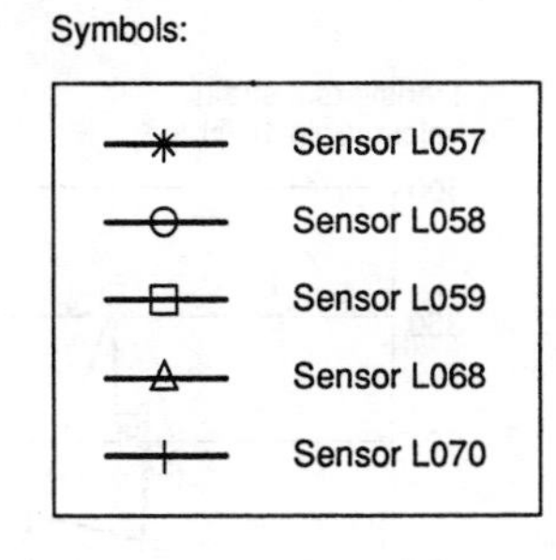

Figure V.32

TYPICAL RESPONSE OF A TRANSVERSAL GAUGE IN THE LOWER PART OF THE LAYER

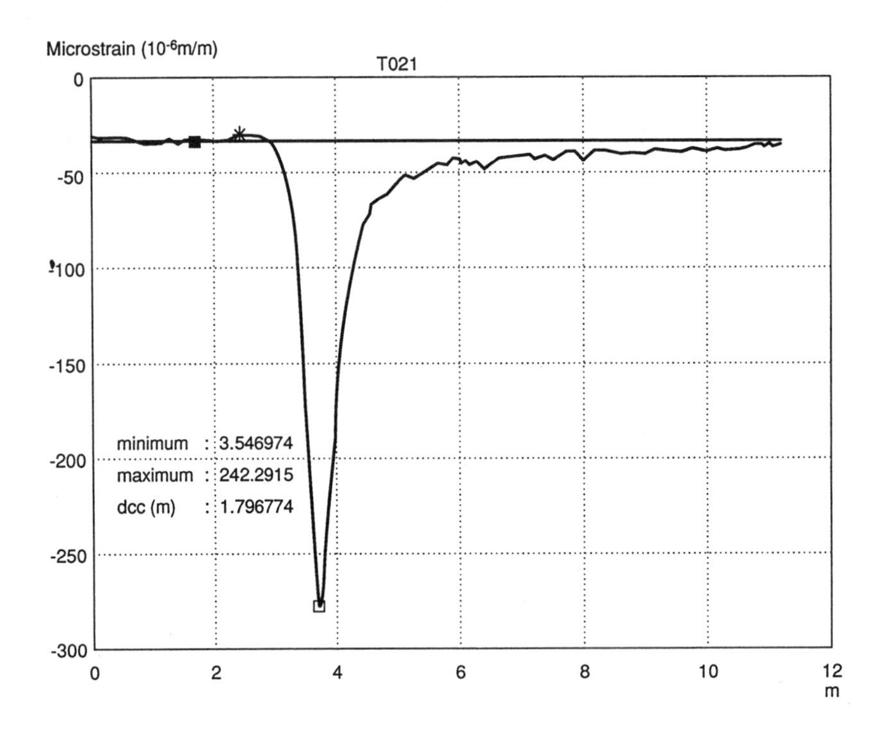

Figure V.33

TRANSVERSAL STRAINS AT THE BOTTOM OF THE THIN FLEXIBLE PAVEMENT STRUCTURE
(SECTIONS 01 & 11)

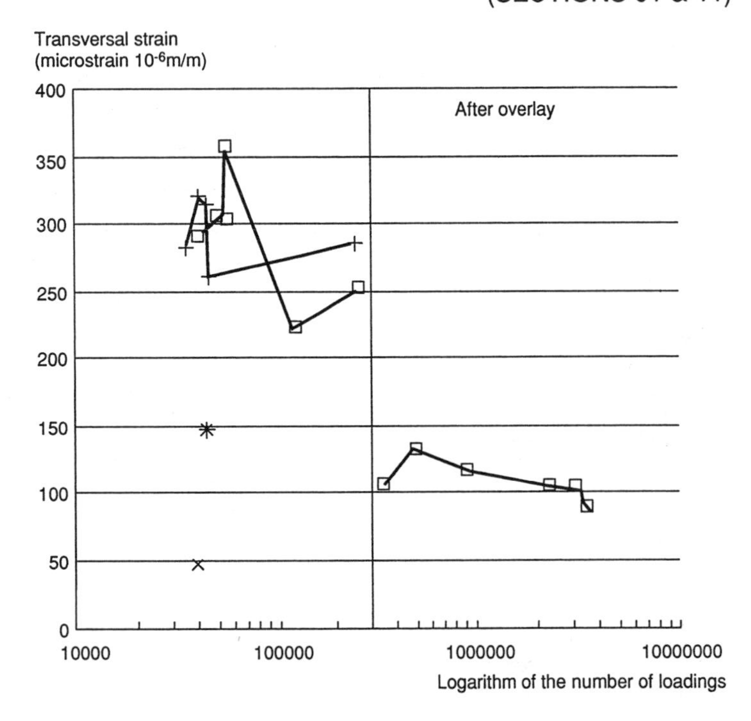

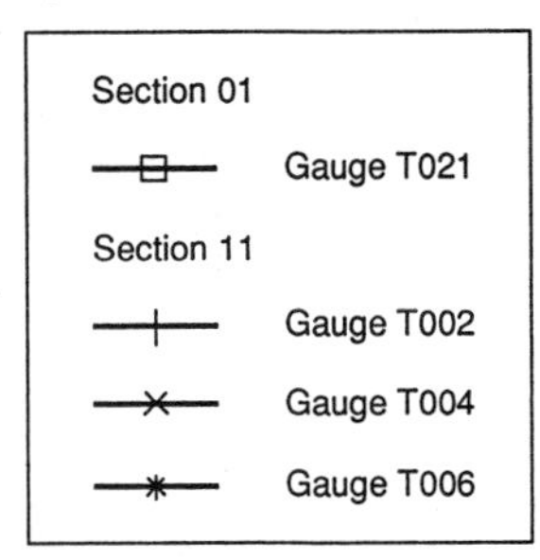

V.3.9 Deformations in the bituminous courses of the semi-rigid structure

The base of these courses is subject to significant longitudinal elongations (Figure V.39) which average around 150.10^{-6} and in some cases reach 350.10^{-6}. There is no continuity in the deformations on either side of the interface separating the bituminous concrete and the cement treated gravel. Several hypotheses have been suggested to account for this; the most likely is slippage occasioned by the presence of a binder-rich tack coat. Transverse elongations are less pronounced, being around 125.10^{-6}.

V.3.10. Deformations in the middle of the bituminous courses of the thick flexible structure

Longitudinal and transverse values are low in view of the closeness to the neutral axis.

Longitudinally, there is a contraction of 20.10^{-6}. This shows that the application of the bituminous course in two successive stages did not lead to discontinuity at the interface. Beyond 2 500 000 loadings, however, levels of deformation were seen to increase which may indicate the beginnings of slippage between the two bituminous layers.

Transverse elongations were limited to about 30.10^{-6}.

V.3.11. Deformations at the base of the overlays

Section 01

Longitudinally, moderate elongations were recorded (Figure V.40) of less than 80.10^{-6}. This value rises with fatigue reaching 150.10^{-6} in the final measurements. Transversally, the readings were too inconsistent to produce any meaningful result. The behaviour of the structure is not similar to that of the thick flexible structure; this is certainly due to the already advanced stage of deterioration of the inferior layer.

Section 03

The only readings are for longitudinal deformations. As seen in Figure V.41, these are small (below 20.10^{-6}). In such a case behaviour may be compared with that of thick flexible structures.

Figure V.34

TRANSVERSAL STRAINS AT THE BOTTOM OF THE THICK FLEXIBLE PAVEMENT STRUCTURE
(SECTIONS 02 and 12)

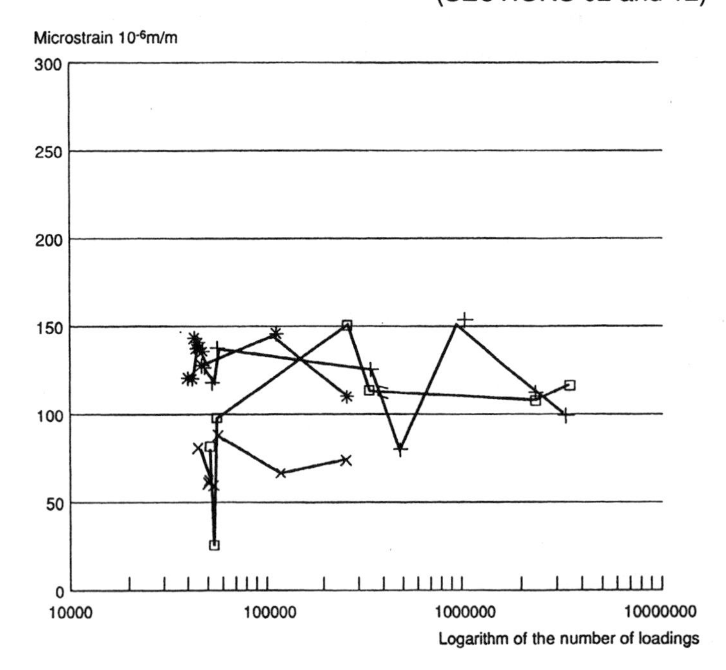

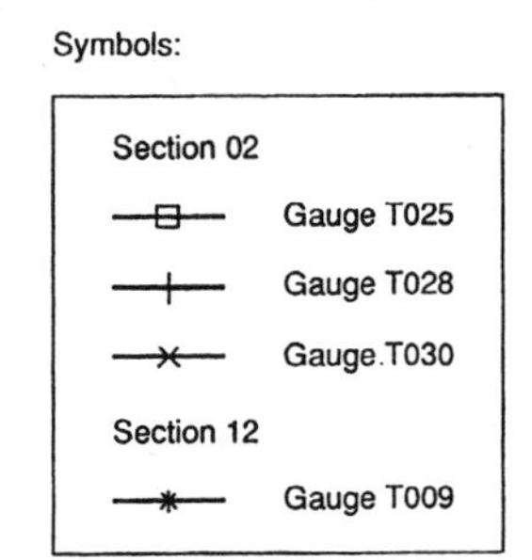

Figure V.35

STRAINS AT THE BOTTOM OF THE CEMENT-TREATED LAYER OF THE SEMI-RIGID PAVEMENT STRUCTURE
(SECTIONS 03 and 13)

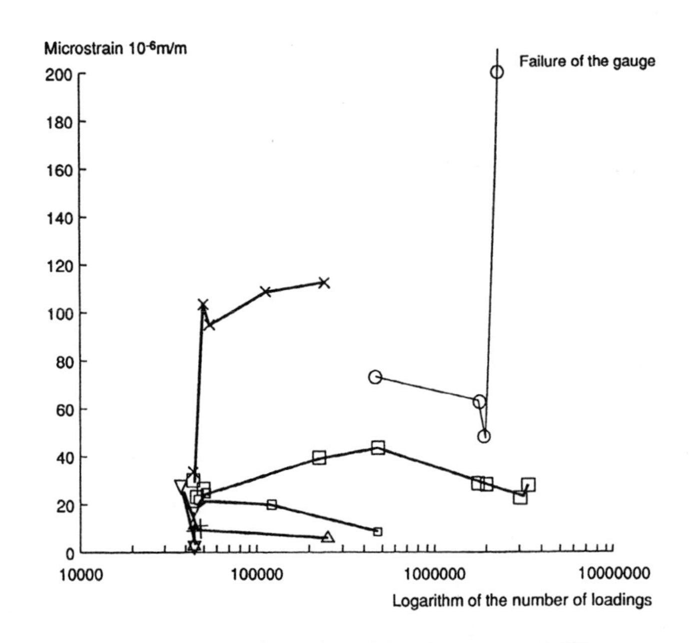

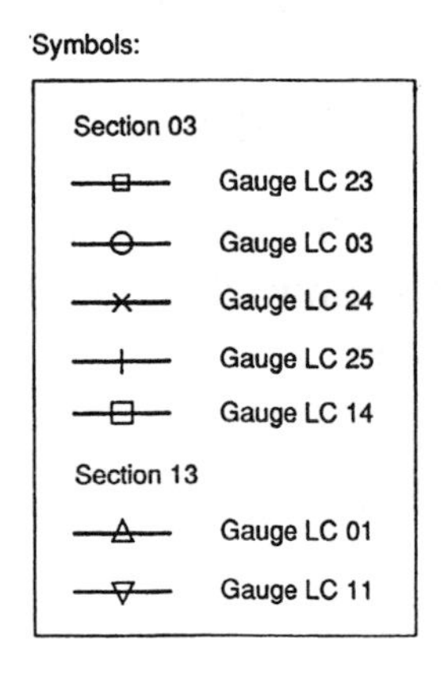

Figure V.36

TRANSVERSAL STRAINS AT THE BOTTOM OF THE SEMI-RIGID PAVEMENT STRUCTURE
(SECTION 03)

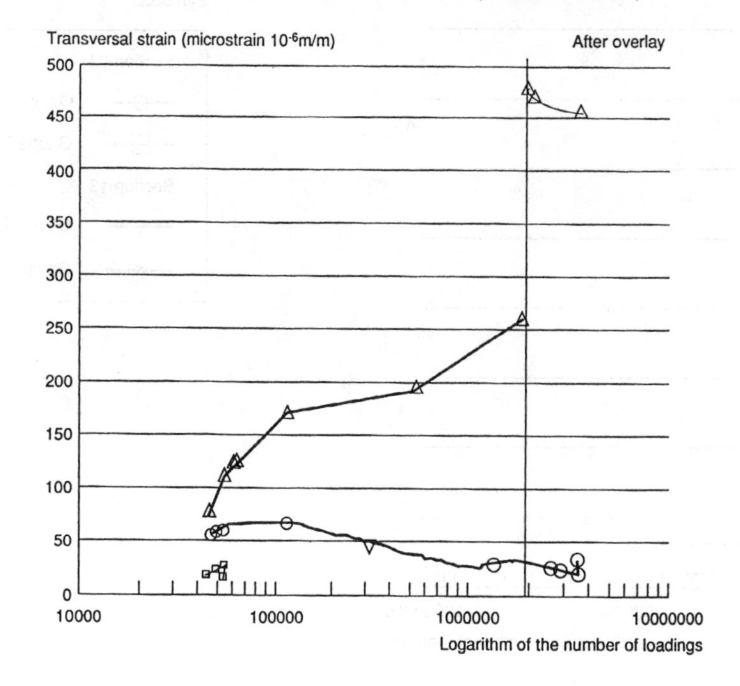

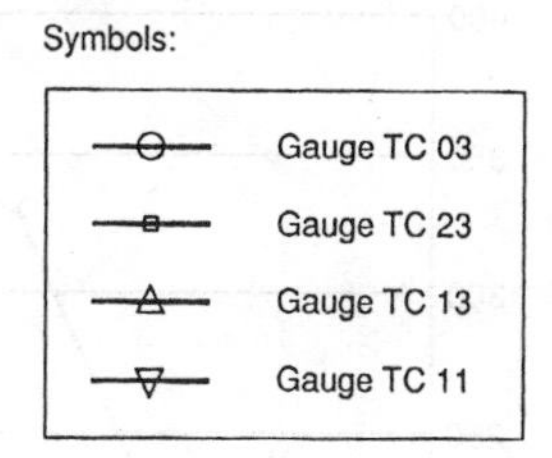

Figure V.37

LONGITUDINAL STRAINS IN THE UPPER PART OF THE CEMENT TREATED MATERIAL— NEGATIVE SIGNALS
(SECTIONS 03 and 13)

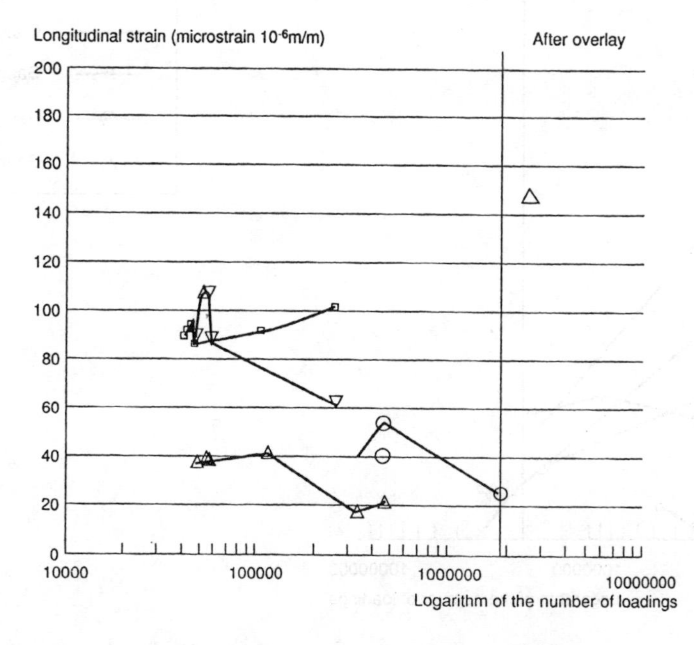

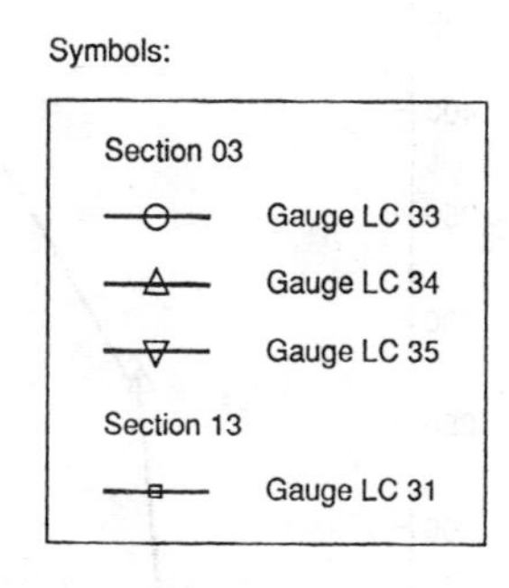

Figure V.38

TRANSVERSAL STRAINS AT THE UPPER PART OF THE CEMENT TREATED MATERIAL

(SECTIONS 03 & 13)

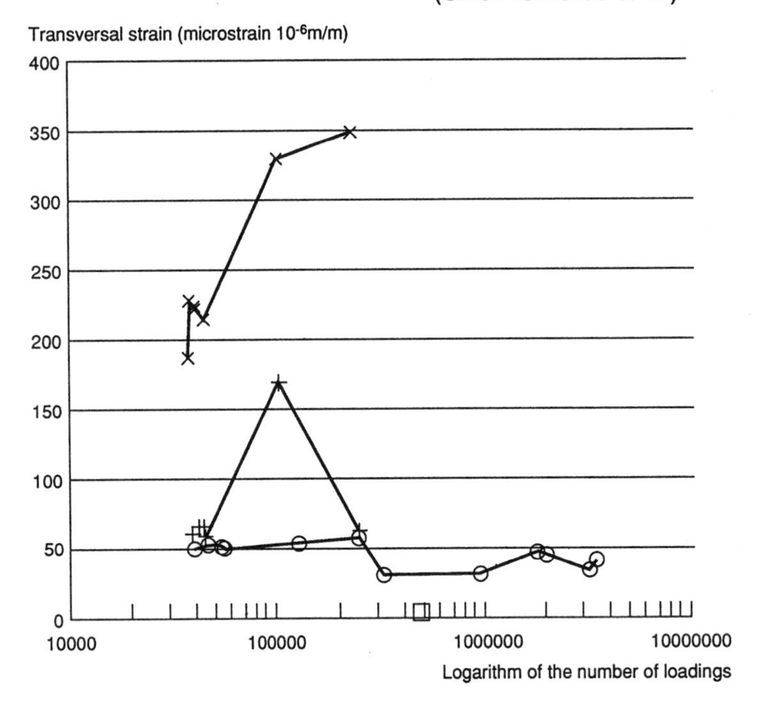

Symbols:

Section 03

Gauge TC 33

Gauge TC 34

Section 13

Gauge TC 31

Gauge TC 32

Figure V.39

LONGITUDINAL STRAIN AT THE BASE OF THE WEARING COURSE OF THE SEMI-RIGID PAVEMENT STRUCTURE

(SECTION 03)

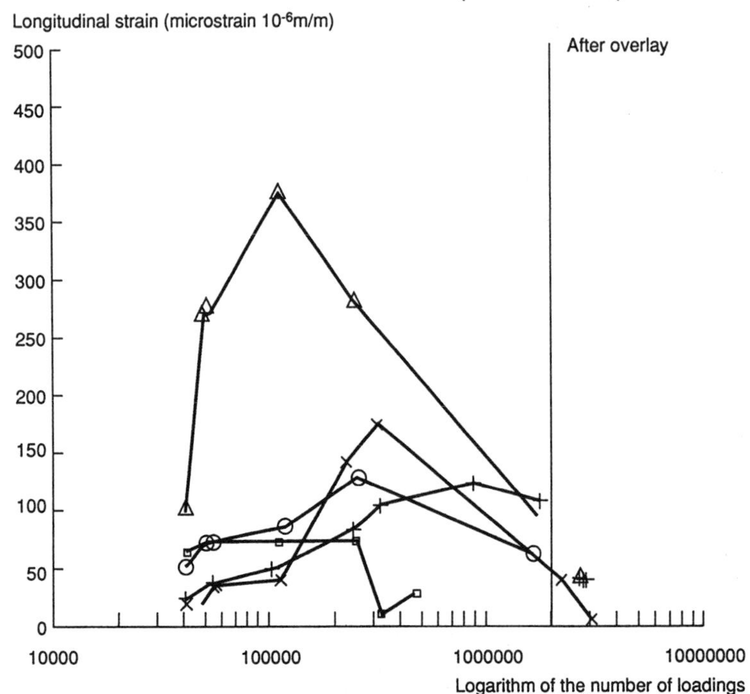

Symbols:

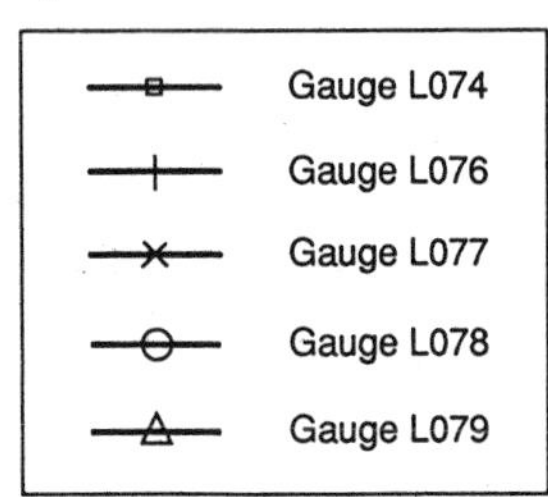

Figure V.40

STRAINS AT THE BASE OF THE OVERLAY OF THE DETERIORATED FLEXIBLE PAVEMENT STRUCTURE

(SECTION 01)

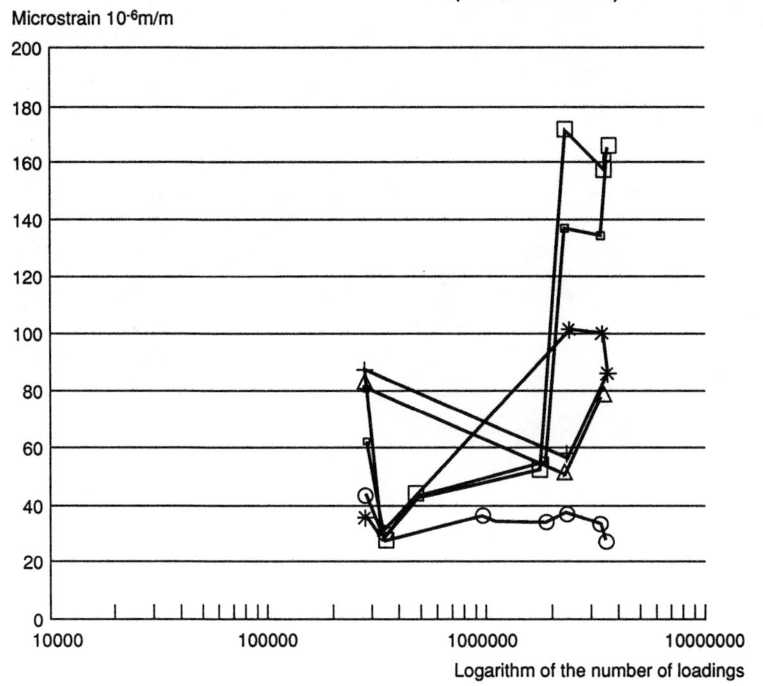

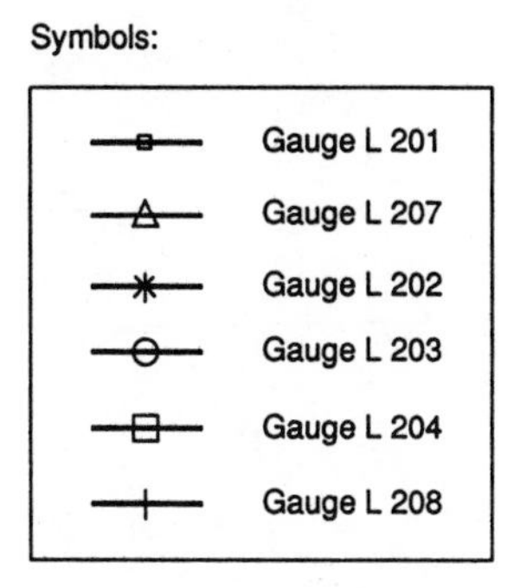

Figure V.41

LONGITUDINAL STRAIN AT THE BASE OF THE OVERLAY OF THE DETERIORATED SEMI-RIGID PAVEMENT STRUCTURE

(SECTION 03)

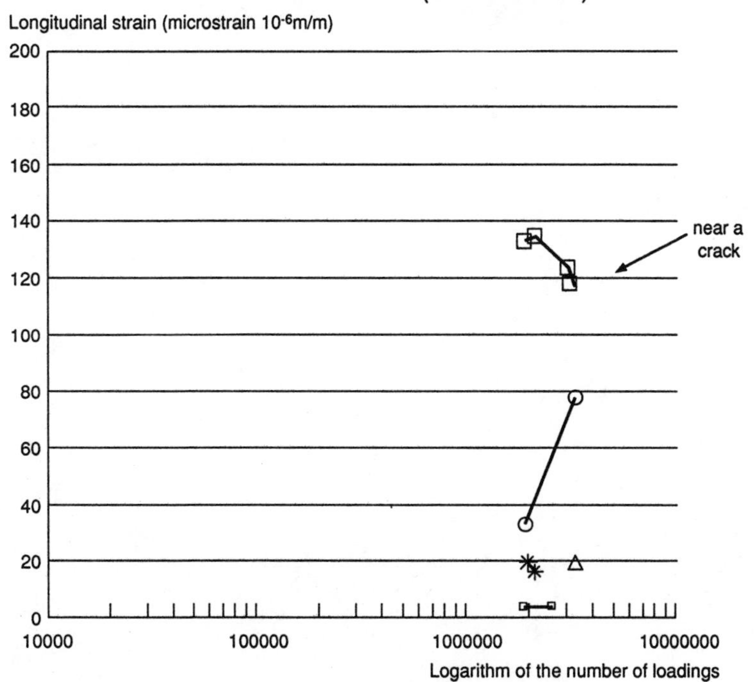

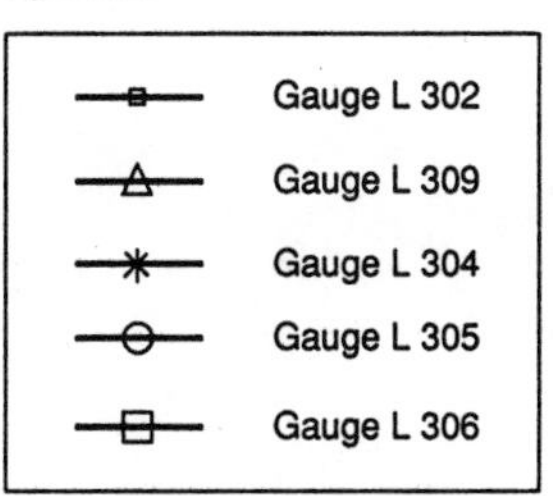

Chapter VI

ANALYSIS AND INTERPRETATION

VI.1. INTRODUCTION

In the course of the FORCE experiment, a great many measurements of pavement properties, responses and performance parameters were made before, during and after the trafficking of the experimental structures. These were designed to generate sufficient information to allow an analysis of the experiment from the point of view of its various objectives. The full and complete analysis of such a vast amount of data from an experiment taking more than one year to complete, is a considerable undertaking, and the remainder of this Chapter describes only those aspects of analysis aimed at the following specific objectives of the common test (see Section I.2.2.):

1. To continue with the standardization and harmonization of test equipment, measurement procedures, data processing, analytical procedures and interpretation of results.

2. To carry out tests on different pavement structures under repeated loads of 11.5 tonnes, and 10 tonnes, and examine the relationship between the two.

3. To verify the validity of design and maintenance procedures used for particular pavement structures and loads in the different participating countries.

Objectives 1 and 2 relate to specific technical issues which the results of the experiment, correctly analysed, should fulfil; Objectives 3, while employing the results of the experiment, does so in a less direct way, and is likely to be the subject of later analyses conducted by participating Member countries. The results of the experiment have therefore been used initially to analyse the experiment in detail from the point of view of the first two objectives.

It is clear that the data gathered will be extremely useful for many other purposes than those stated as the direct objectives of the test. It is therefore anticipated that further analyses, with other specific aims, will be undertaken by various individual participants in the experiment -- who each have access to all the data gathered -- and published elsewhere.

In the first two sections of this Chapter, data from the experiment are used to examine relationships between pavement performance and axle load, and performance of pavement instrumentation respectively. The final sections discuss the use of models of pavement performance and response, particularly in respect of the values calculated by the models. None of the models so far developed claims to predict performance or response to a high degree of accuracy, and these sections of the analysis are simply used to draw attention to differences between types of model, between input data requirements, and between output formats. Because this is a complex field, requiring careful and lengthy interpretation, no attempts have yet been made to compare predicted and observed results.

PART A -- ANALYSIS OF MEASURED DATA

VI.2. THE RELATIVE DAMAGING EFFECTS OF AXLE LOADS

VI.2.1. Background

The effect of different axle loads on pavement deterioration was first thoroughly studied in the AASHO Road Test and the concept of Present Serviceability Index (PSI) was developed (see also Section V.2.6). This included cracking, rutting, patching and roughness as parameters of the deterioration of the road. The data was analysed and the effects of axle loads were expressed by equations that were later simplified to the so-called "fourth power law". This law implies that if an axle is twice as heavy as another, their relative effects on pavement performance are in the ratio $(2)^4$, i.e. sixteen. Thus the pavement trafficked by the heavier load has a life only one sixteenth that of the pavement trafficked by the lighter load. The fourth power law is expressed mathematically as follows:

$$\left(\frac{P_x}{P_y}\right)^4 = \frac{N_y}{N_x} \qquad \text{Eq. VI.1}$$

where P_x and P_y are axle loads and N_x and N_y are the corresponding number of load applications.

The exponent in the fourth power law is not constant but was found in the AASHO Road Test to vary from about 3.6 to 4.6. Later experimental and theoretical research has indicated greater variability in the power, but has not been conclusive.

The OECD/FORCE project provided a good opportunity to compare the effect of different axle loads because it was possible to use two axle loads simultaneously. The proposed new axle load limit of 11.5 tonnes for driving axles within EC Member countries was selected as the basic axle load in the OECD/FORCE test and the 10 tonne axle load was selected in order to compare the effects of the two. As described before, the 11.5 tonne axle load was used on the outer ring (sections 01, 02, 03), where the radius of rotation was 19 metres, and the 10 tonne axle load for the inner ring (sections 11, 12, 13), on a 16 metre radius. Cracking and rutting of the pavements were used as the principal performance indicators for comparison of the effects of different wheel loads. Roughness or unevenness of the pavement could not be used because of the special type of suspension used on the test machine, which eliminates the effect of dynamic loads. The analysis of the effects of different wheel loads described in this section of the report is based separately on cracking and rutting.

During the experimental phase of the comparison, it was intended that trafficking under each wheel load would continue until structure I (sections 01 and 11, bituminous layers 60 mm) had reached a failure condition. By the end of this phase sections 03 and 13 of the structure III (cement treated base course) had also cracked, although to different degrees, and this allowed some indications of the "power" applying to cement treated base course materials to be calculated.

In this analysis the "power" is calculated from the performance of the pavement as determined by cracking and rutting. It can also be determined from the response measurements. Strain, stress or deflection caused by different axle loads were measured during the experiment, and using a failure criterion or fatigue curves, the "power" can be estimated. The "power" will thus depend on the stress dependency of the different materials.

VI.2.2. Effect of different axle loads: rutting

As noted earlier, during the common test three structures were loaded at an inner and an outer wheel path and under a different wheel load, i.e. half the nominal axle loads required in the experiment. In total, the outer wheel path was subjected to about 4 million load applications, the inner one to about 570 000. Sections 01 and 03 of the outer wheel-path were overlayed by 60 mm of bituminous concrete in the course of the test: section 01 at beginning of June 1989 and section 03 at the end of July 1989.

It can be assumed that in the case of rutting, permanent deformation took place within the pavement, the result of which is evident as "rutting" at the pavement surface. On completion of the experimental phase of the project, trenches were cut in the pavement, and slabs of materials removed for testing. Observations at this stage confirmed that where rutting had occurred it was generally confined to the bituminous and granular layers; much smaller deformations took place within the soil. Measurements carried out with the Dynaflect revealing no effect of loading. It is assumed that the magnitude of the permanent deformation, and therefore of the rutting, depends on the magnitude of the axle-load applied, and it is this structural rutting, rather than the plastic deformation of the surface layer which is investigated here.

Influence of Temperature

The trafficking period of the test was between 23rd December 1988 and 5 November 1989. This means that during the course of the year different temperatures occurred within the different layers of the pavement and at the surface. Temperatures were measured in two sections at different depths and the air, and the results of these measurements were taken as being representative of the whole test track.

Following the philosophy of some pavement behaviour models and/or programs (VESYS for example), it can be assumed that the permanent deformation at a given point within the pavement, however small, is proportional to the transient deformation at that point. Thus, permanent deformations depend on the magnitude of the transient ones, and moreover on the number of load repetitions, decreasing with increasing number of load applications as a result of the stiffening effect of the material. The temperature dependent fraction of the stiffness is determined by the thickness and the properties of the bituminous layers; temperature therefore strongly influences permanent deformation, and, in consequence, rutting.

The loading of the structures with the different axle loads took place over differing lengths of time in the year, as noted above. This gave rise to loads being applied at different temperatures, and in order to examine the influence of the axle load on rutting, it is first necessary to study the influence of temperature on rutting.

The temperatures measured at different depths -- which altered after the overlay of course --were first transposed into temperature gradients in the pavements. Temperatures at different depths were then combined, using the formula developed in the analysis of the Nardo test (Figure VI.1) to give a single effective temperature T_{eff}, valid for the whole of the bituminous layer. This led to the following formulae describing the effective temperature for the different structures (see Figure VI.1)

Structures I: $T_I = (T_6 + T_2) / 2$

II: $T_{II} = (2.T_{14} + T_6) / 3$

III: $T_{III} = (T_7 + T_2^*) / 2$

and after overlay

III_{ov}: $T_{III,ov} = (2.T_7 + T_2^*) / 3.$

This simplification of temperature distribution allowed a time / temperature distribution to be made, in which load repetitions N_i correspond to temperatures T_i. Figure VI.2 shows a shortened example of this distribution.

Two assumptions concerning the effect of temperature were made; first, that the pavement deformation only takes place within the bituminous layer and proceeds following the laws of visco-elasticity, and, second, that the permanent deformation is proportional to the stiffness.

Figure VI.1

DEFINITION OF TEMPERATURES

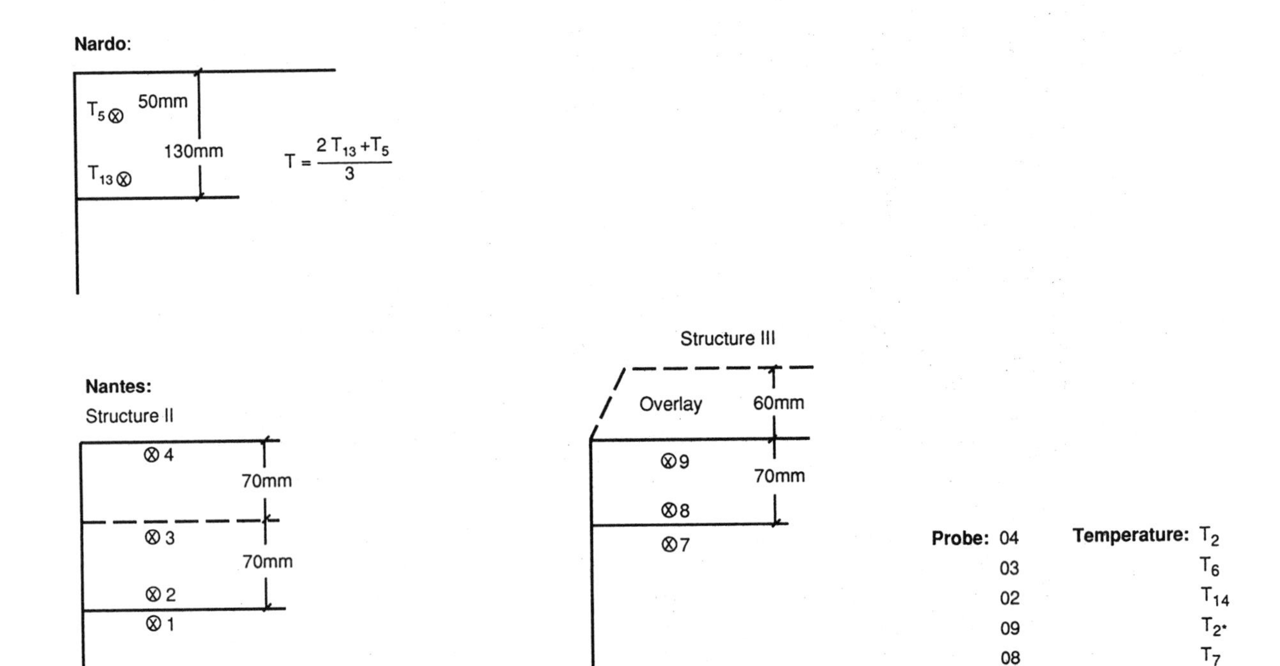

Figure VI.2

EXAMPLE OF N_i/T_i DISTRIBUTION

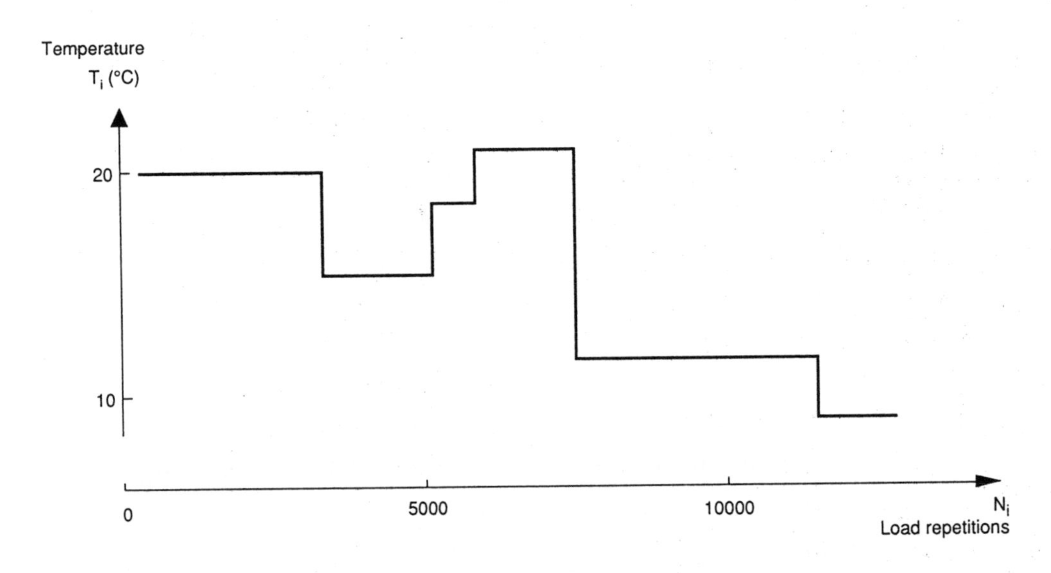

The viscoelastic behaviour of the bituminous material can be described using the materials characteristics determined by appropriate testing, as described in Chapter V. Using these measurements, an attempt was made to back-calculate the rutting in section 11, and to compare the predicted values with the rut-depth measurements recorded by the Project Manager. The results of this exercise, however, showed that the predicted influence of temperature was strongly overestimated, the back-calculated curve oscillating up and down along the measured one. This suggests, therefore, that the first assumption is false.

Again, using the E-moduli E_2 and E_3 of a three-layered system, back-calculated from the deflection-bowls of Falling Weight Deflectometer measurements on the test pavements, and taking the temperature dependent modulus E_1 from Dynamic Material Testing with samples of the material, the stiffness was calculated for temperatures between +10 °C and +40 °C and related to that at +20 °C (Figure VI.3). This coefficient, ranging from 0.75 to 1.75 over the temperature range investigated, may be used later in the analysis to develop a so-called "rutting-factor". However, it is not possible at this stage to test the second assumption, and for this reason temperature cannot be allowed for when evaluating rutting. There remains, however, the possibility of evaluation without considering temperature, and this was carried out as follows.

Rutting - Possible Basis for Evaluation

Full-scale test facilities in a number of countries have frequently been used to investigate and quantify relationships between pavement performance, axle loads and the number of load applications. Some of these have provided valuable information which can be used as a basis for the present analysis. For example, a total of 48 tests at the Bundesanstalt fur Strassenwesen (BASt) in Germany have led to the formulation of a law to describe permanent deformation (rutting), w_{P}, as a function of the number of load repetitions N:

$$w_P = w_O + a \cdot N^k$$

The power k was found to be 0.5 ±0.2 in 90 per cent of the tests carried out. The value w_O - see Figure VI.4, which shows an example of the development of rutting - characterizes a phase of consolidation early in the life of a pavement. The amount of this consolidation is perhaps dependent more on construction variables than on the materials properties that govern the structural rutting that take place later. Structural rutting follows a straight line when plotted against the square-root of the number of load repetitions ($N^{0.5}$), and it is this rutting which is used in comparisons of the effect of different axle loads. The slope a of this straight line contains the influences of load, temperature and pavement type. If two of these can be kept constant, the influence of the third can be quantified. To investigate this, a rutting factor a^* was defined, being the rut depth after one million loadings. From the formula noted above, therefore

$$a^* = a.10^3$$

Figure VI.3

RELATIVE STIFFNESS COEFFICIENTS OF SECTION 11

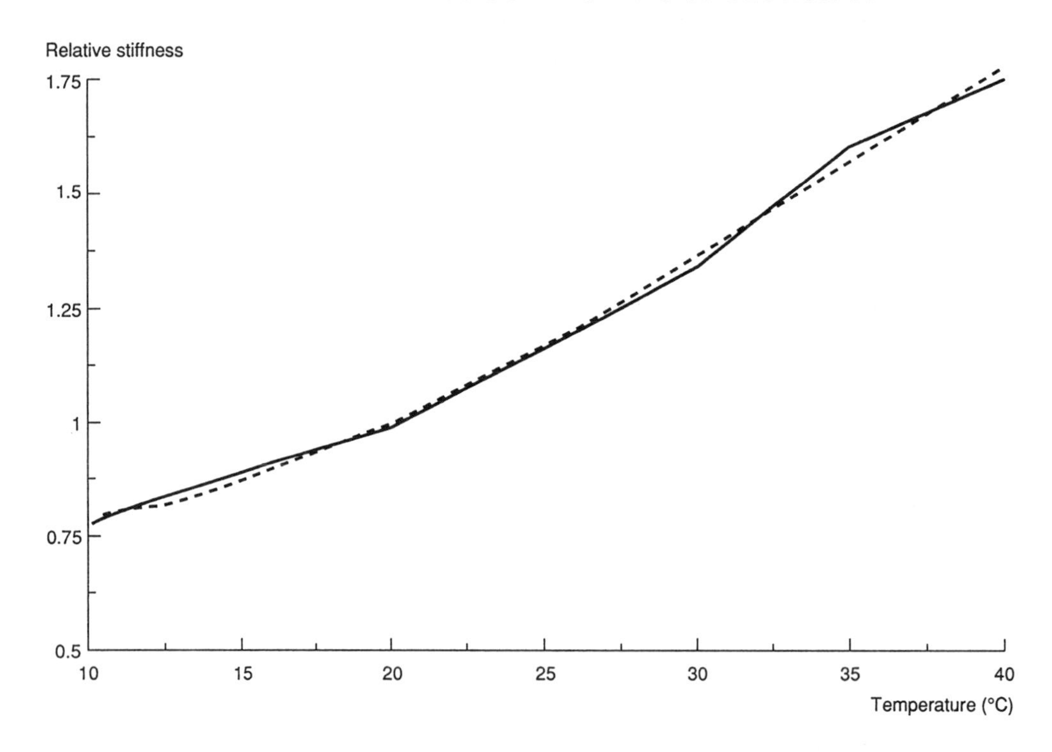

Figure VI.4

EXAMPLE OF THE DEVELOPMENT OF RUTTING, BASt MEASUREMENT

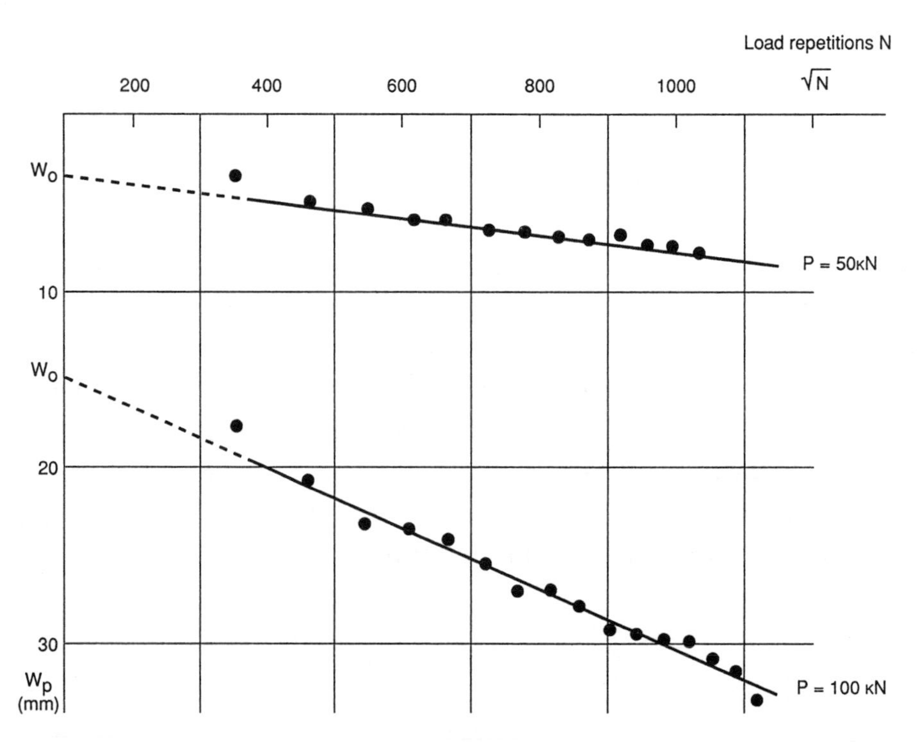

OECD/FORCE Results of Rutting Evaluation

The rutting measurements performed give rut-depth values that follow a straight line when plotted against $N^{0.5}$, even though the test track has no means of temperature control. On this basis, assuming that the principles described above also apply, it is possible to analyse rutting in the FORCE experiment without taking account of temperature changes during the test.

As a result of the overlay applied to sections 01 and 03, their behaviour changed completely. For this reason only the performance of the sections up to the point of the overlay was considered in the analysis. Figures V.5 to V.7 show this early behaviour for each of the three structures. The final number of load applications considered was therefore about 500 000 ($N^{0.5}$=750). It is for this number of load applications that a comparison of the rutting effects of 10 tonne and 11.5 tonne axle-loads is possible, since the 10 tonne loading ended at about 570 000.

For each of the three structures the heavier load led to a steeper slope of the straight line, giving a higher value of a^* (Table VI.1). For structure I, the test was completed after the first half million of loads, when the structure had reached the end of its life.

Table VI.1.

RUTTING FACTOR FOR 10/11.5 TONNES

Structure	**Rutting factor $a^* = a.10^3$**	
	10 t	**11.5 t**
I - thin bit.	31.4	70.0
II - thick bit.	4.46	6.67
III - cement treated	8.83	10.85

Both the remaining structures were loaded further with a 11.5 tonne axle load. The continuation of the evolution of rut depth is given in Figure VI.8. A very different behaviour of the two pavement types is clear:

-- section 02 shows a straight line with a slope very similar to that before: $a^*(N \leq 500\ 000) = 6.67$ and $a^*(N \geq 500\ 000) = 4.33$

-- section 03 by contrast shows a much steeper slope, even when this slope is characterised by only 3 measurements: $a^*(N \leq 500\ 000) = 10.85$ and $a^*(N \geq 500\ 000) = 24.80$

Structure III, section 03, can therefore be supposed to be degraded, perhaps as a consequence of increasing cracking within the cement-bound base. Because of this degradation it was necessary to overlay section 03 also. When evaluating the results of rutting of the overlayed sections 01 and 03, it must be assumed that each performed as if it were a completely new pavement. The formula used in the evaluation:

$$w_P = w_O + a \cdot N^{0.5}$$

requires therefore, because of the $N^{0.5}$ scale, a new zero-point. Even though the development of rutting is defined by only a few points (Figure VI.9), there is in both cases (01 and 03) a straight line, following the consolidation phase.

Figure VI.5

RUTTING OF STRUCTURE I

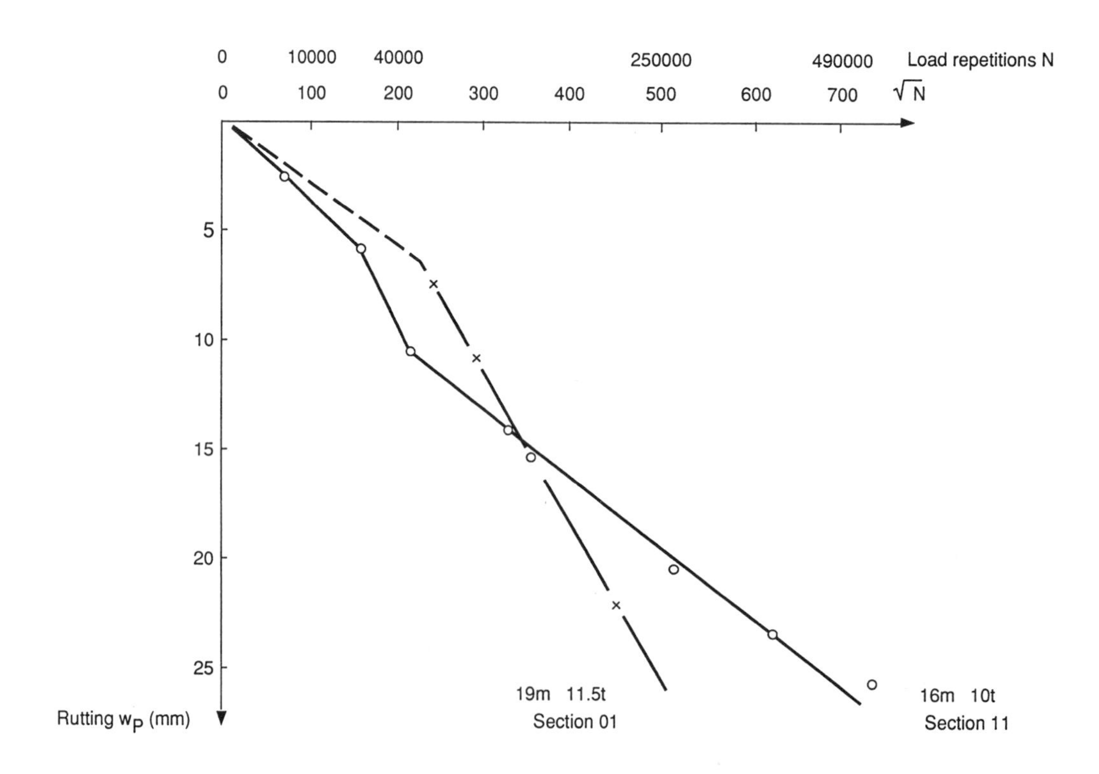

Figure VI.6

RUTTING OF STRUCTURE II

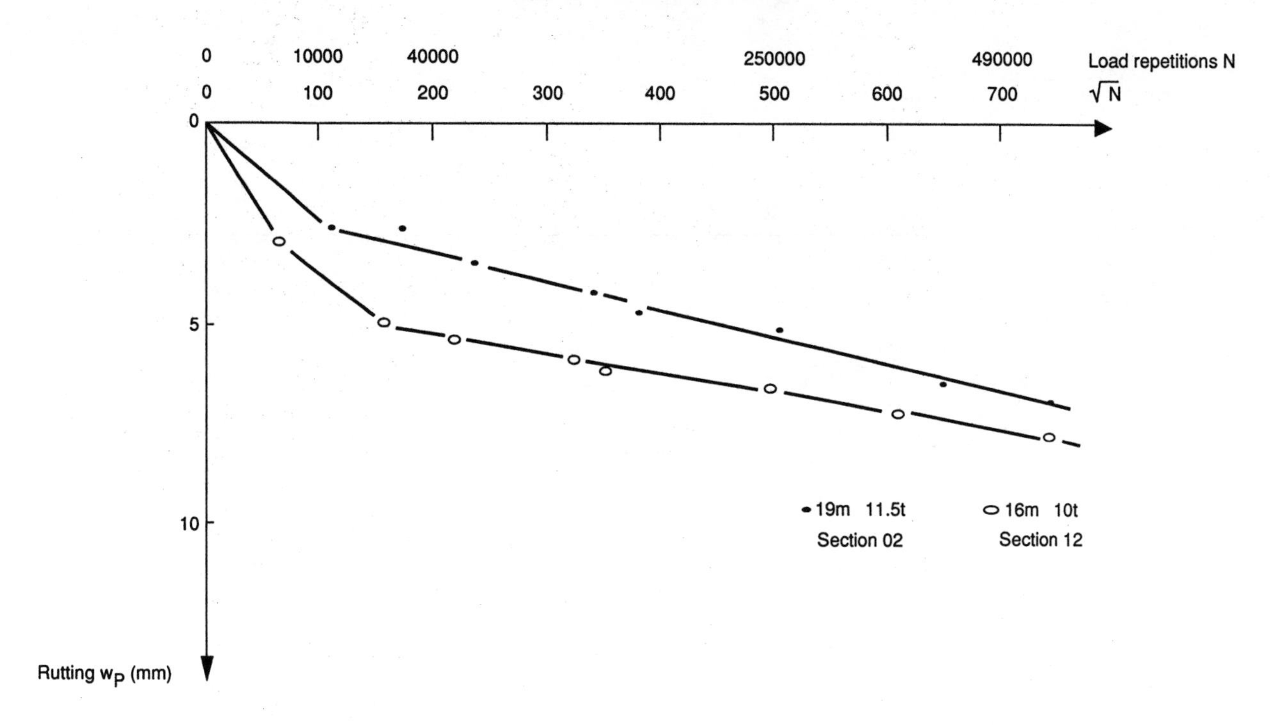

Figure VI.7

RUTTING OF STRUCTURE III

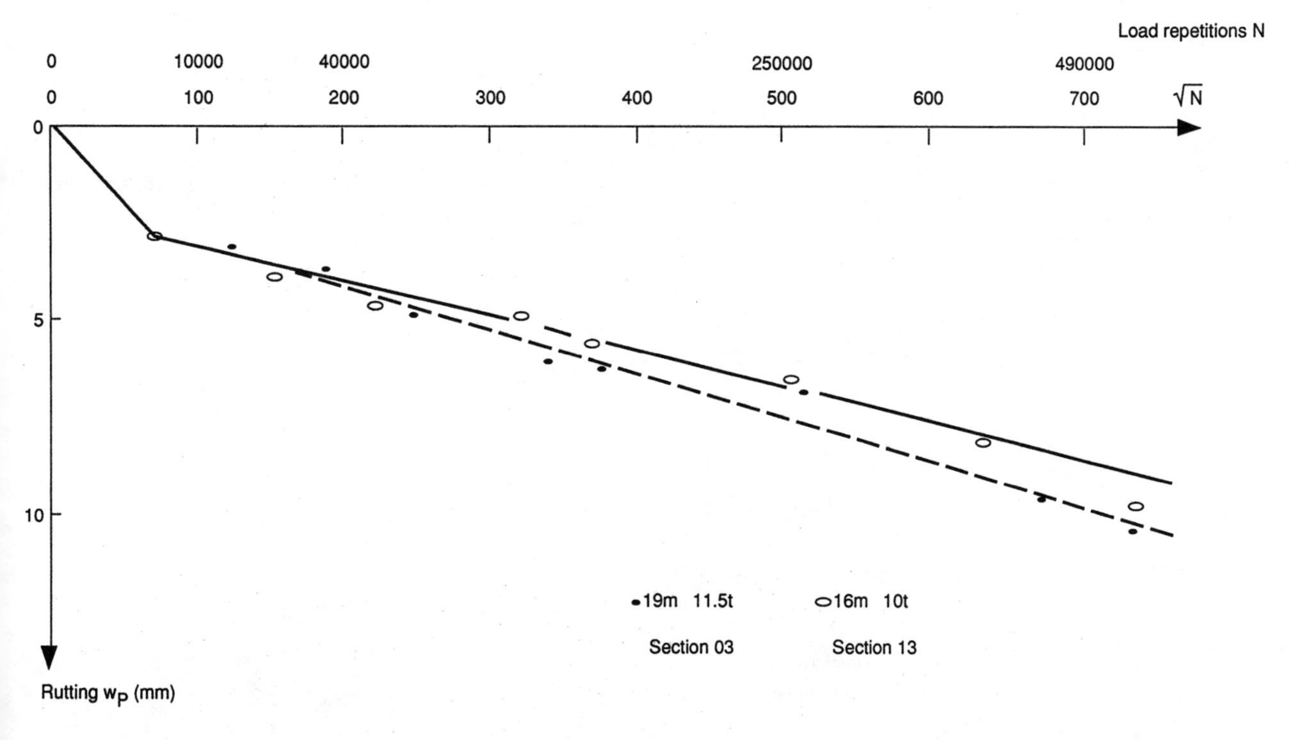

Figure VI.8

DEVELOPMENT OF RUTTING

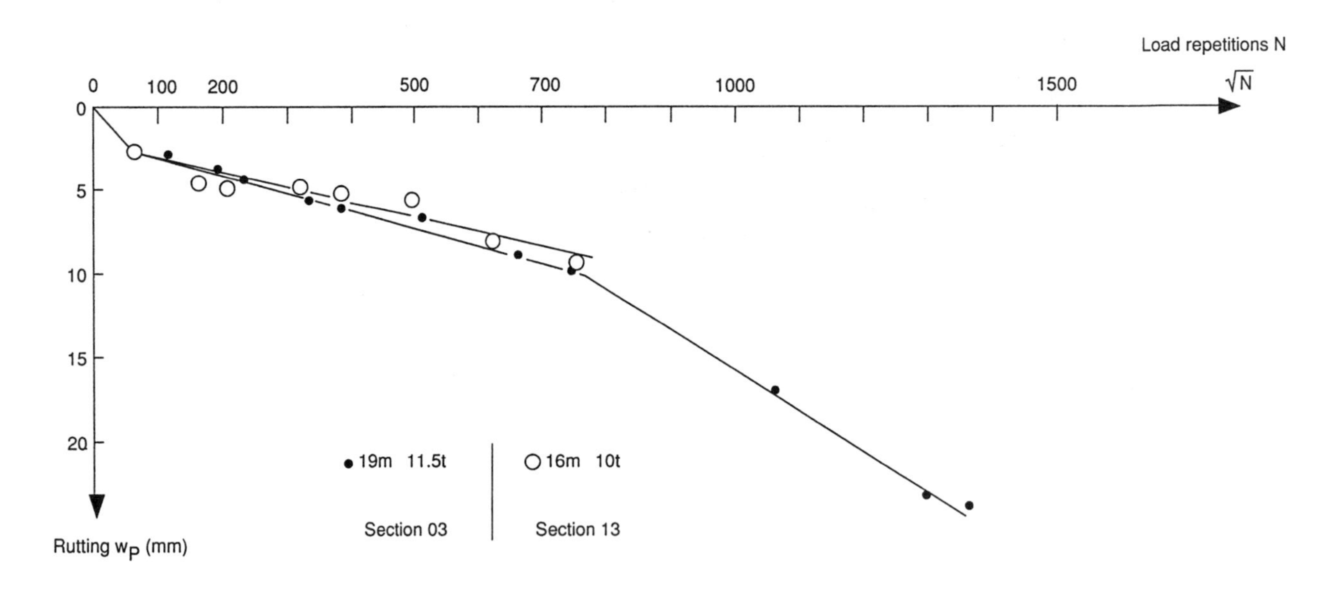

Structure III
cement treated

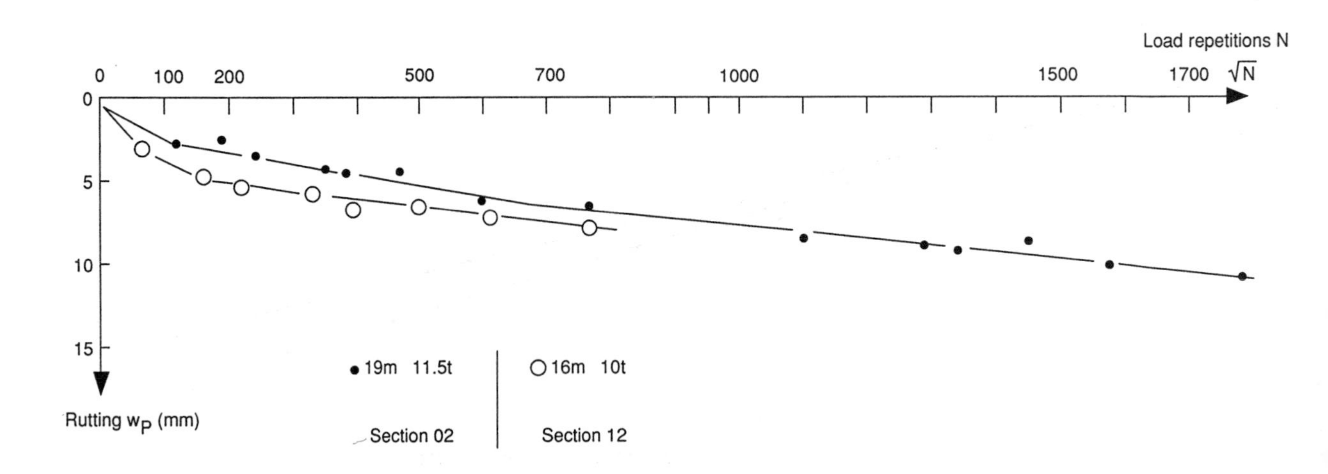

Structure II
thick bituminous

Figure VI.9

RUTTING AFTER OVERLAY IN SECTIONS 01 AND 03

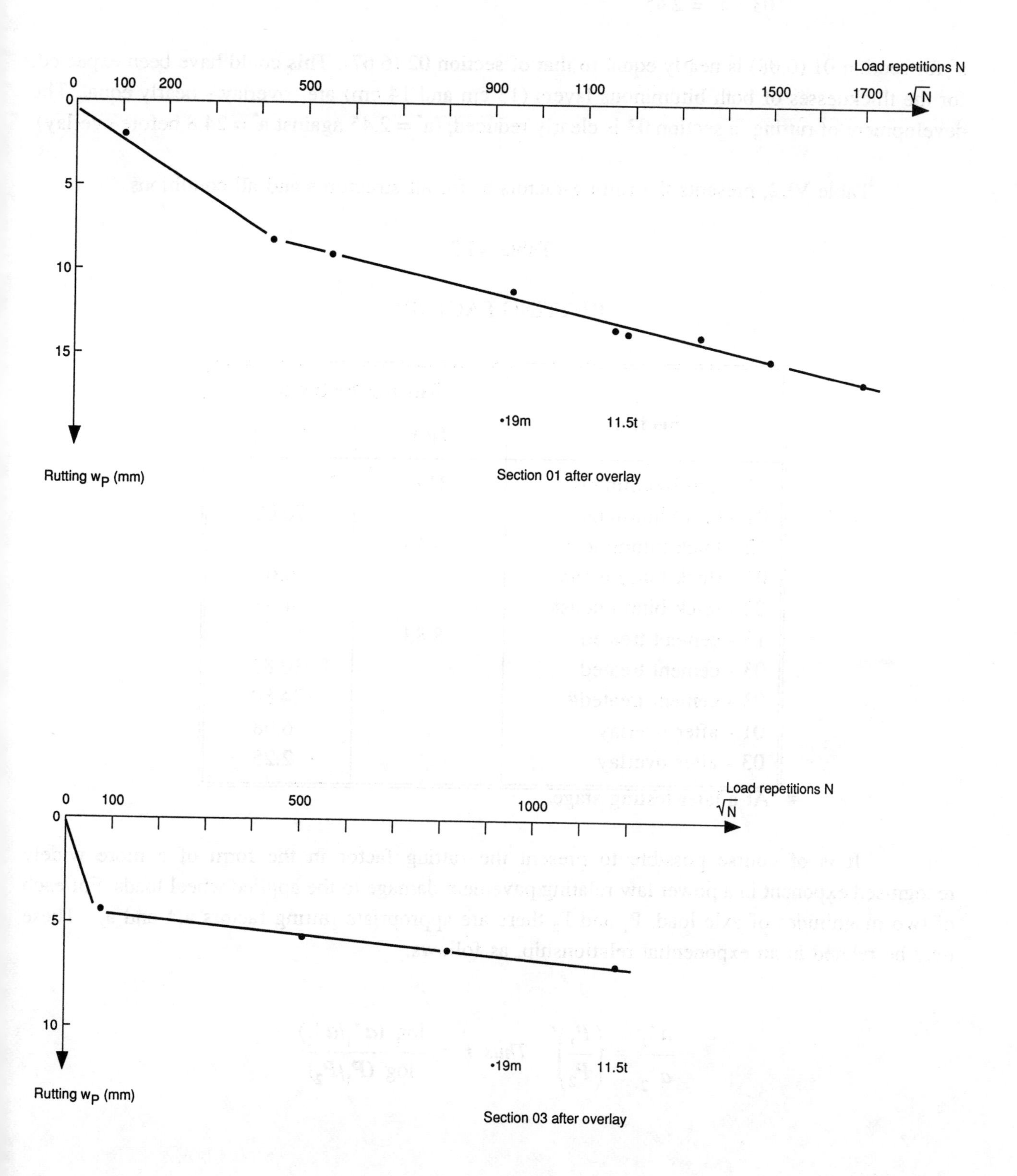

For the two sections, each overlayed with 6 cm of bituminous concrete, the rutting factors are:

$$01 : a^* = 6.08$$
$$03 : a^* = 2.45$$

a^* for section 01 (6.08) is nearly equal to that of section 02 (6.67). This could have been expected, for the thicknesses of both bituminous layers (13 cm and 14 cm) are -overlay - nearly equal. The development of rutting in section 03 is clearly reduced, ($a^* = 2.45$ against $a^* = 24.8$ before overlay).

Table VI.2, presents the rutting-factors a^* for all structures and all conditions.

Table VI.2.

RUTTING FACTORS

Section	**Rutting factor a^***	
	10 t	**11.5 t**
11 - thin bituminous	31.4	
01 - thin bituminous		70.00
12 - thick bituminous	4.46	
02 - thick bituminous		6.67
02 - thick bituminous#		4.33
13 - cement treated	8.83	
03 - cement treated		10.85
03 - cement treated#		24.80
01 - after overlay		6.08
03 - after overlay		2.25

\# At a later testing stage

It is of course possible to present the rutting factor in the form of a more widely recognised exponent in a power law relating pavement damage to the applied wheel loads. For each of two magnitudes of axle load, P_1 and P_2 there are appropriate rutting factors a_1* and a_2. These may be related in an exponential relationship, as follows:

$$\frac{a^*_1}{a^*_2} = \left(\frac{P_1}{P_2}\right)^r \quad \textit{Thus } r = \frac{\log\ (a^*_1/a^*_2)}{\log\ (P_1/P_2)}$$

Using the values of Table VI.2, therefore, allows values of r to be calculated for the two axle loads used and for each of the structures examined, as shown in Table VI.3.

Table VI.3.

SUMMARY OF POWER LAW EXPONENTS ON THE BASIS OF RUTTING

Structure	r
11/01	5.74
12/02	2.88
13/03	1.47

VI.2.3. Effect of different axle loads: cracking

At the FORCE test, the length of cracking was defined as the longitudinal length + 250 mm on each side (the length of a transversal crack is thus 500 mm) as presented in Figure IV.14. The total length of cracking was then divided by the length of the test section, to give the percentage, which was used as the principal measure of cracking. No index of severity was used in the assessment.

All visible cracks were also painted over with different colours so that the progress of cracking over time could be easily seen; they were also transferred to scale on paper and the coordinates of their starting, finishing and intermediate points were later digitized for easier analysis. The length of cracks were calculated from the digitized data by the Road and Traffic Laboratory of the Technical Research Centre of Finland (VTT). Cracks were also characterised as either transverse, longitudinal or diagonal. The lengths from the digitized data were used as the second measure of cracking.

Cracking was defined in the AASHO Road Test as the area, in sq feet per 1,000 sq ft of pavement surface, exhibiting class 2 or class 3 cracking. Class 2 cracking is defined as that which has progressed to the stage where cracks have connected together to form a grid-type pattern. The definitions of cracking used in the AASHO and in the FORCE tests are thus quite different and comparisons are not easily undertaken.

The percentage of cracking observed in the FORCE test is expressed as a function of the number of load applications in Figures VI.10 and VI.11 on linear and logarithmic scales respectively. It is clear that the development of cracking is linear on the logarithmic scale.

Figure VI.10

CRACKING PERCENTAGE OF STRUCTURE I AS A FUNCTION OF LOADINGS

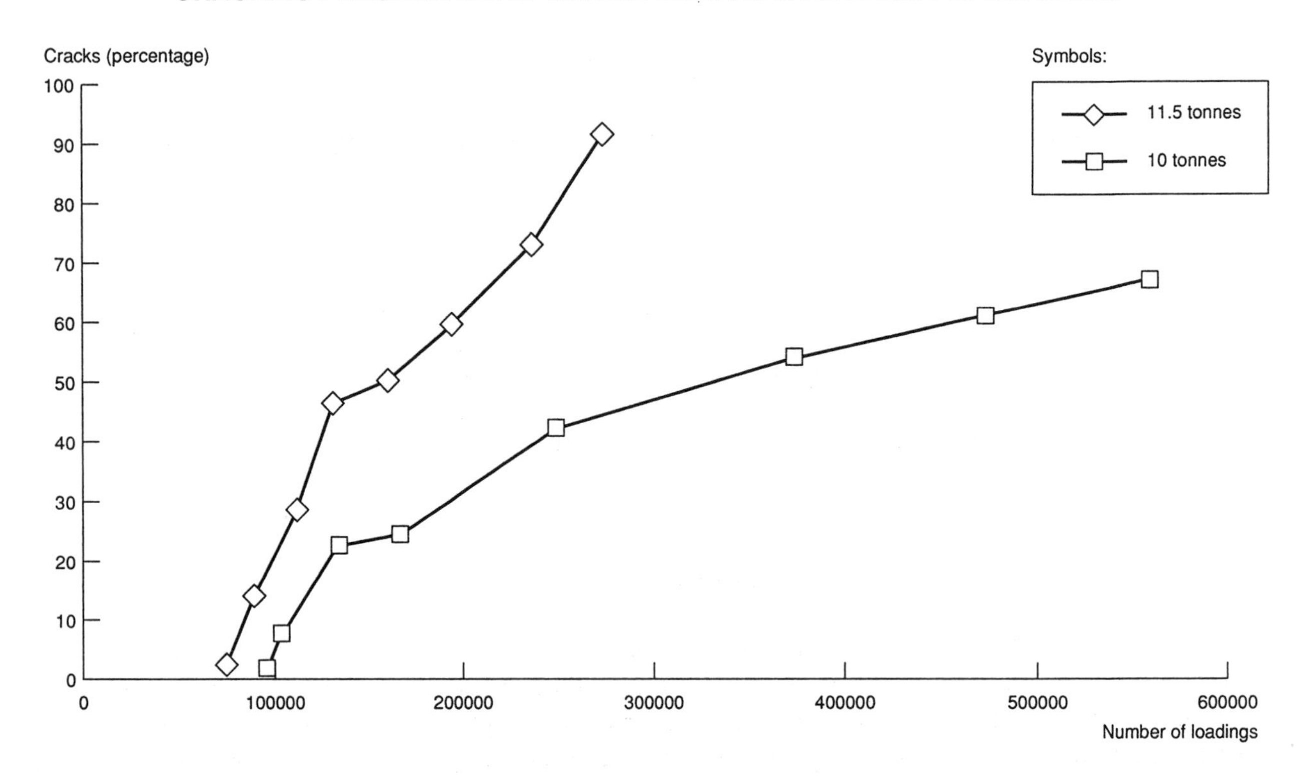

Figure VI.11

CRACKING PERCENTAGE OF STRUCTURE I AS A FUNCTION OF LOADINGS IN LOGARITHMIC SCALE

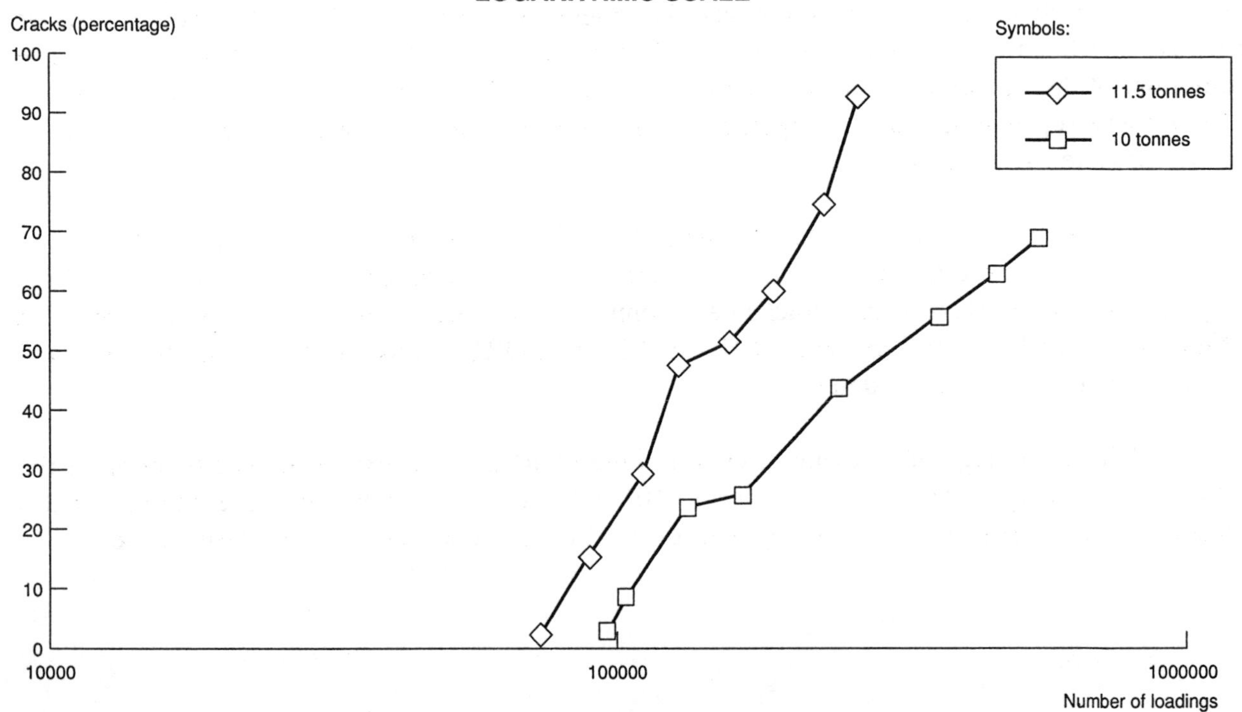

The basic principle for comparison is presented in Figure VI.12. The number of load applications bringing about the same defined degree of cracking for the 11.5 and 10 tonnes curves is noted. These are defined as $N_{11.5}$ and N_{10}. The appropriate power law relating deterioration to axle load can then be calculated from the formula

$$\left(\frac{11.5}{10}\right)^{x} = \left(\frac{N_{10}}{N_{11.5}}\right) \qquad \text{Eq. VI.2}$$

The value "x" has been calculated for different levels of deterioration and is shown in Figure VI.13. The values "x" vary between 1.80 to 6.68 increasing linearly with the degree of cracking (Figures VI.14 and VI.15).

Using the digitized cracking data, it was possible to calculate the exact length of cracks and to distinguish longitudinal, transversal and diagonal cracks. The total crack lengths were divided by the length of the section and later expressed as crack length / 100 linear meters. These are presented in Figure VI.16 which again illustrates the linear relationship between crack length and number of load applications. The corresponding "x" values were calculated in the same way as above and the results are presented in Figure VI.17. In this case, values vary from 2.40 to 8.85, increasing linearly up to about 400 000 applications and becoming less linear beyond this figure (Figures VI.18 and VI.19); the values are slightly greater than those based on cracking percentage.

For the sections trafficked by the 10 tonne axle load, there are many more transverse than longitudinal cracks, but the rate of development of both the longitudinal and transverse crack formation is very similar for an axle load of 11.5 tonnes (Figures VI.20 and VI.21). The two phenomena are therefore different and may be a result of the effects of the different radii or because of the relatively heavy load applied to a weak structure.

Because not enough cracking developed on the other structures it was not possible to carry out axle load comparisons.

VI.2.4. Effect of different axle loads: response measurements

During the course of the experiment, many measurements were made of the response of the pavement to the applied wheel loads. Stresses, strains and deflections generated in the pavement were recorded for the Project using specified gauges and sensors, and by other participating teams using their own measuring techniques.

In addition to the comparison of the effects of the 10 tonne and 11.5 tonne axle loads by rutting and cracking, it is possible to use some of these response measurements to make similar comparisons. The principle of the use of response measurements for analysing the effects of axle loads is presented in Figure VI.22. The behaviour of the pavement materials is generally not linear

Figure VI.12

THE PRINCIPLE OF THE COMPARISON OF THE EFFECTS OF 10 TONNE AND 11.5 TONNE AXLE LOADS

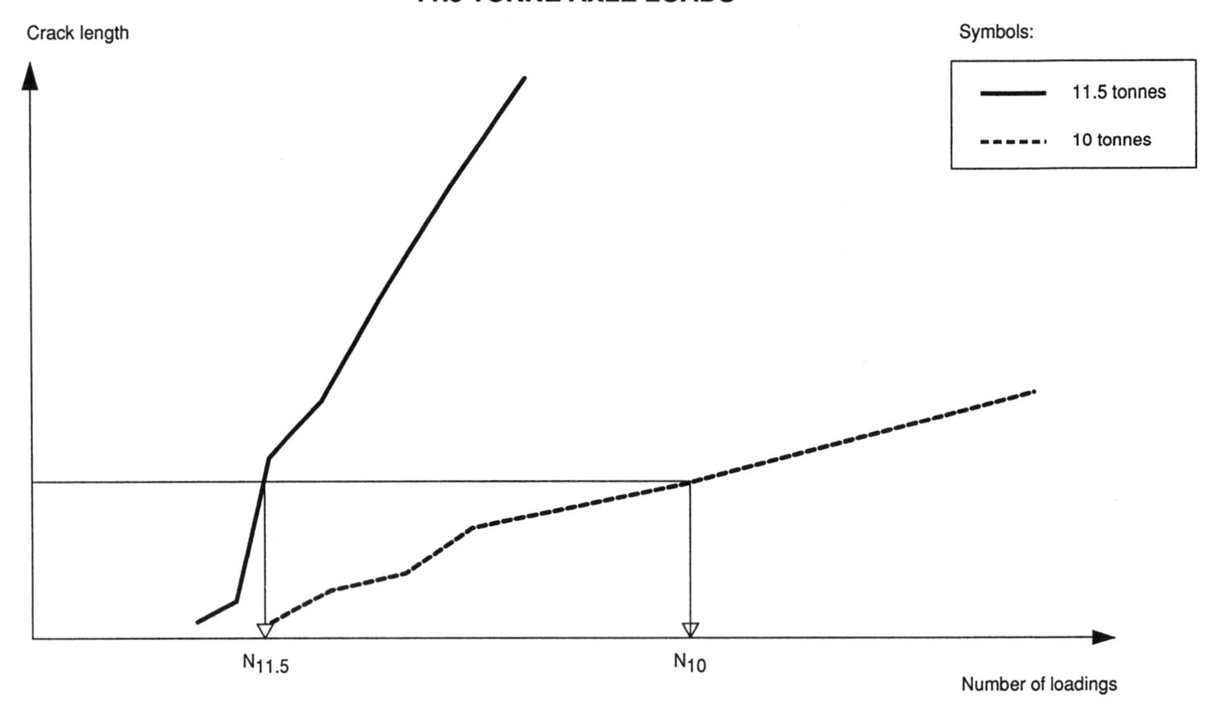

Figure VI.13

THE "POWERS" BASED ON CRACKING PERCENTAGE

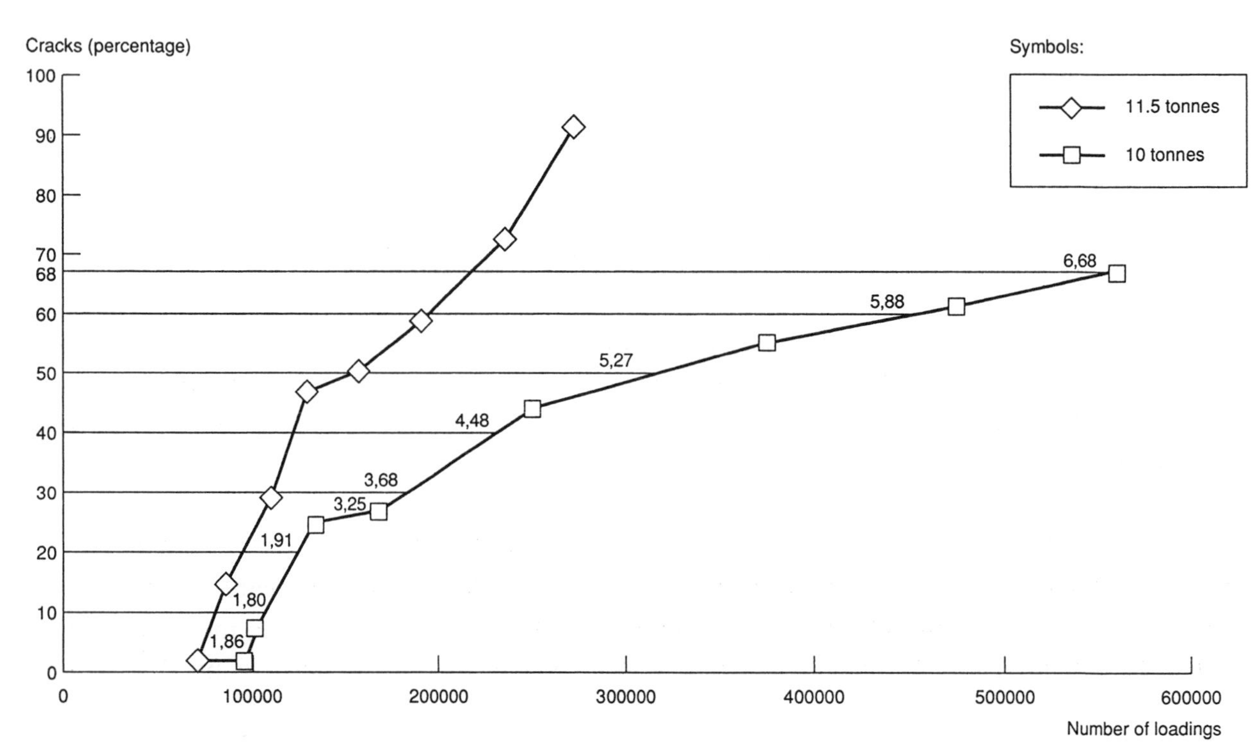

Figure VI.14

THE "POWERS" BASED ON CRACKING PERCENTAGE AS A FUNCTION OF LOADINGS

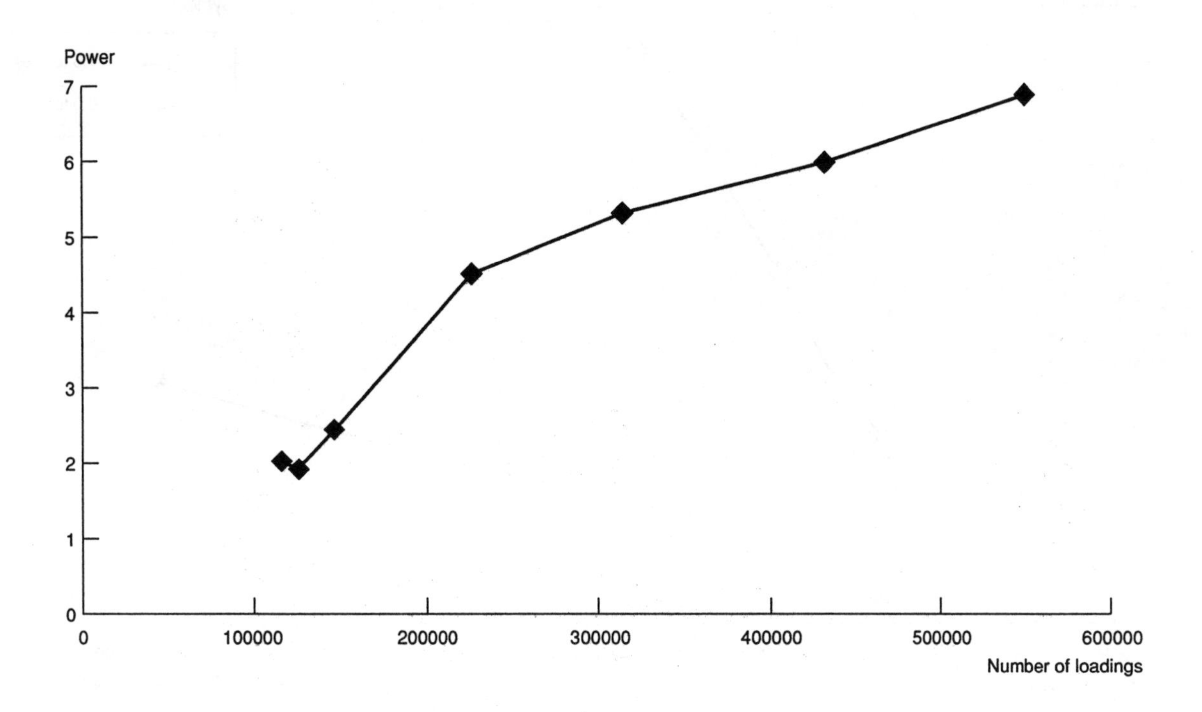

Figure VI.15

THE "POWERS" BASED ON CRACKING PERCENTAGE AS A FUNCTION OF CRACKING

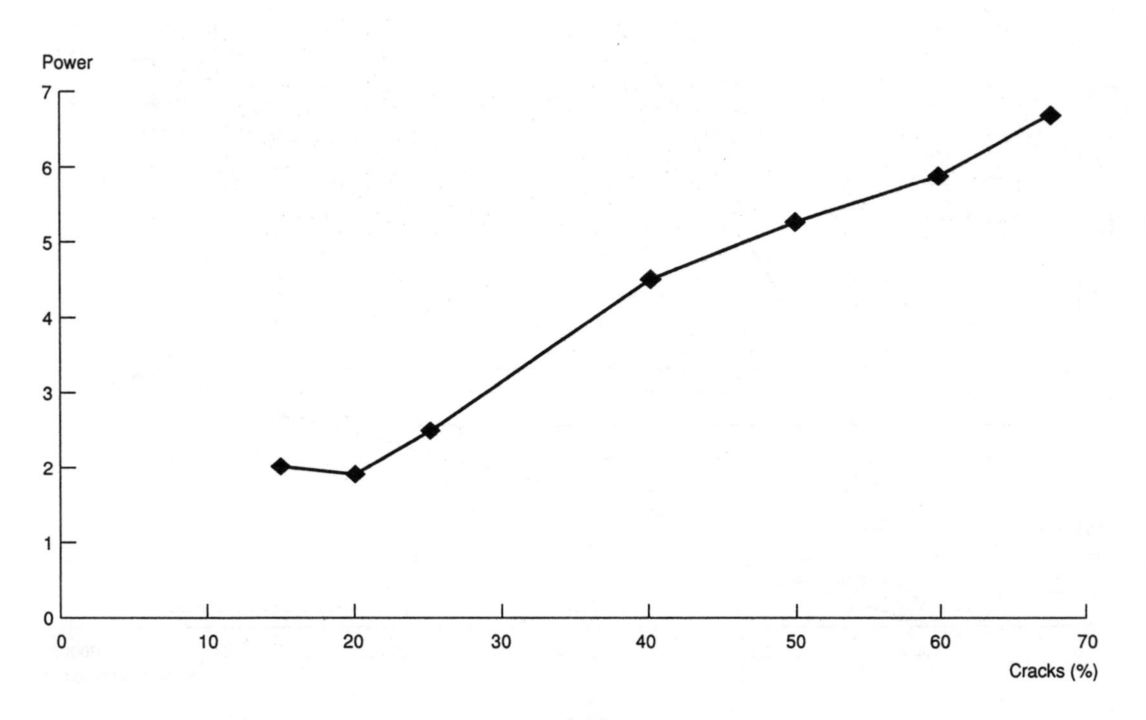

Figure VI.16

CRACK LENGTH OF THE STRUCTURE I AS A FUNCTION OF LOADINGS

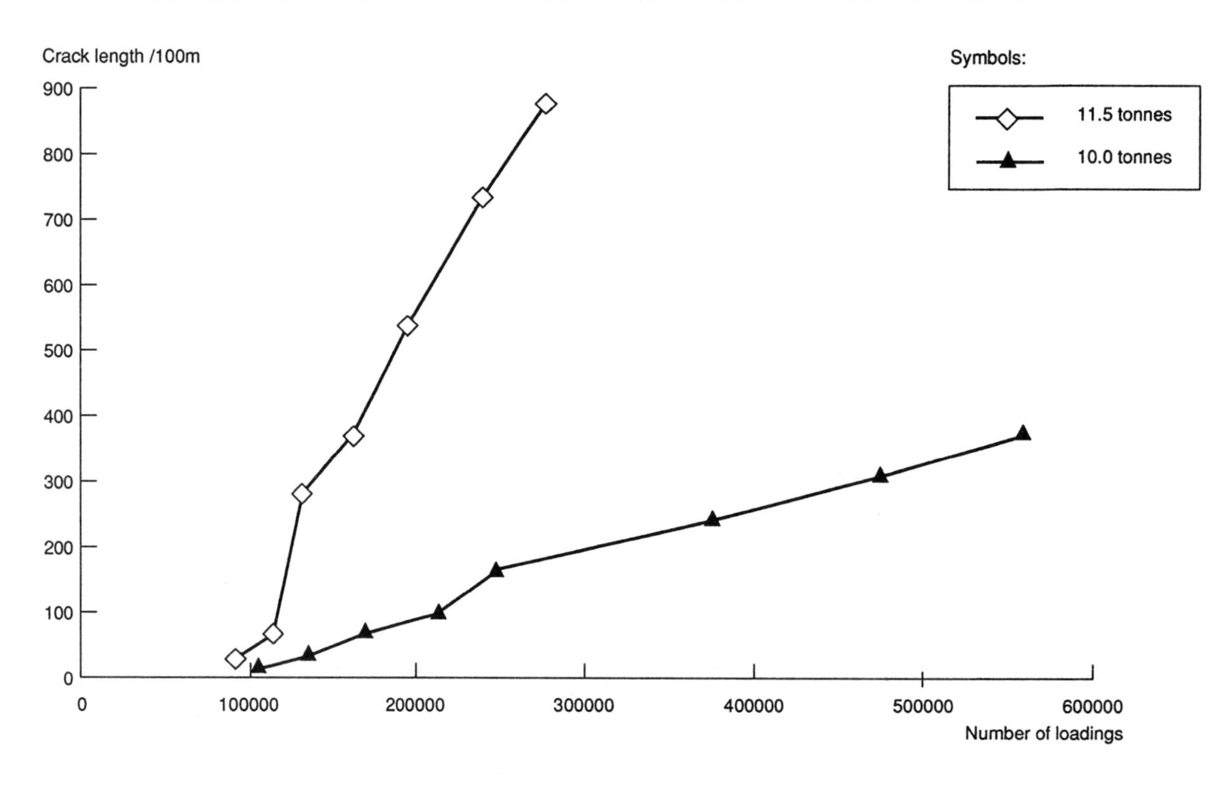

Figure VI.17

THE "POWERS" BASED ON CRACK LENGTH

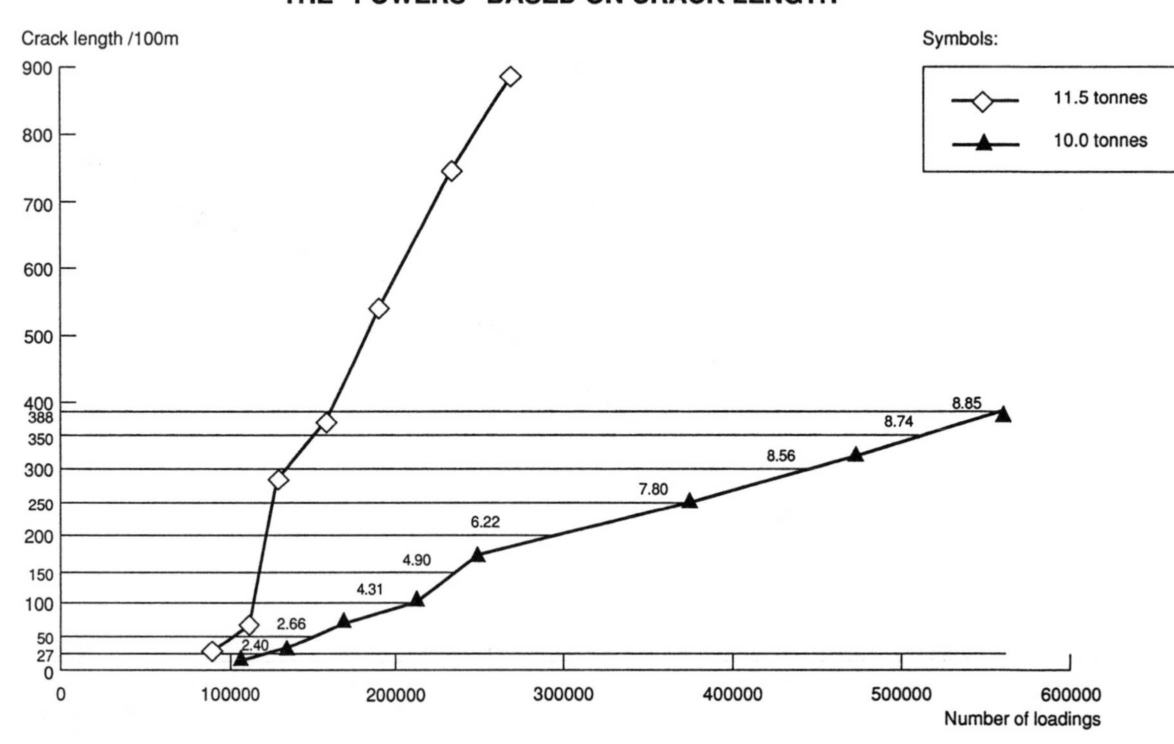

Figure VI.18

THE "POWERS" BASED ON CRACK LENGTH AS A FUNCTION OF LOADINGS

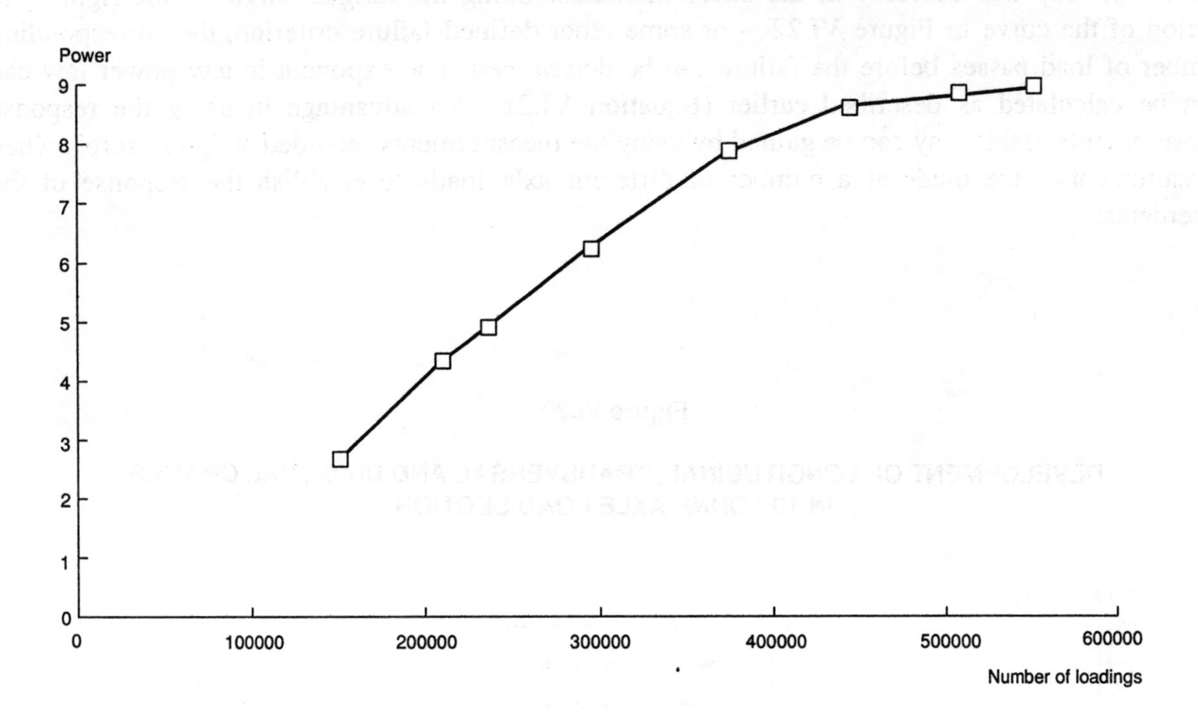

Figure VI.19

THE "POWERS" BASED ON CRACK LENGTH AS A FUNCTION OF CRACKING

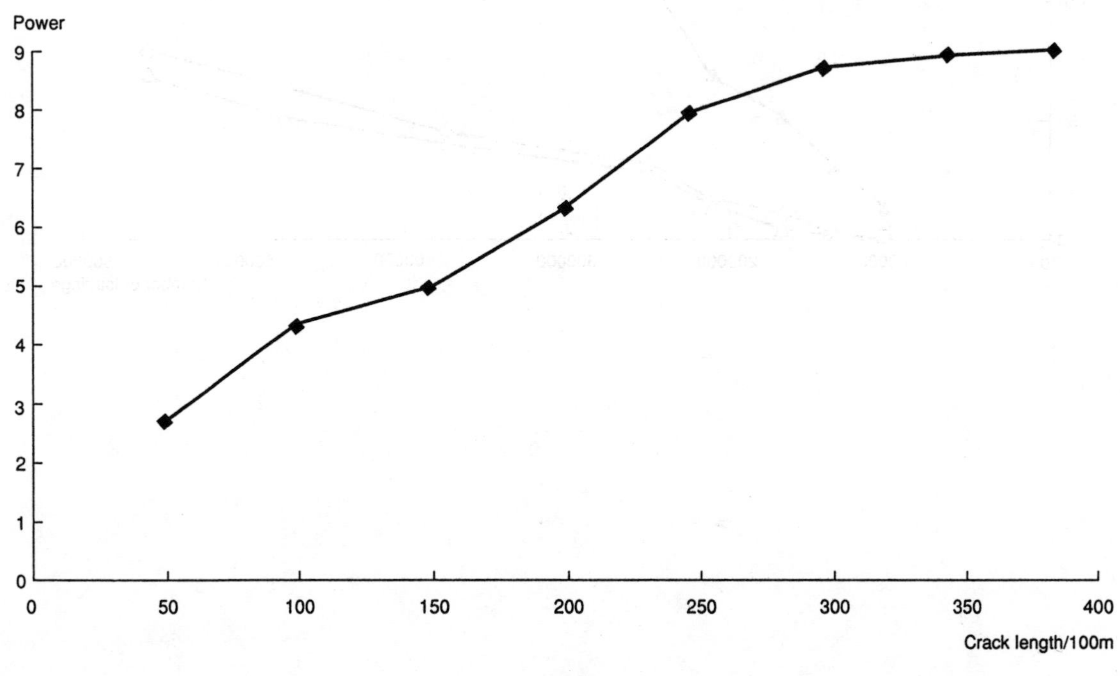

(cf. dotted line) but non-linear, (cf. solid line). In principle the elastic modulus of materials like the crushed rock will increase as the stress increases and the elastic modulus of cohesive materials like silt or clay will decrease as the stress increases. Using the fatigue curve -- the right hand portion of the curve in Figure VI.22 -- or some other defined failure criterion, the corresponding number of load passes before the failure can be determined. The exponent in any power law can then be calculated as described earlier (Equation VI.2). An advantage in using the response measurements in this way can be gained by using the measurements recorded at "point zero", when measurements were made at a number of different axle loads to establish the response of the pavements.

Figure VI.20

DEVELOPMENT OF LONGITUDINAL, TRANSVERSAL AND DIAGONAL CRACKS IN 10 TONNE AXLE LOAD SECTION

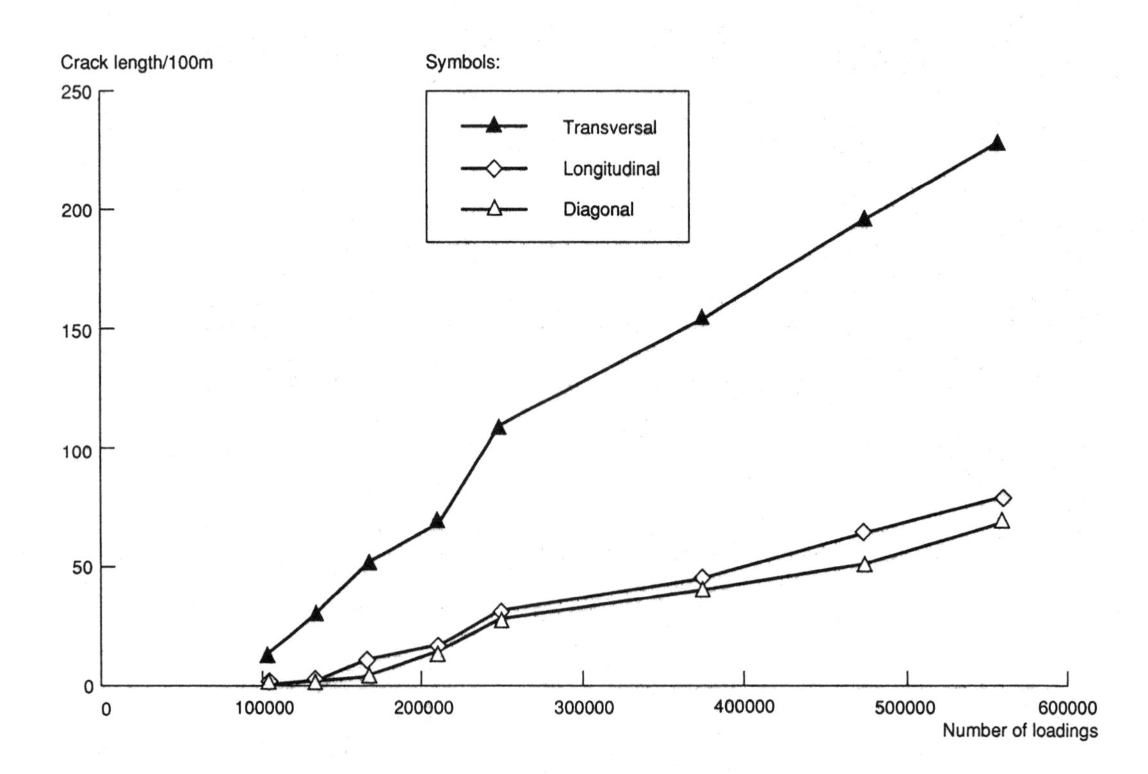

Figure VI.21

DEVELOPMENT OF LONGITUDINAL, TRANSVERSAL AND DIAGONAL CRACKS IN 11.5 TONNE AXLE LOAD SECTION

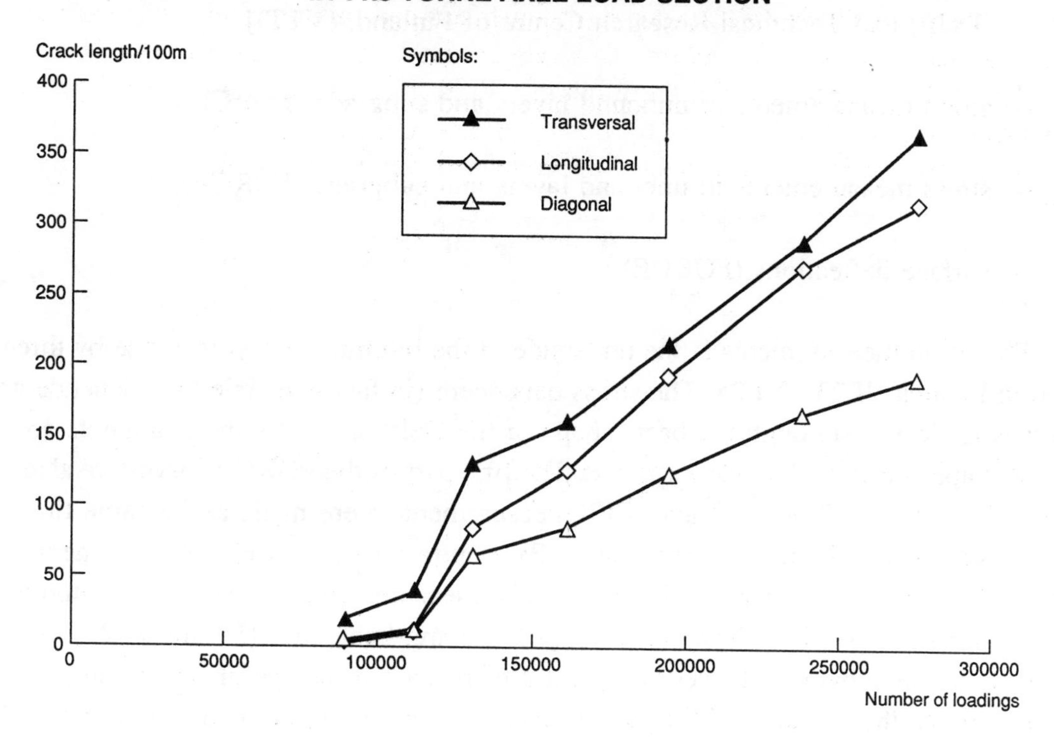

Figure VI.22

PRINCIPLE OF THE USE OF RESPONSE MEASUREMENTS FOR DETERMINING THE "POWER"

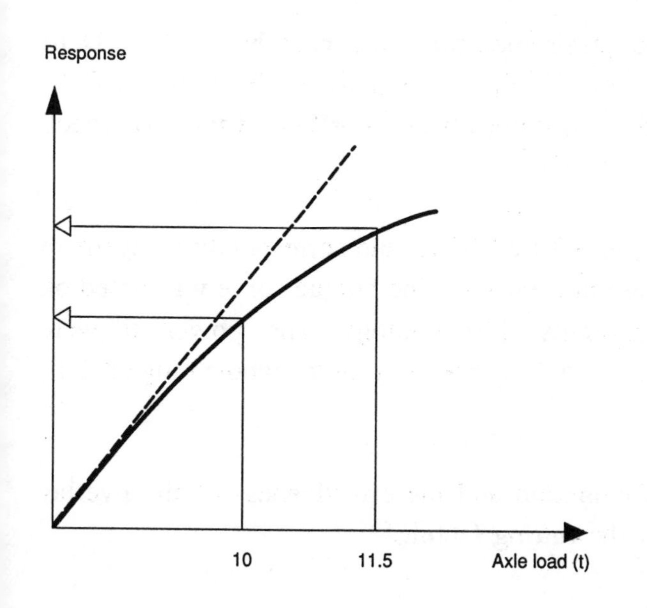

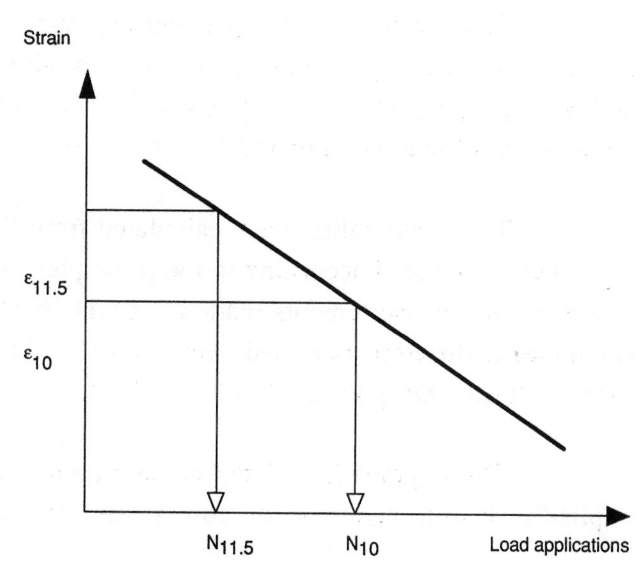

For the purposes of this comparison, the following response measurements were used:

-- strain measurements in bituminous layers [FORCE, Delft University of Technology (Delft) and Technical Research Centre of Finland, (VTT)],

-- strain measurements in unbound layers and subgrade (FORCE),

-- stress measurements in unbound layers and subgrade (FORCE),

-- surface deflections (FORCE).

The strain measurements at the underside of the bituminous layers, made by three teams, are shown in Figures VI.23 - VI.25. The stress dependent (in fact here axle load dependent) nature of the curves is clear. Although the basic shape of the Delft and VTT measurements are similar, the concave shape was not what was expected. The first part of the FORCE curves are also concave but the remainder is not. The Delft and VTT measurements were made at the same time and the FORCE measurements about a month later. By contrast to the strain measurements, surface deflections seemed to behave linearly (Figure VI.26). Measurements of strain in the unbound layers and in the subgrade seemed to show some stress stiffening behaviour (Figure VI.27). Stress measurements in the subgrade showed too great a dispersion to be useful for the purposes of this analysis (Figure VI.28). Because of this, and because of the considerably greater volume of results available, the remainder of this analysis employs the measurements of strain in the bituminous material.

The stress dependent behaviour of the materials was not possible to be explained with measurements made during the test. The tyres were made for 13 tonne axle load and when smaller loads were used, the tyre inflation pressure was correspondingly altered. The contact area was more or less constant but the contact pressure distribution might have been different.

The varying stress dependent behaviour of strain measurements made by FORCE, Delft and VTT is not easily explained by other measurements. However, comparisons between the Delft and VTT gauges, for the 11.5 tonne axle load, and for different lateral position of the test wheel, do show good relative agreement.

The strain values were calculated from Figures VI.23-VI.25 and corresponding pavement lives were calculated according to the principles presented earlier. The fatigue curve was based on the laboratory measurements made by the Delft University of Technology. The "powers α" were calculated at different axle load ranges (e.g. 8.2-11.5, 11.5-13 tonne) and for the whole range 8.2-13 tonne. Results are presented in Table VI.4.

The degradation of the cement-treated foundation and the effectiveness of the overlay applied to it were also evident from an analysis of the rutting factor.

Figure VI.23

STRAINS CAUSED BY DIFFERENT AXLE LOADS, FORCE MEASUREMENTS

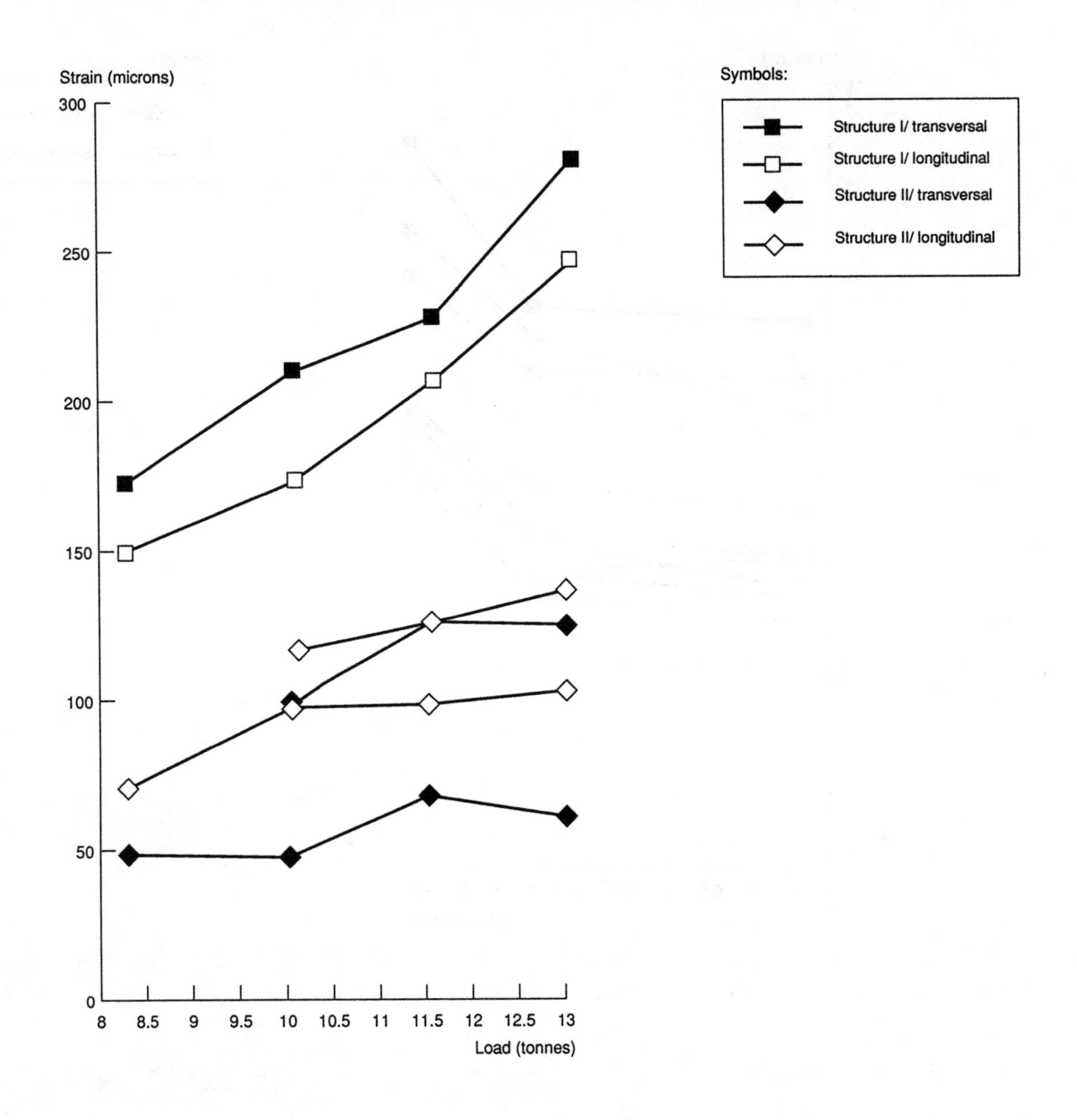

Figure VI.24

STRAINS CAUSED BY DIFFERENT AXLE LOADS, DELFT UNIVERSITY OF TECHNOLOGY MEASUREMENTS

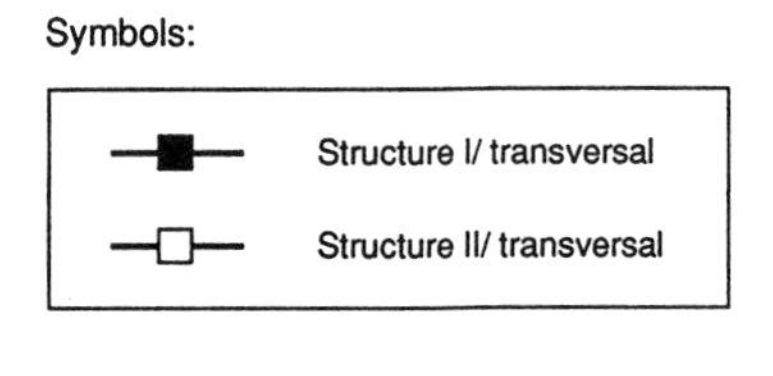

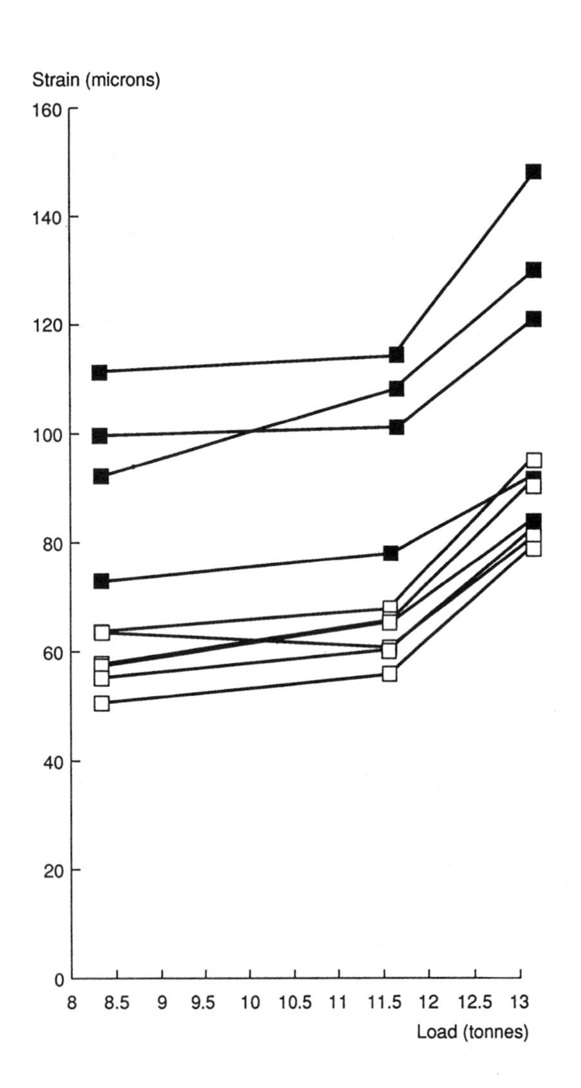

TABLE VI.4.

THE POWERS CALCULATED FROM STRAINS IN BITUMINOUS LAYERS WITHIN DIFFERENT AXLE LOAD RANGES

Structure	Strain gauge	FORCE				DELFT			VTT		
		8.2/ 10	10/ 11.5	11.5/ 13	8.2/ 13	8.2/ 11.5	11.5/ 13	8.2/ 13	8.2/ 11.5	11.5/ 13	8.2/ 13
I	Transversal	4.5	2.6	8.7	5.4	1.3	12.1	4.3	4.2	9.8	5.7
	Longitudinal	3.9	6.4	-11.1	0.7				2.1	11.4	4.6
II	Transversal	0.0	13.1	-4.4	2.8	1.2	8.8	3.2	5.0	14.6	7.6
	Longitudinal	8.6	0.7	1.6	4.3				6.9	14.8	8.7

VI.2.5. Discussion

In sections VI.2.2 to VI.2.4, attempts have been made to draw conclusions about the relative damaging effects of two different axle loads on the basis of different criteria. In spite of the apparent simplicity of the task, many considerations have to be made before conclusions can be drawn. The following discussion of the analyses, and by implication the results on which they are based, presents some of the more important considerations. First, however, it must be noted that the degree of deterioration at which the condition of the road becomes critical and in need of structural maintenance is defined differently in different countries. Conclusions based on the condition of the FORCE test track, where deterioration was extensive, therefore need to be treated with some caution when applied to in-service roads elsewhere.

Rutting

On the basis of the analysis of rutting performance of the pavements it is clear that more frequent measurements of rutting would have simplified the analysis and improved the quality of results. Although some trafficking took place under a 13 tonne axle load, there was insufficient information on rutting collected during this phase to allow this heavier axle load to be considered in the analysis.

The method of analysis selected led to useful results, even without consideration of the influence of temperature, and permitted the influence of the axle load on rutting to be related to the rutting factor a^*, the rutting factor varying with the pavement type. Similarly, the rutting factor developed in the analysis is equally able to distinguish between the performance of the pavements before and after the overlay was applied. In this respect, the two structures of similar type (Structure I and Structure II, sections 01 and 02) gave very similar rutting factors after overlay.

Figure VI.25

STRAINS CAUSED BY DIFFERENT AXLE LOADS, VTT MEASUREMENTS

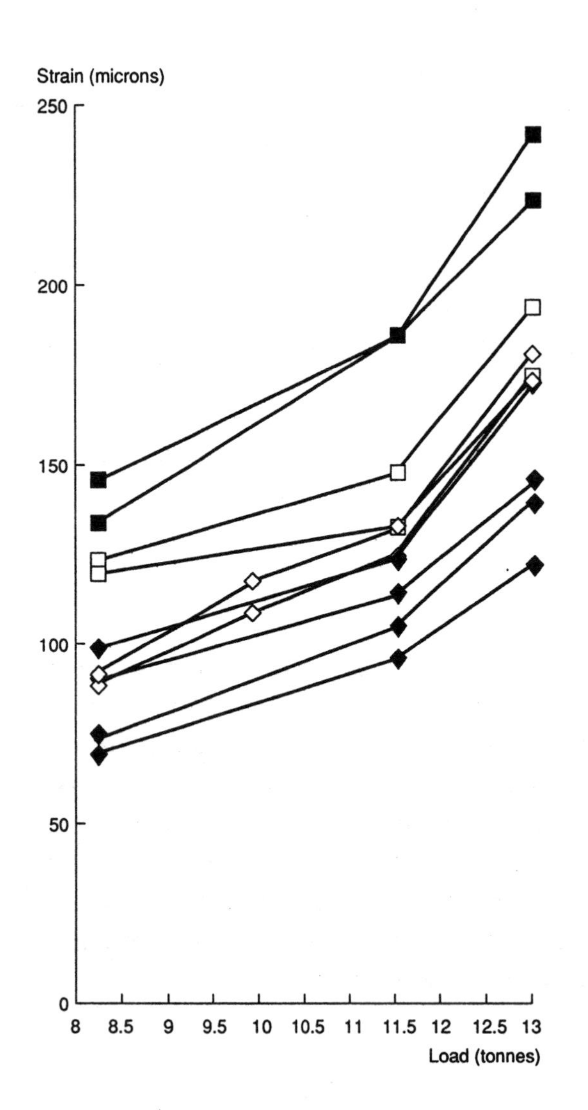

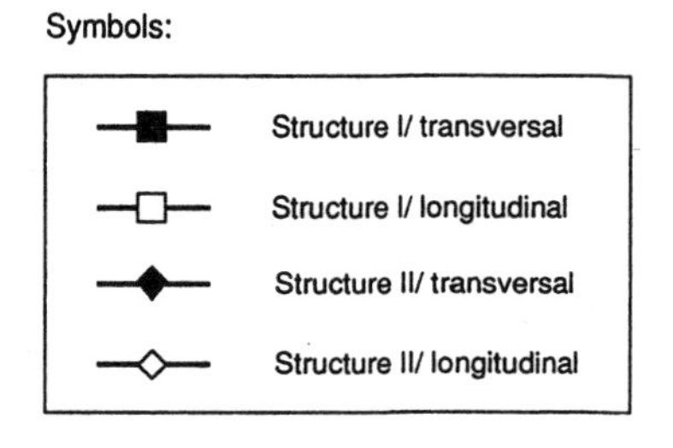

Figure VI.26

SURFACE DEFORMATIONS CAUSED BY DIFFERENT AXLE LOADS

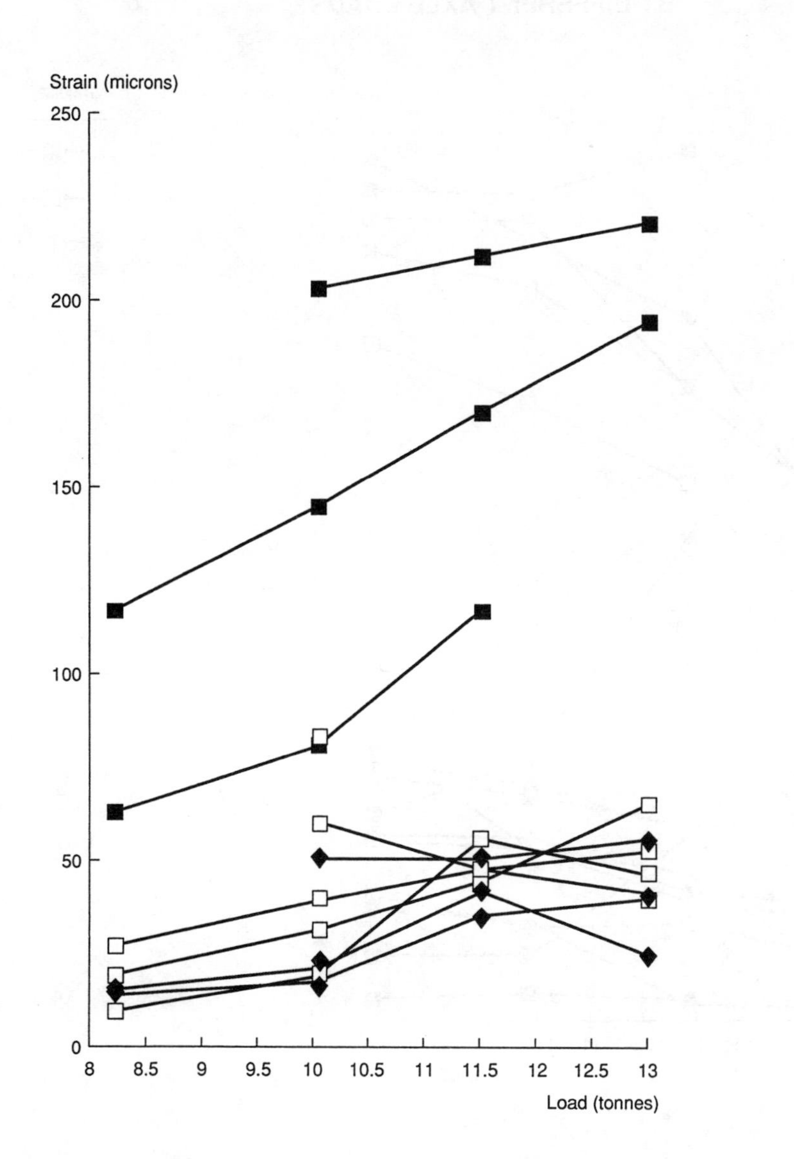

Symbols:

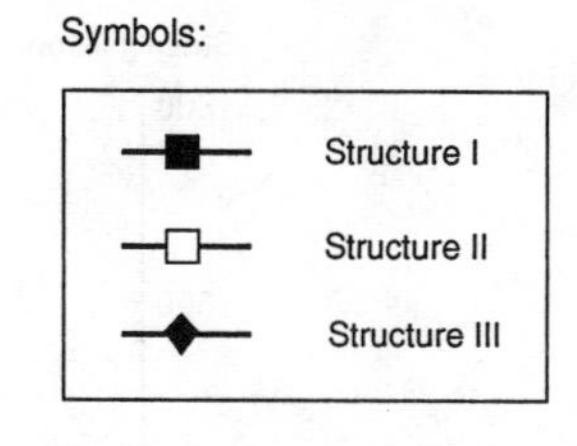

Figure VI.27

VERTICAL STRAINS IN UNBOUND LAYERS AND SUBGRADE CAUSED BY DIFFERENT AXLE LOADS

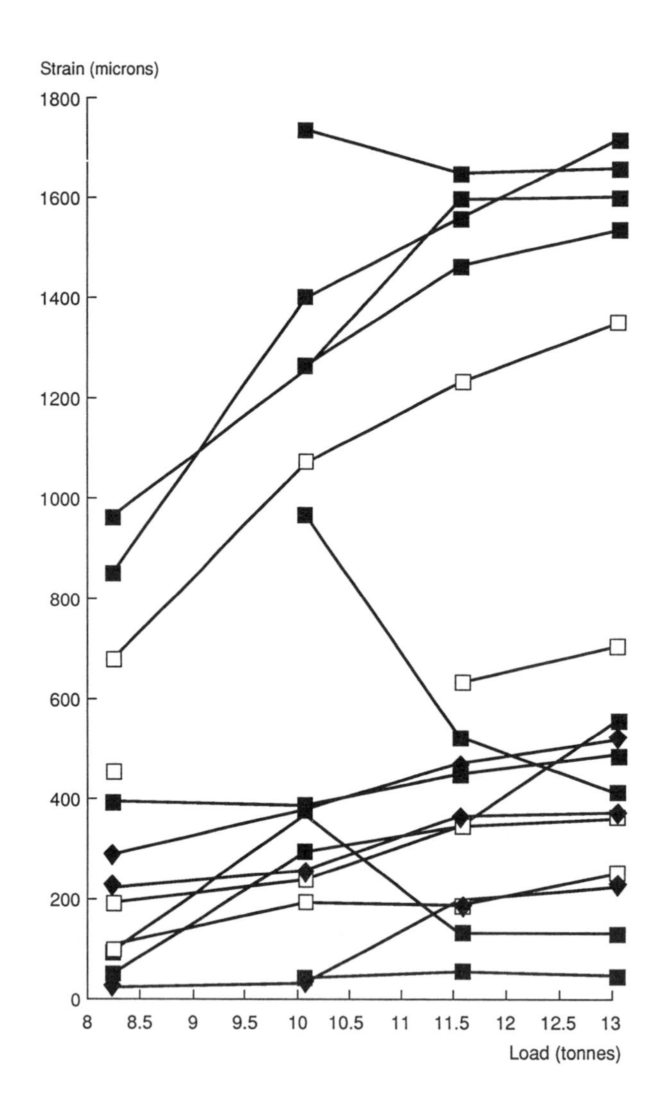

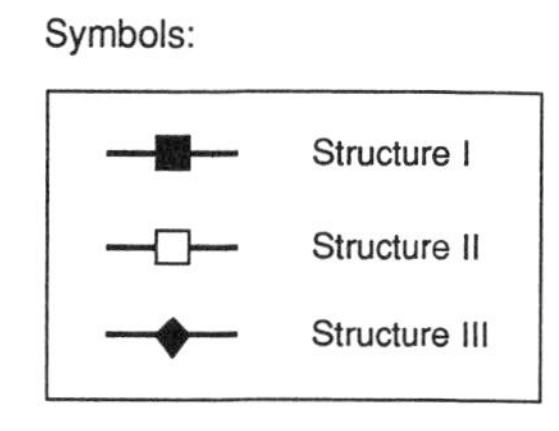

Figure VI.28

VERTICAL STRESSES IN UNBOUND LAYERS AND SUBGRADE CAUSED BY DIFFERENT AXLE LOADS

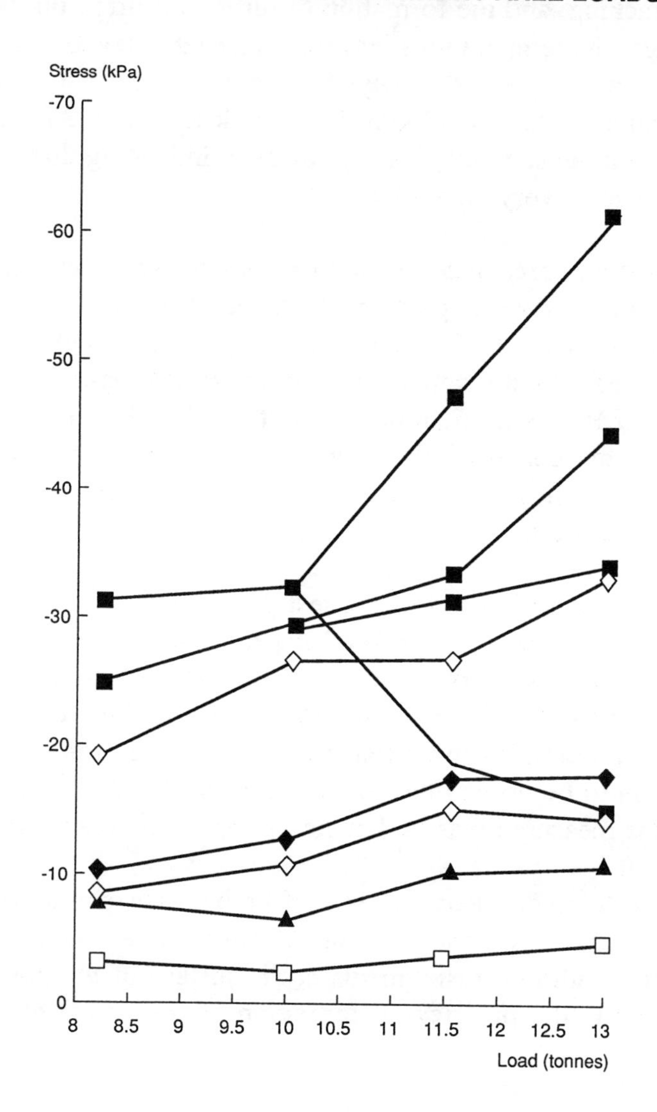

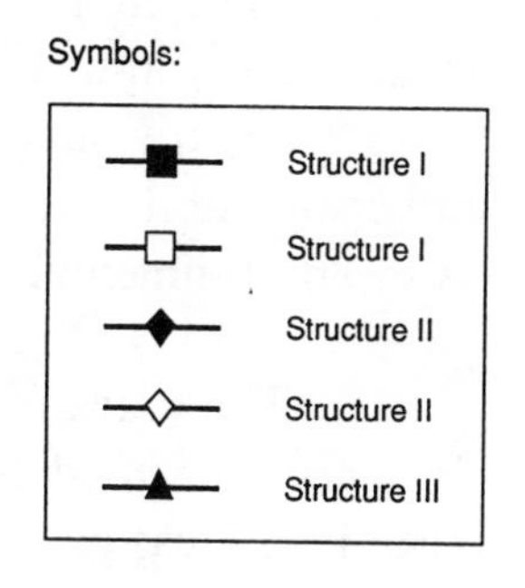

Cracking

From the point of view of the analysis of cracking, a number of physical parameters need to be considered. The initiation of cracking, and the formation of rutting occurred on the 10 tonne and 11.5 tonne radii at different times; the temperatures and the water table levels were therefore not the same for each axle load. This may affect the analysis to some degree, but no procedures for verifying any such effects are available. The development of crack length as a function of the number of axle loads (Figure VI.16) was substantially linear, however, indicating that any changes due to environmental conditions have been very small.

The cracked area expressed as a percentage of the total area of the pavement is perhaps a less accurate method of assessing the degree of cracking than the absolute crack length. The cracked area was generally a logarithmic function of axle load passes (Figure VI.11) so that the rate of increase in percentage cracking decreased with increasing numbers of axle passes. Crack length, however, developed linearly (Figure VI.16). The slight non-linearity in the 11.5 tonne section may indicate some effect of changes due to environmental conditions. Because the non-linearity is small, however, it is likely that the reason for this lies in the inaccuracies in defining the cracked area and not in the change of environmental conditions.

The predominant mode of cracking in each of the test pavements was initial transverse cracking followed by longitudinal cracking at a rather later stage. However, observed cracking patterns in the 10 tonne section (11) are different from those in the 11.5 tonne section (01) (Figures VI.20 and VI.21). While the total length of transverse and longitudinal cracking is very similar for the 11.5 tonne section there are many more transverse cracks than longitudinal cracks in the 10 tonne section. There appears to be no obvious explanation for this and a comparison of the longitudinal and transverse strains measured was undertaken in order to understand the cause.

The FORCE Project and VTT made measurements of both transverse and longitudinal strain at the bottom of the bituminous layers in sections 01 and 02 (bituminous layers 6 cm and 14 cm thickness); VTT also made corresponding measurements at the surface of the pavement. Any differences in these strains may indicate the preferential formation of transverse or longitudinal cracks.

The transverse strains appeared to be 20 to 35 per cent greater than longitudinal strains in Structure I, according to the VTT measurements, and 10 to 20 per cent greater according to the FORCE measurements made later at different temperatures and using only two transverse gauges. Previous measurements at the Virttaa Test Site in Finland have indicated a difference of the order of 20 to 60 per cent greater strains depending on temperature and thickness of the bituminous layers. From the VTT measurements made at Nantes the difference between transverse and longitudinal strains was independent of axle loads (from 8.2 to 13 tonnes).

Transverse strains in Structure I were certainly greater than longitudinal, suggesting that longitudinal cracking should take place in preference to transverse. This was not what was observed in practice, however. Structure 01 (loaded by 11.5 tonnes) exhibited similar degrees of transverse and longitudinal cracking, and that loaded by 10 tonnes showed much more severe transverse cracking. Whether this is due to weakness of the structure in relation to the loads applied is not clear.

In the stronger Structure II, the behaviour was more consistent. Measured longitudinal strains were greater than transverse, and this was consistent with the fact that when cracks did appear late in the experiment, they were transverse.

One further possible effect influencing the analysis needs to be mentioned. The radii on which the 10 tonne and 11.5 tonne axle loads travelled were, of course, different. The true linear speed on the 10 tonne section was thus 16 per cent less than that on the 11.5T section (60.6 km/h instead of 72 km/h). The observed strains decreased monotonically with the speed (Figure VI.29). On an in-service road, increased speeds would often bring about greater dynamic effects, compensating for the decrease in strain. The suspension on the LCPC machine at Nantes, however, is excellent and no effect of dynamic loads can be seen. The deterioration observed may thus be somewhat different from that which takes place on the normal road.

Because of the small radii, there is a greater shear effect between the tyre and the pavement than would occur on a normal road. Although shear at the pavement surface was measured the results have not yet been analysed nor compared to shear on a normal road.

Response Measurements

In principle the elastic modulus of materials such as gravel and crushed rock used in pavement layers increases as the stress increases, and the elastic modulus of cohesive materials such as silts and clays decreases as the stress increases. The changes are not linear. Some materials may have both properties deriving from both frictional and cohesive effects. The subgrade at the FORCE test is very unusual in its material and grading, and its behaviour is equally unusual.

As the applied load on a pavement increases, the stresses, strains and deflections increase, but because of the presence of three materials of different behaviour, the combined response to the load may be very complicated. Although the behaviour of the strains at the underside of the bituminous layers also seemed relatively complicated -- the stress dependency seeming to be different at different stress levels for example -- and in spite of the fact that different gauges exhibited different behaviour, only strains at the bottom of the bituminous layers could be used in this study.

The effect of different axle loads is very difficult to calculate because the theoretical enough. Test roads built into the public network are a very expensive method of gaining information for this purpose and seasonal effects may have drastic effects which cannot be easily analysed. Ideally, the test pavements used for a comparison of the effect of different axle loads should deteriorate simultaneously in order to avoid this seasonal variation. Test tracks with artificial loading like that at Nantes offer the only real possibility to study the effects of different axle loads.

Figure VI.29

THE EFFECT OF SPEED ON STRAINS IN STRUCTURE II, VTT MEASUREMENTS

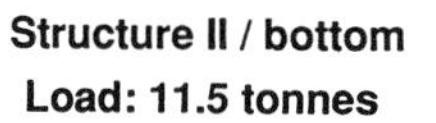

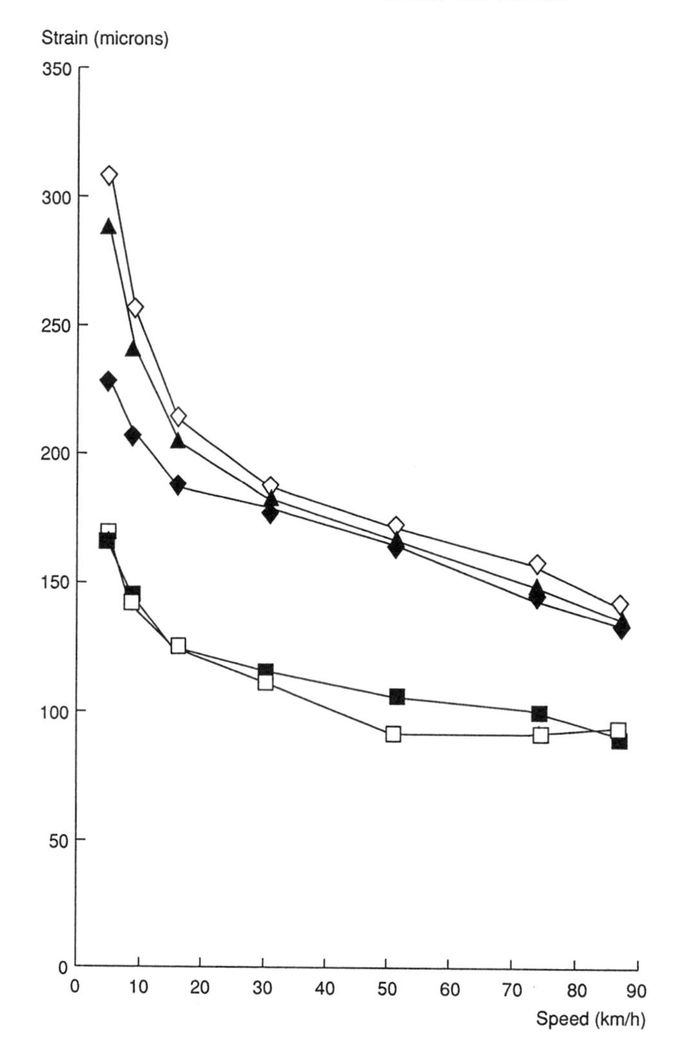

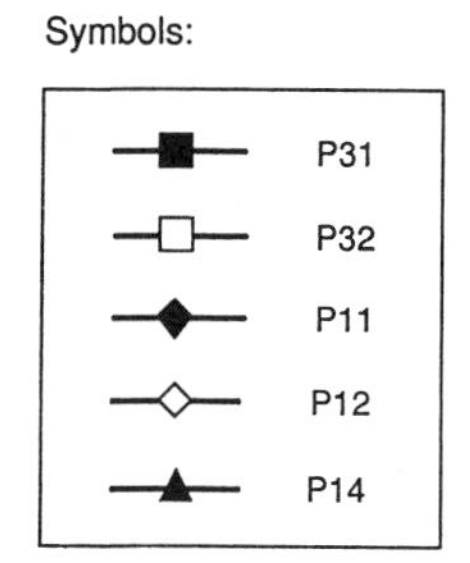

VI.2.6. Summary and conclusions

The OECD/FORCE project afforded a good opportunity to compare the effect of axle loads because it was possible to use two axle loads simultaneously. The new axle load limit of 11.5 tonne for driving axles within EC was selected as the basic axle load in the OECD/FORCE test and the 10 tonne axle load was selected as being representative of current legal maximum axle loads in many countries. The 11.5 tonne axle load was used on the outer ring (sections 01, 02, 03), where the radius of rotation was 19 metres and a 10 tonne axle load for the inner ring (sections 11, 12, 13), where the radius was 16 metres. Cracking and rutting were used as the performance indicators; roughness could not justifiably be used because of the special type of suspension which eliminated the effect of dynamic loads.

Although the experiment was carried out on a limited number of experimental structures, and with only two axle loads, analysis of the results to show their relative damaging effects was valuable because of the simultaneous trafficking of the test pavements. The relative damaging effect was calculated both from the performance of the pavement in terms of cracking and rutting, and on the basis of response measurements.

The exponent in the power law appeared to depend strongly on the degree of deterioration. The values of the exponent are from 1.86 to 6.68 if the estimated cracked area was used and from 2.40 to 8.85 if the measured length of the cracks was used.

The deterioration experienced in the test was expressed as the total length of cracking in relation to the length of section (as a percentage), and this does not correspond directly to criteria used in most countries. However, if the 25 - 30 per cent degree of cracking at the FORCE experiment is assumed to be roughly equivalent to 60 - 100 crack metres per 100 linear metres of road, the "power" values would be 3.2 - 3.7 based on cracked area and 2.7 - 4.3 based on crack length.

In spite of the many problems encountered in the analysis, it is considered that the results are both reliable and valuable.

VI.3. ANALYSIS OF RESPONSE MEASUREMENTS

The FORCE accelerated pavement testing experiment at Nantes was designed to assess the relative performance of three different pavement structures. To assist in monitoring the condition of the pavements as trafficking progressed, an extensive programme of measurement of various transient responses - stresses, strains and deflections - was undertaken. The purpose of these measurements was not only to assess the responses of the pavements to the repeated applications of loads, but also to assess at a more fundamental level the measurements themselves. This would allow comparisons to be made with a similar, but less comprehensive exercise undertaken by OECD at Nardo in 1985. The following paragraphs describe the measurement programme and present an initial analysis and assessment of the results.

VI.3.1. Instrumentation

Details of the instrumentation of the test pavements was given in Chapter IV. As is common with pavement instrumentation, not all gauges survived the construction process and remained in working order long enough to be used in the measurement programme. For a variety of other reasons, some data from the gauges had to be rejected, and other gauges did not survive the duration of the experiment. These and other aspects of the analysis of response measurements are discussed hereunder.

VI.3.2. Measurement programme

An extensive set of measurements was obtained between 6th March 1989 and 14th March 1989, before commencement of the main trafficking programme. These were designated the "point zero" measurements. The purpose of these was to ascertain the as-laid condition of the pavements and provide data which might be useful in the validation of theoretical models. Measurements for the same purpose were also obtained from overlaid sections, mostly from the newly installed gauges, before these were subjected to extensive trafficking. The initial 'point zero' measurements were taken under a wide range of controlled conditions of load, speed and lateral displacement of the test wheel. The initial measurements on overlaid sections were taken only under the standard load and speed conditions for those sections, and covered only a relatively small range of values of lateral displacement of the test wheel.

Details of the test conditions that were used for different sets of initial measurements are given in Table VI.5.

Following initial testing, measurements were made at intervals throughout the trafficking programme to record the course of change in the transient responses. In most cases measurements were taken only under standard load and speed conditions with the wheel running on the pavement centreline. However, for the final measurements on the outer test sections, measurements were made also with the wheel running on changed trafficking lines +/-52 cm either side of the centreline.

Pavement temperature conditions at different times could not be controlled. In consequence, they became a major source of variability in the collection of the data. To provide a basis for treating the results to take account of this variability, additional measurements, under standard load and speed conditions and with the wheel running on the pavement centreline, were made early on in the experiment during a period in which pavement temperatures were steadily increasing. Measurements were obtained repeatedly from a sample of the gauges over a period of a few hours during which average temperatures in the bituminous layers increased from about 9 to 20°C.

Table VI.5.

INITIAL MEASUREMENTS FOR "POINT ZERO" INVENTORY

No. of Measurements	Load r = 19 m	Load r = 19 m	Speed No. rot/min.	Point no.
1	10.0	11.5	10	1
1	10.0	11.5	10	2
1	10.0	11.5	10	3
1	10.0	11.5	10	4
1	10.0	11.5	10	5
1	10.0	11.5	10	6
1	10.0	11.5	12	6
1	10.0	11.5	7	6
1	10.0	11.5	4	6
1	10.0	11.5	2	6
1	10.0	11.5	1	6
1	10.0	11.5	0.5	6
1	10.0	11.5	10	7
1	10.0	11.5	10	8
1	10.0	11.5	10	9
1	10.0	11.5	10	10
1	10.0	11.5	10	11

Check on consistency

In line with the approach developed in Section IV.3.2., all outputs with a C marking were rejected. The data made generally available, therefore, were the values of the principal parameters listed above for those outputs that had been marked either A or B.

An initial examination of the data revealed the presence of a small number of clearly implausible values, for example deflections with upward components in excess of 10 mm. Such data was probably due mostly to errors in the earlier marking and were rejected.

Rather more frequent were instances where the gauge response had apparently been inconsistent during the course of a single cycle of data capture. It was less straightforward in this case deciding how to deal with the problem. It seemed reasonable to require at least some evidence of consistency between different responses for data to be retained. It was less clear, however, whether it was desirable also to require total consistency; low level responses could, for instance, be spurious features due to noise.

A limited study was therefore made of the effects of applying alternative criteria. From this it became apparent that the choice of criterion made very little difference to the overall picture. A minimum criterion was therefore applied in order to retain as much data as possible. In detail the criterion applied was that the two largest responses, as represented in each case by the sums of the maximum and minimum values, should agree to within 20 per cent. The larger of the two responses was then retained to represent the output. Generally, whenever this criterion was met, the agreement was much closer than 20 per cent, and the other responses, where present, were either also in close agreement or relatively small.

Output Parameters Selected for Analysis

Once the major sift of data described above had been completed, attention was focussed mainly on the maximum values of the gauge responses, representing the tensile components of horizontal strains, the compressive components of vertical stresses and strains, and the downwards components of deflections. These components are those normally considered in relation to pavement fatigue and rutting and were, for the majority of cases, the major components.

VI.3.3. Correction for temperature differences

As indicated earlier, pavement temperature conditions were a major source of variability in the collection of the data. Therefore, to enable the effects of other variables to be investigated, adjustments were first needed to standardise the results so that they corresponded to a single temperature.

In both the development of adjustment procedures and their subsequent application pavement temperature profiles had to be estimated from a fairly limited amount of data. No temperature measurements had been obtained from structure I (sections 01 and 11) due to early sensor failures, while the records at certain depths in the other structures were also far from complete, due to later sensor failures in the case of section 02 and changes in depth caused by the addition of an overlay in the case of section 03; no instrumentation was included in the inner sections.

In dealing with these problems, gaps in the temperature records were filled using data for matching times and similar depths from other sections. In this process the results from section 03 were used where possible for sections 01, 11 and 13, as all these sections had similar initial thicknesses of bituminous material, while the results for section 02 were used for section 12. Temperatures at depths other than those at which measurements were made were estimated, where required, by either linear interpolation or extrapolation, as appropriate.

Consideration had to be given early on to the question of how to represent pavement temperatures in the calculations. Trial of various alternatives showed that generally the strongest correlations between gauge output and pavement temperature were obtained when the latter was represented by the average temperature in the lower half of the bituminous material. This representation was therefore adopted for subsequent work. It is noted, however, that other representations gave very similar correlations, and adjusted results would have been very similar whatever choice had been made.

An initial study was made to examine the relationship between temperature sensitivity of gauge response and other variables.

To provide a standardized representation of gauge outputs, measured responses were expressed in fractional terms of the measured response at 20 degrees C (approx) i.e. in SIG(T)/SIG(20). These standardized responses for different pavement structures and types of measurement are shown plotted against pavement temperature in Figures VI.30 to VI.32. No clear systematic variation of temperature effects with either type of measurement or depth is evident from these plots.

Figure VI.33 shows the same data on a single plot, different symbols being used for the different pavement structures, together with linear regressions derived from them. These show a clear difference in temperature effects between structures II and III. The effects for structure I are rather variable but intermediate on average between those applying to the other structures.

The presence of this pattern in the results is consistent with theory. Temperature effects arise largely because of the viscoelastic properties of the bituminous material in the constructions, and can be expected to be largest where this material contributes most to the strength, as represented by the overall load spreading ability. Structure II contained a relatively large total thickness of such material, and therefore would have owed a relatively large proportion of its strength to this. In contrast, structure III had a relatively small total thickness of such material and would have gained much of its strength from the non-viscoelastic cement treated sub-base. The contribution of the bituminous material to overall strength for structure I would have been smaller than for structure II due to its smaller thickness, but greater than for structure III due to the absence of any other layer of comparable or greater stiffness. The greater variability of temperature effects in structure I suggests some lack of uniformity in this relatively weak structure.

The presence of the observed differences in temperature effects coupled with the theoretical support for them provides a basis for relating adjustments for temperature to the structure. For each structure, therefore, adjustments were based on the regression equation applying to it. This was used to adjust all gauge readings for the structure to equivalent values at a temperature of 24°C.

For consistency, separate adjustment procedures should have been developed and applied to the overlaid sections. However, since no data had been obtained for this purpose, continued use was made of the adjustment procedures developed for the original constructions. Generally, adjustments following the time at which the first of the overlays was applied were relatively small. In consequence, the continued use of the original procedures would not have caused a serious increase in error.

Figure VI.30

SIG(T)/SIG(20) VS PAVEMENT TEMPERATURE
(SECTION 01)

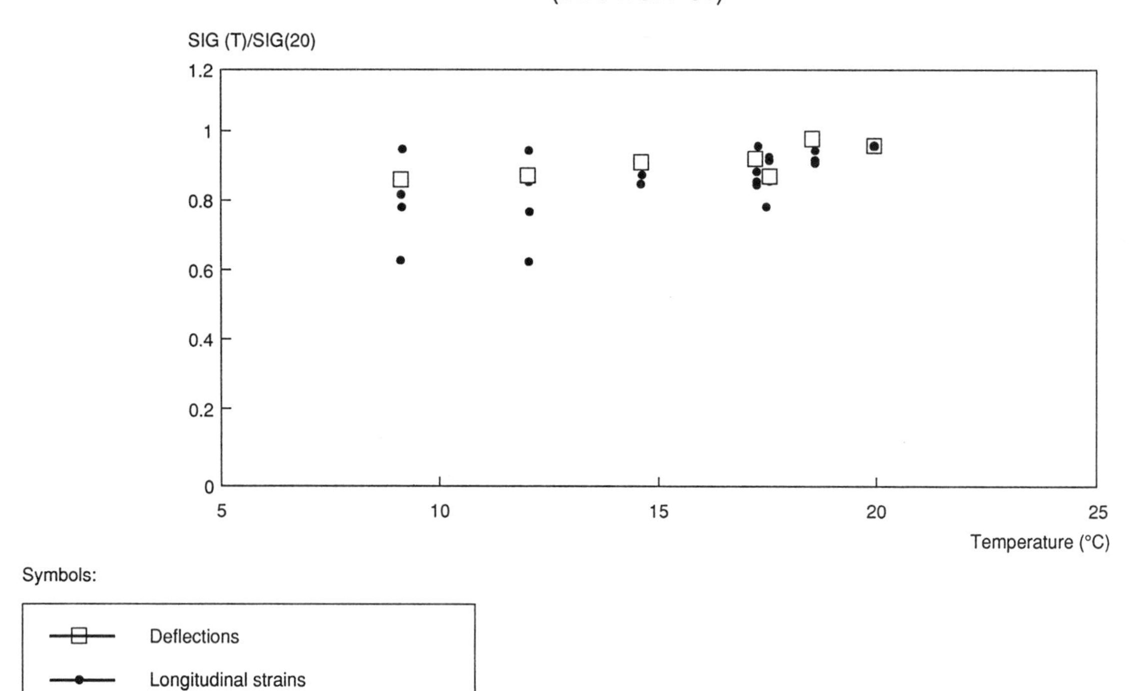

Figure VI.31

SIG(T)/SIG(20) VS PAVEMENT TEMPERATURE
(SECTION 02)

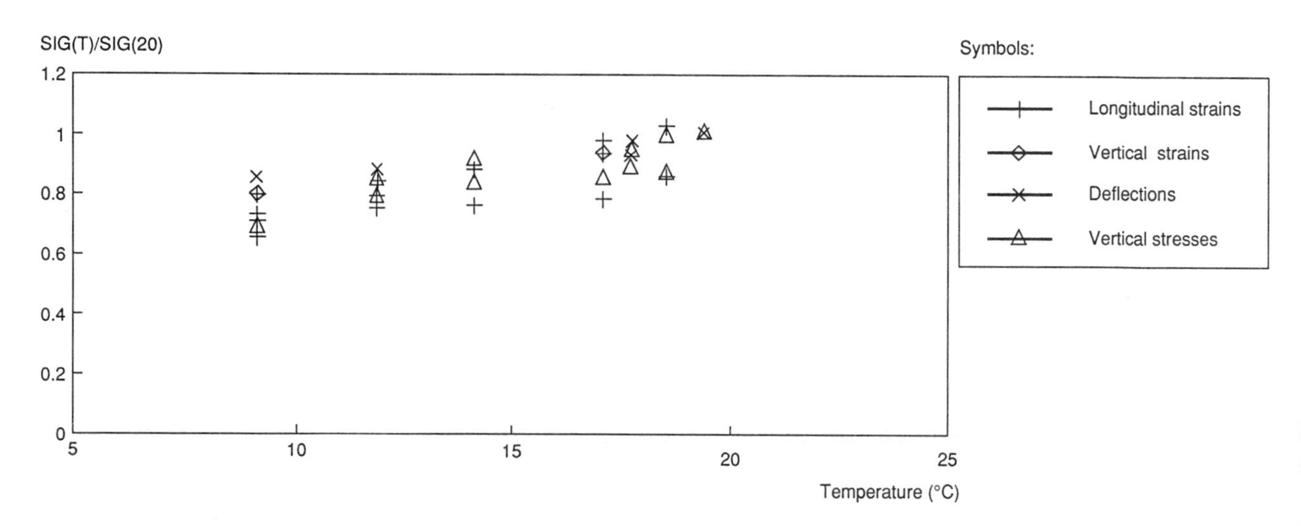

Figure VI.32

SIG(T)/SIG(20) VS PAVEMENT TEMPERATURE
(SECTION 03)

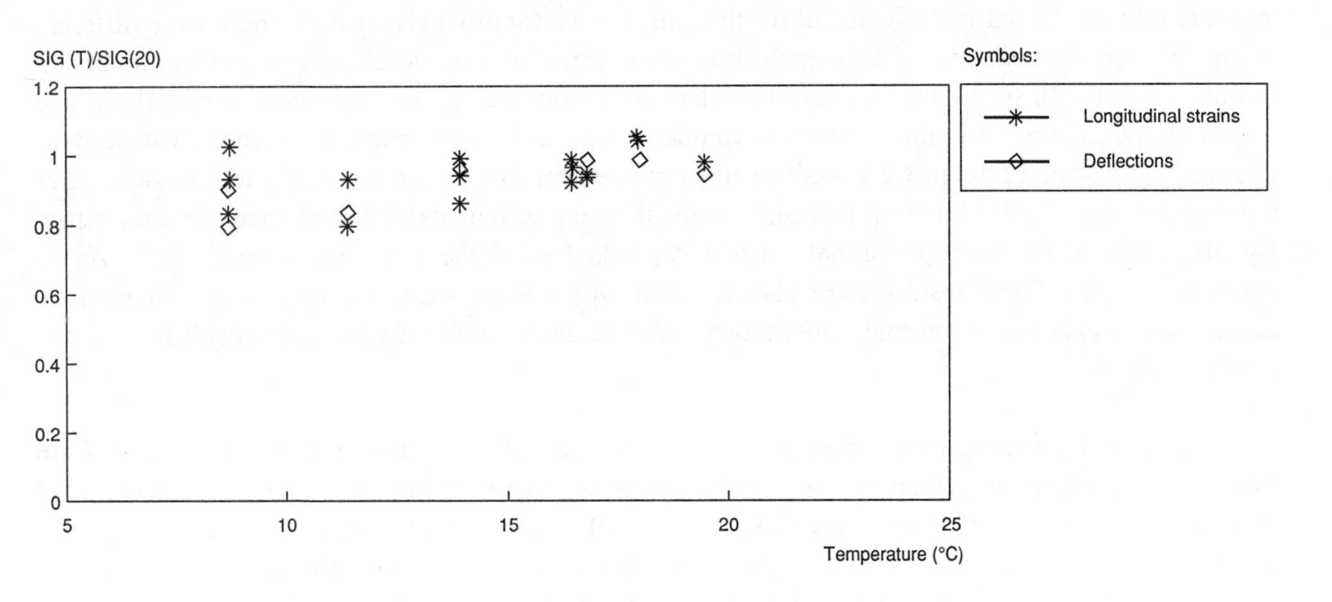

Figure VI.33

SIG(T)/SIG(20) VS PAVEMENT TEMPERATURE
ALL SECTIONS

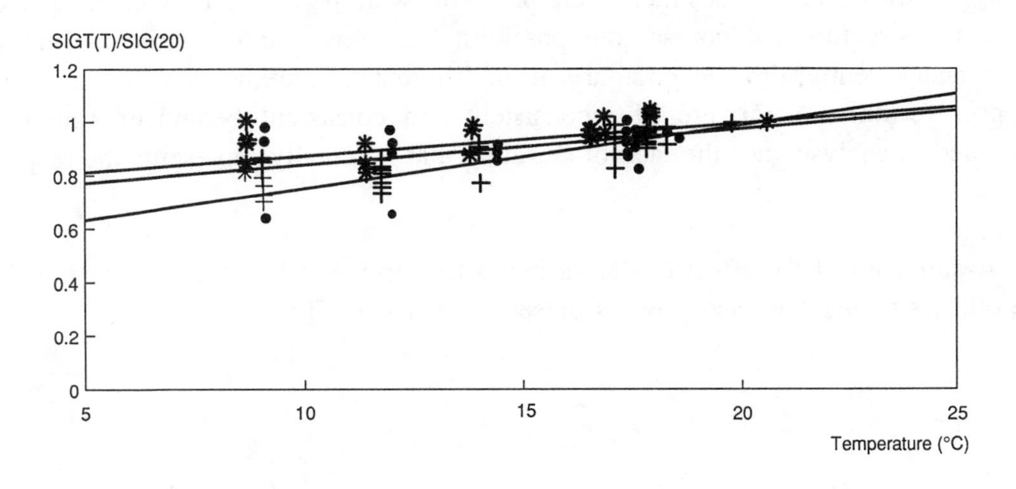

Symbols:

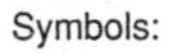

•	Section 1	——	Regression 1
+	Section 2	——	Regression 2
✳	Section 3	——	Regression 3

Regression 1 = SIG(T)/SIG(20) = .70+.015 *T

Regression 2 = SIG(T)/SIG(20) = .52+.024 *T

Regression 3 = SIG(T)/SIG(20) = .76+.012 *T

VI.3.4. Further consistency checks

Once the data had been standardized to correspond to a single temperature, it was possible to examine further the consistency of the data obtained from each gauge. The "point zero" measurements were particularly useful for this purpose as, for any given gauge, there were different groups of measurements that should each show some clear form of variation, eg a gradual reduction of output level with speed, which could be determined from the results in general. Where the gauge output at "point zero" was found to show frequent large and erratic departures from clear norms -- usually on a scale of at least 2:1 -- all results obtained for that gauge were rejected. In such cases the data set was usually far from complete, indicating a previous detection of many unsatisfactory signals, either at the time the signal form was marked or at the first consistency check. As an extension of this check results were also rejected where there were simply too few of them to provide any evidence of internal consistency. In most such cases only a single result had passed previous checks.

Finally, consideration was given to a number of large but isolated departures from established patterns of variation or trends. Most of these occurred within two batches of measurements in the 'point zero' measurements involving the same gauges but different speeds. Some gauges had apparently provided their only good output in these batches of measurements while others appeared to have provided successive bad outputs in a sequence of good outputs. Quite clearly, therefore, some problem must have occurred in gauge identification or equipment set-up at this stage. The results giving rise to these departures, together with a small number of similar problematic data at other times, were therefore rejected.

The main concern underlying most of checks applied to the data was internal consistency. For most gauges fairly consistent output was obtained where it was reasonable to expect this, which tends to suggest that in other cases there were problems with the functioning of the gauges or their bonding to the structure. Of course, the possibility remains that the structure in places was responding inconsistently, although comparisons of different measurements in the same vicinity give little support for this. A mixture of inconsistent and consistent behaviour cannot easily be accommodated in analysis, nor the lack of certainty that it actually represents the response of the structure.

A summary of the effect of the various sifts applied to the data in terms of the number of gauge outputs retained at each stage is presented in Table VI.6.

VI.3.5. Results

The variation of the maximum signal components with wheel displacement, load, speed and number of load applications is shown through a series of graphical presentations in Figures VI.34 to VI.48. The results obtained during the "point zero" inventory provide information on initial signal form, initial signal levels and their dispersion. In addition the 'point zero' measurements show the effects of load and speed.

Initial Signal Form

Information on the initial signal form is provided by the relative values of the maximum and minimum signal components and the variation of the maximum values with wheel displacement. Overall, there are some wide variations in the way these characteristics vary between different gauges. Both systematic tendencies related to the depth and type of the measurement and more erratic variations are present in these variations.

Vertical stresses and strains. These were, as would be expected, predominantly compressive responses. The results showing the effect of wheel displacement tend to confirm the usual expectation for the depths concerned of a single maximum only, broadly in the central region of the response. In some cases there is a noticeable fluctuation of level within this region, but generally this is slight and could simply be due to factors affecting reproductibility, errors in correcting for temperature differences, for example. One gauge, in section 11, shows a marked departure from the norm, but other gauges in the same vicinity do not confirm this as representing a general feature of the pavement response. Another gauge, in section 01, shows a relatively flat response over a wide range of wheelpaths. This suggests the gauge was close to the limit of its working range and could not give a full response.

Longitudinal strains at the underside of base layers. These were predominantly tensile strains, although there were some wide variations between different gauges in the same structure. Overall, the effect of wheel displacement was less consistent than for vertical stresses and strains. Some results indicate the presence of a single maximum only, in the central region, while others indicate the presence of separate maximum values, not usually very pronounced, under the individual wheels. Yet other results show more erratic variations. There appears, however, to be no clear relationship between the differences and structural variables.

Transverse strains at the underside of bituminous layers. The transverse strains at these depths were, overall, more tensile than the corresponding longitudinal strains. This is in general agreement with theoretical expectations. In some cases there appear to be two positions where the response had a maximum. It must be presumed that these correspond to the positions of the individual wheels. For most of the gauges the results are few in number, and have no clear pattern to them.

Other horizontal strains in bituminous layers. These comprise the longitudinal and transverse strains at a depth of 6cm in structure II, and the strains measured at the interface between the original construction and the overlay for overlaid sections. These are dealt with separately in the following paragraphs.

Table VI.6.

AMOUNTS OF DATA BEFORE AND AFTER SIFTS

Type of measurement	**Number of gauge outputs**			
	Logged	**After check on signal form**	**After first check for consistency**	**After final checks**
Longitudinal strain	2240	1529	1294	1178
Transverse strain	913	466	391	382
Deflection	493	435	415	415
Vertical strain	604	584	566	509
Vertical stress	503	304	286	281

(i) Structure I after overlay

The relative values of the maximum and minimum components show some large differences, but generally the initial responses were slightly more compressive than tensile. Generally, also, the responses show separate maximum values under the individual wheels. This feature is likely to have been promoted by the relatively high temperatures at which these measurements were made.

(ii) Structure II

Most of the measured strains were quite small, indicating that these depths were, initially at least, close to neutral axes in the bituminous material. The positions of neutral axes are likely to be very sensitive to the effects of temperature and local variations in material properties. Not surprisingly, therefore, the signal form, as represented by the relative values of maximum and minimum components and the pattern of variation with wheel displacement, is quite variable between different gauges.

(iii) Structure III after overlay

There were relatively few results in this case. Those that were obtained indicate a predominantly tensile response with a tendency towards showing separate maximum values under the individual wheels.

Horizontal strain measurements in sub-base layers. These comprise measurements obtained from a single depth only of each of the unbound sub-base layers of structures I and II, and from a range of depths in the cement treated sub-base of structure III. The number of working gauges at any given depth was usually very few, in many cases only one.

Relative values of maximum and minimum components. There are few cases where comparisons can be made between results from several gauges at the same depth. However, the main features of the available results indicate that:

i) signals near the top of the cement treated material are predominantly compressive. This is in contrast to the results at the underside of the base which were predominantly tensile, and suggests a lack of bonding between these layers.

ii) the variation of signal form with wheel displacement is generally either similar to that for vertical strains or has no clear pattern.

Deflections. The deflection measurements show separate maximum values occurring under the individual wheels in several cases. This characteristic applies only to type 1 gauges. The effect is too pronounced to be plausibly related to conditions well below the pavement surface. A large component of these responses must therefore be due to localised deformation close to the pavement surface, possibly a movement largely confined to the gauge housing itself, which could get pressed into the structure as the wheel passes over it. There must therefore be doubts about the general reliability of measurements made with this type of gauge until these possibilities are checked.

Effect of Speed

The effect of speed on the various parameters measured, for each of the structures tested, is shown in Figures VI.49 to VI.54. Signals decrease approximately linearly with the logarithm of speed. The effect tends to be relatively small for vertical stresses and strains. For longitudinal strains, however, the effect is most pronounced for structure I, the weakest of the three structures.

Effect of Load

The effect of load is presented in Figures VI.55 to VI.60. These appear to show linear relationships between stresses and strains and load. The uncertainties brought about by the confidence limits of the data tend to swamp any possible non-linearity in the relationship.

Initial Signal Levels

There are no statistically significant differences between inner and outer sections for any particular structure and type of measurement. Combined results for inner and outer sections show a significant difference in longitudinal strain at the underside of the base between structure I and the other structures, (see Figure VI.61, in which the results for the inner sections were first scaled by 11.5/10 to adjust for load differences). Results of other types of measurement are too few in relation to their dispersion to show any other clear differences in response between the different structures.

Effect of Trafficking

The examples of plots referred to earlier indicate the presence of considerable variability in the way signal levels changed. Very few systematic tendencies can be seen. Indeed, similarly positioned gauges sometimes follow very different trends, suggesting these are largely unrelated to general changes in the structure. A general tendency for signals to increase early on can be noted. There is also a general drop in signal levels for section 01 as a result of the overlay.

An interesting feature is the limited tendency for horizontal strains at the base of the overlay on section 01 to increase later in the experiment. This could indicate further weakening of the underlying structure at this time.

Figure VI.34

LONGITUDINAL STRAIN VS LOAD
SECTION 01, Depth 63mm

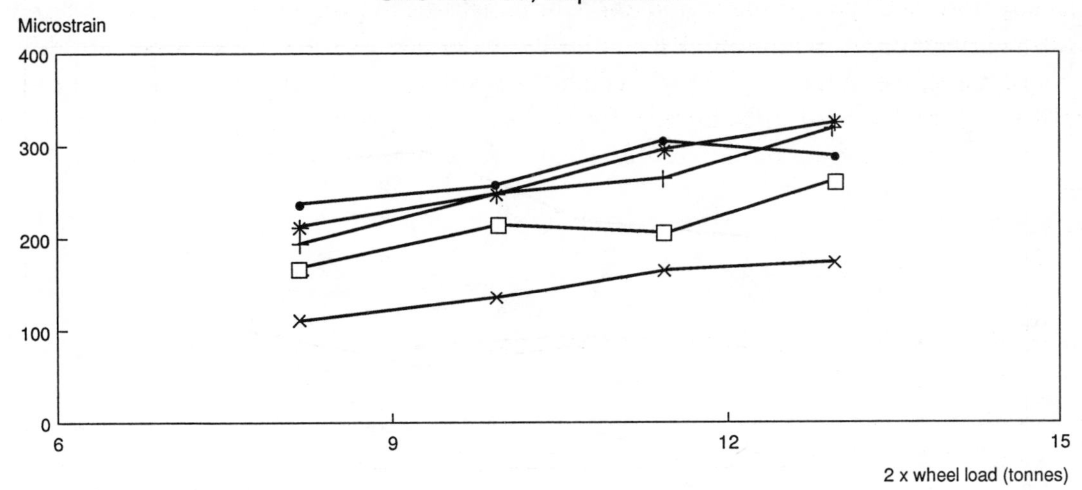

Symbols:

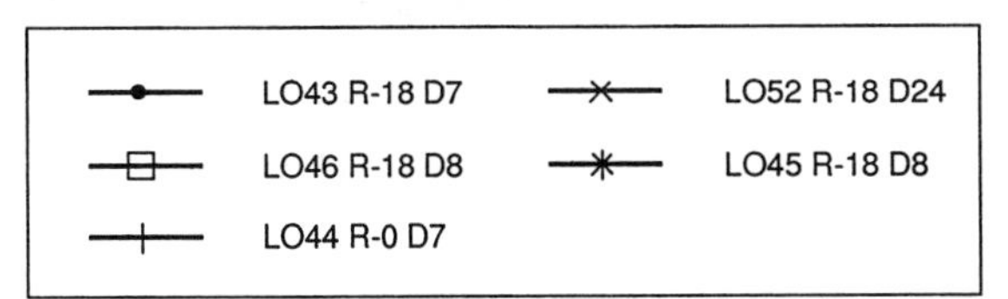

Figure VI.35

VERTICAL STRAIN VS LOAD
SECTION 01, Depths 163/443/643mm

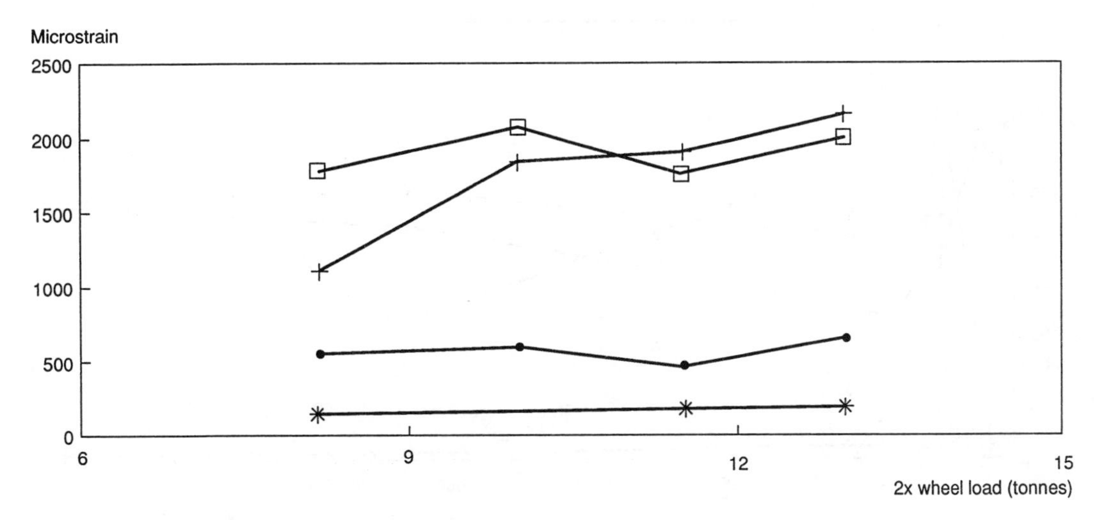

Symbols:

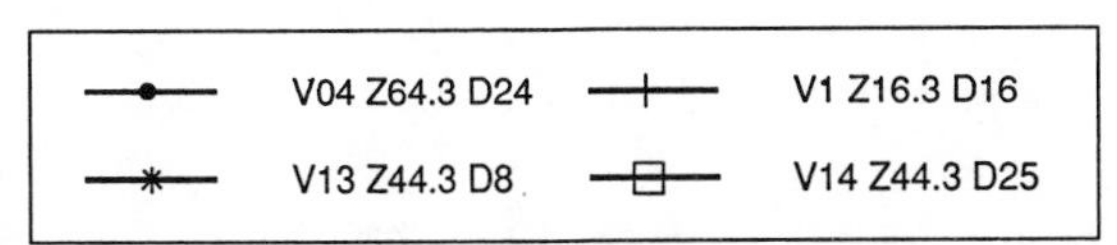

Figure VI.36

DEFLECTION AT SURFACE VS LOAD
SECTION 01

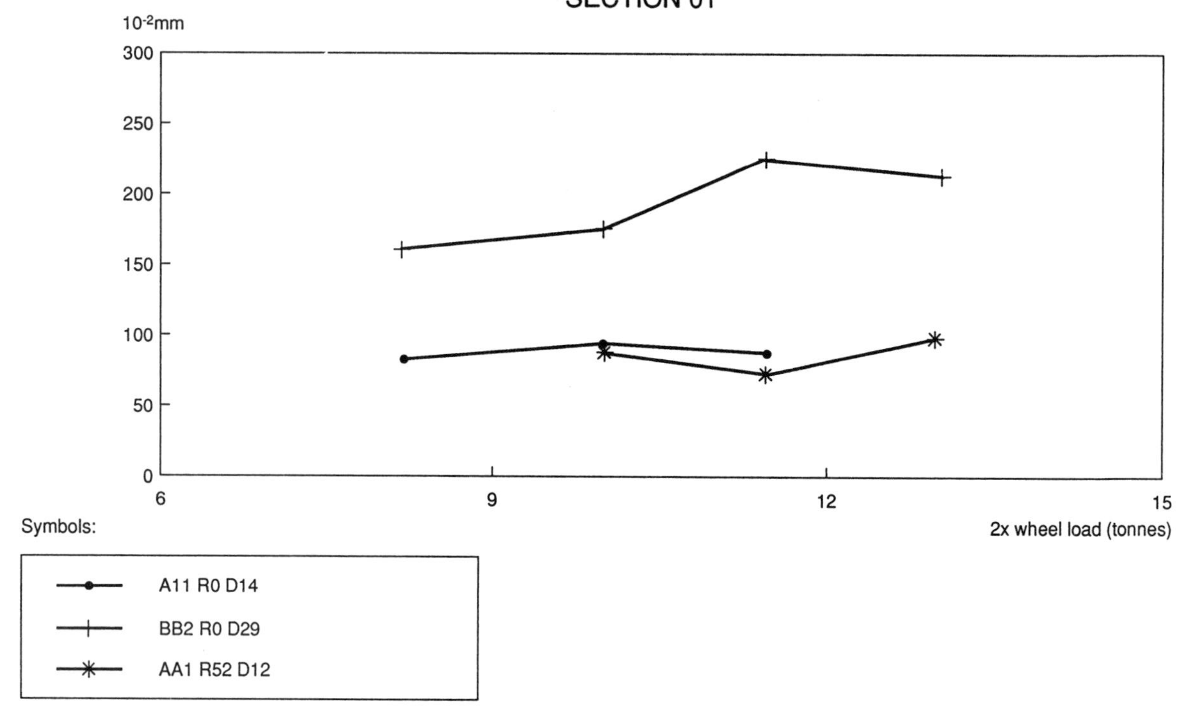

Figure VI.37

VERTICAL STRAIN VS TRAFFICKING
SECTION 01, Initial Depths 163/443/643mm

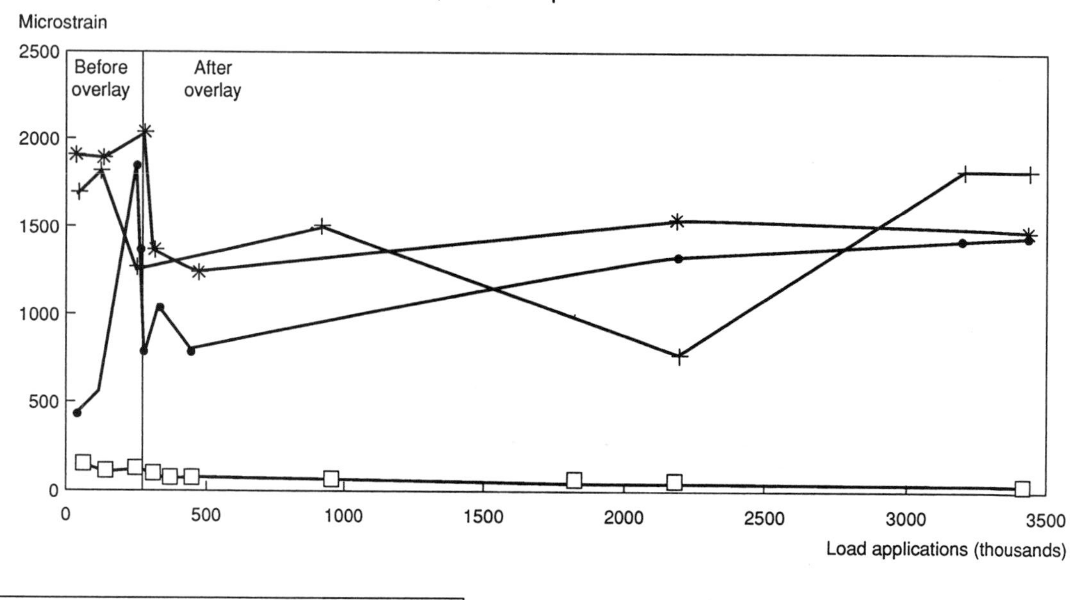

Figure VI.38

LONGITUDINAL STRAIN VS WHEEL DISPLACEMENT
SECTION 01, Depth 63mm

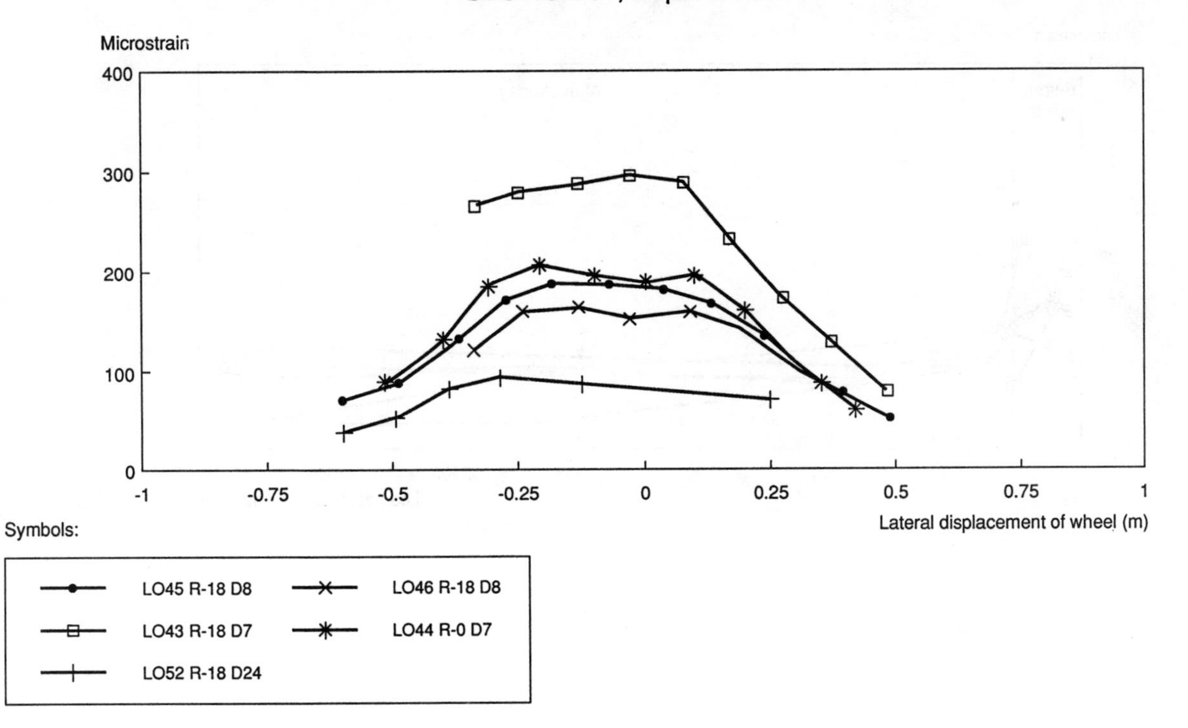

Symbols:

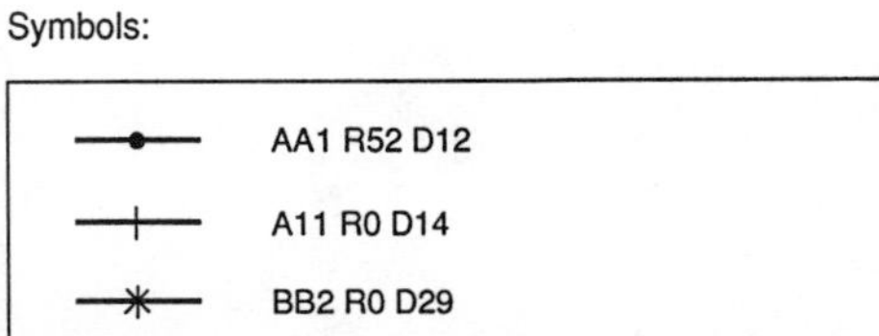

—●—	LO45 R-18 D8	—×—	LO46 R-18 D8
—□—	LO43 R-18 D7	—✳—	LO44 R-0 D7
—+—	LO52 R-18 D24		

Figure VI.39

DEFLECTION AT SURFACE VS WHEEL DISPLACEMENT
(SECTION 01)

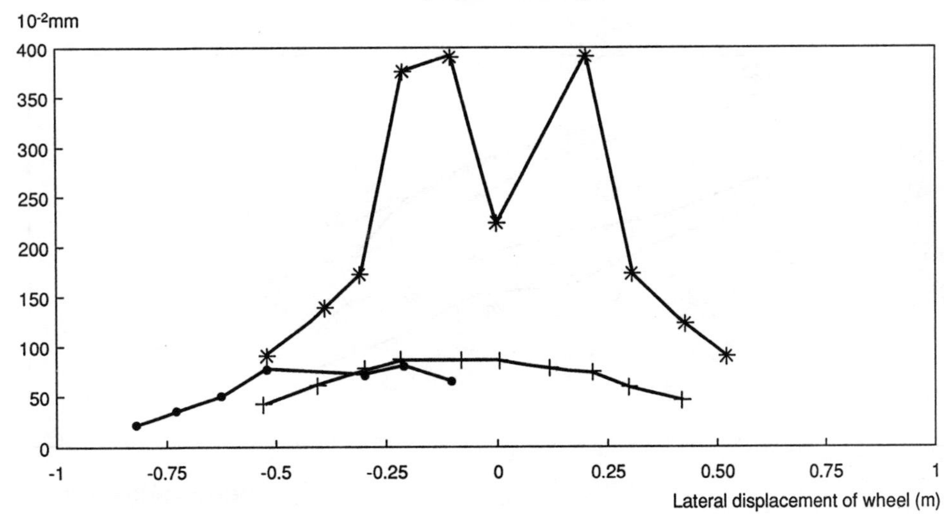

Symbols:

—●—	AA1 R52 D12
—+—	A11 R0 D14
—✳—	BB2 R0 D29

Figure VI.40

LONGITUDINAL STRAIN VS TRAFFICKING
(SECTION 01, Initial Depth 63mm)

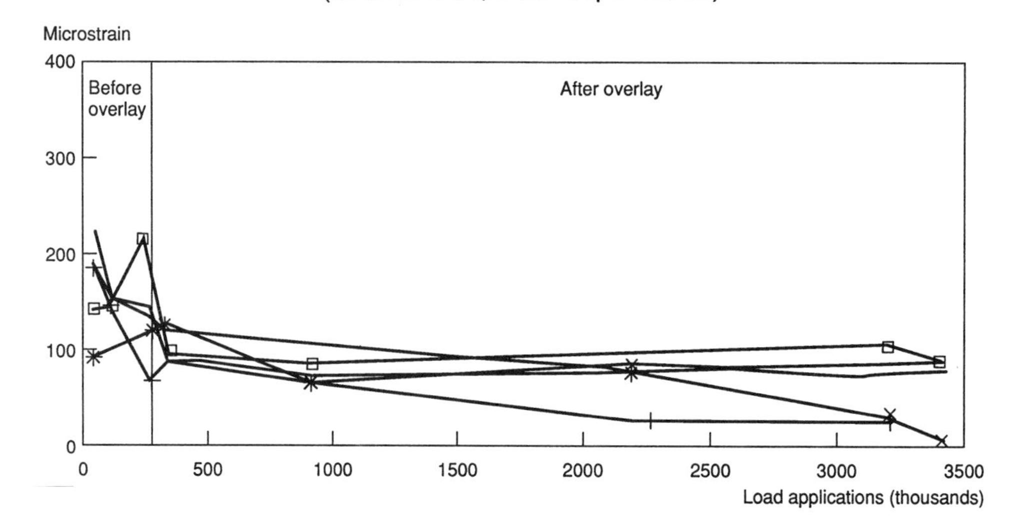

Symbols:

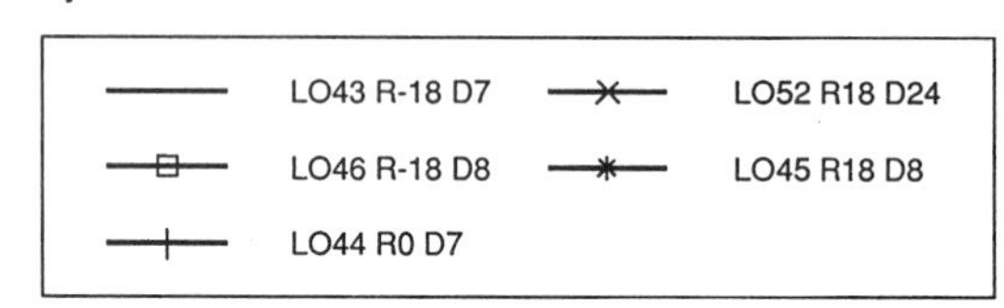

Figure VI.41

LONGITUDINAL STRAIN VS SPEED
(SECTION 01, Depth 63mm)

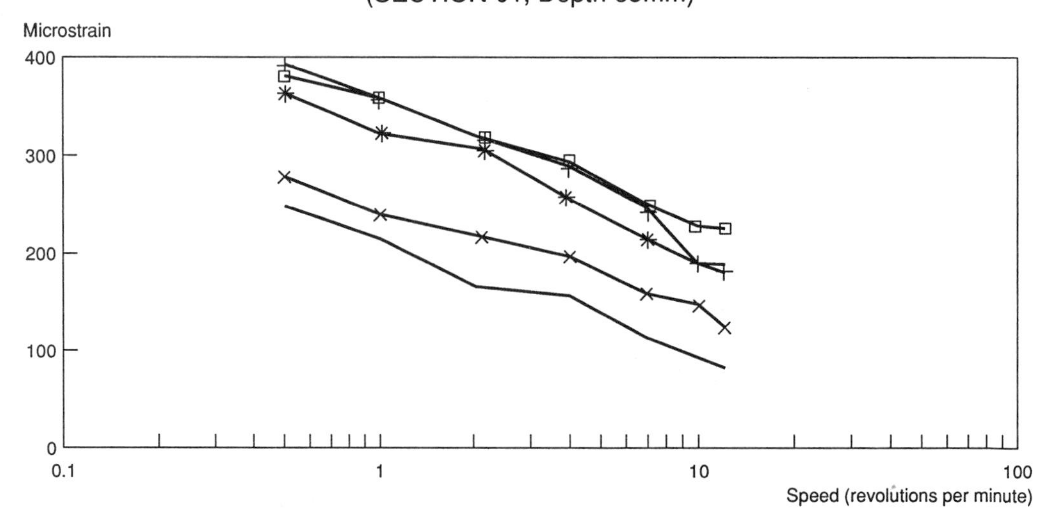

Symbols:

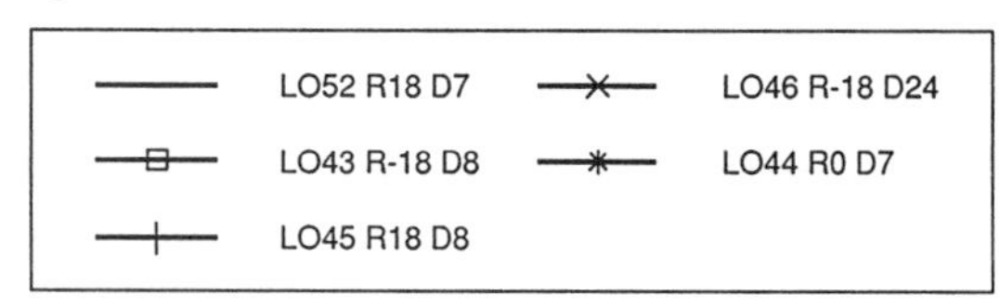

Figure VI.42

LONGITUDINAL STRAIN VS LOAD
(SECTION 02, Depth 139mm)

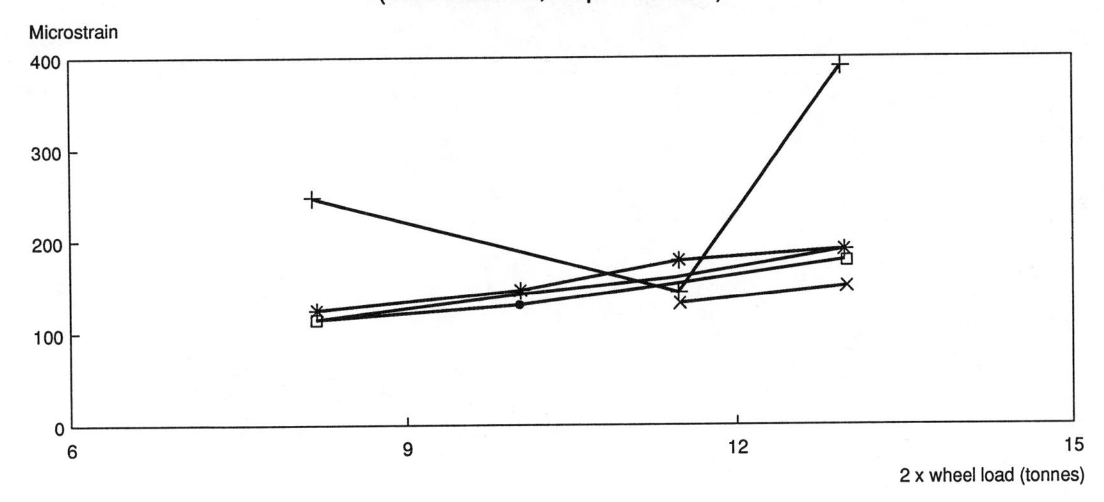

Symbols:

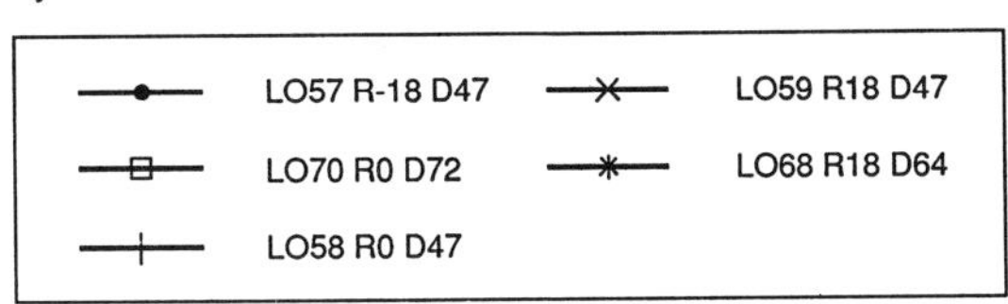

Figure VI.43

VERTICAL STRAIN VS LOAD
(SECTION 02, Depths 239/519/719mm)

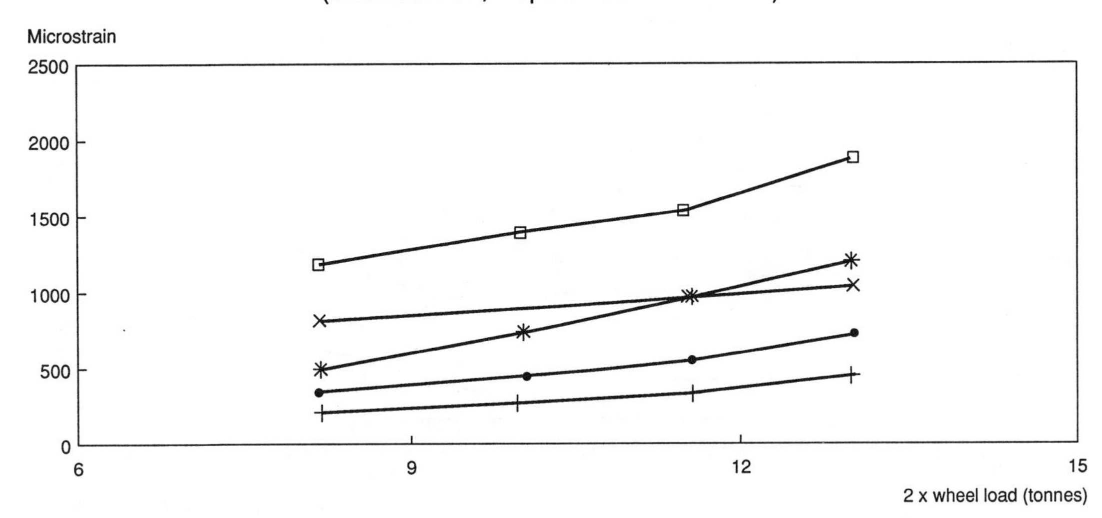

Symbols:

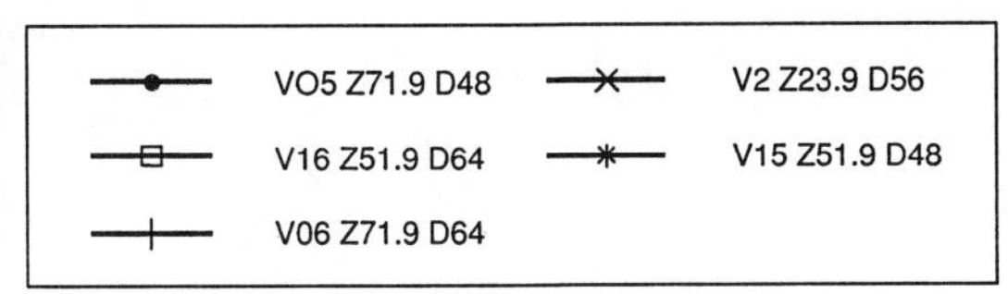

Figure VI.44

DEFLECTION AT SURFACE VS LOAD
(SECTION 02)

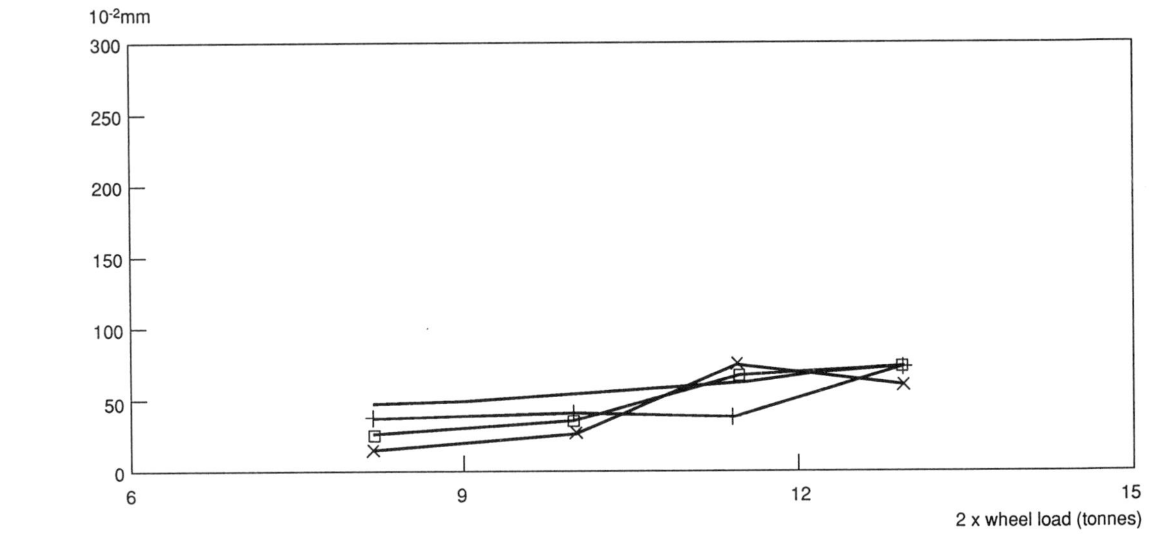

Symbols:

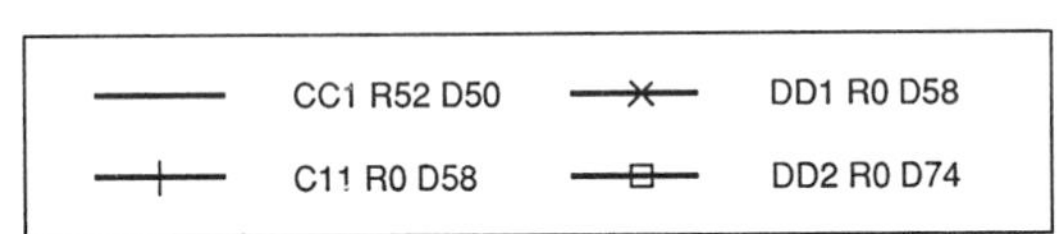

Figure VI.45

LONGITUDINAL STRAIN VS LOAD
(SECTION 03, Depth 75mm)

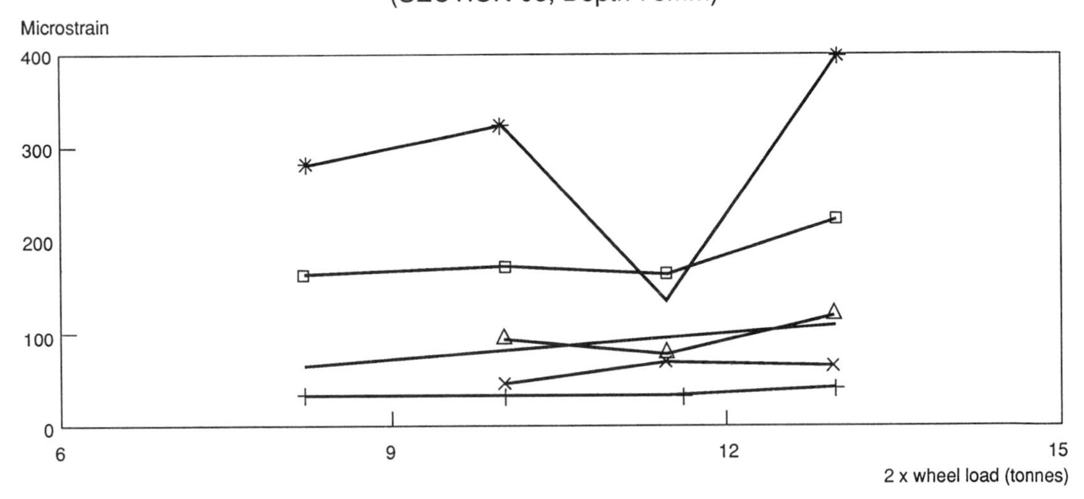

Symbols:

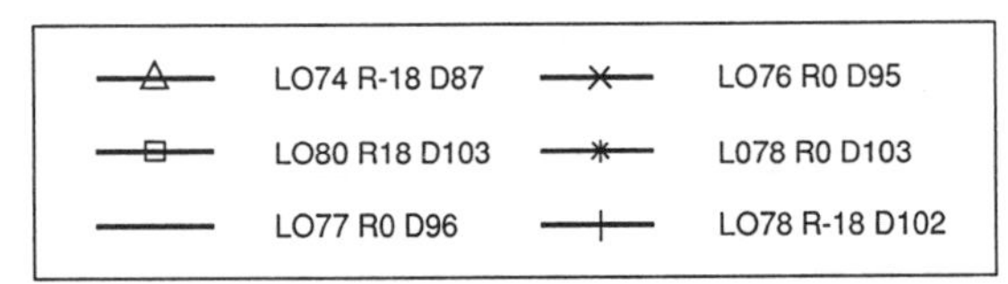

Figure VI.46

LONGITUDINAL STRAIN VS TRAFFICKING
(SECTION 03, Initial Depth 75mm)

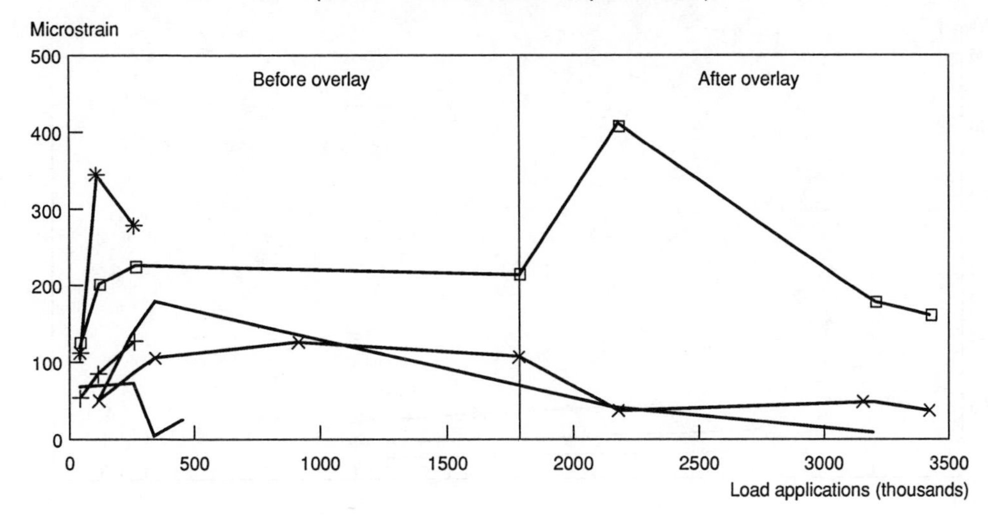

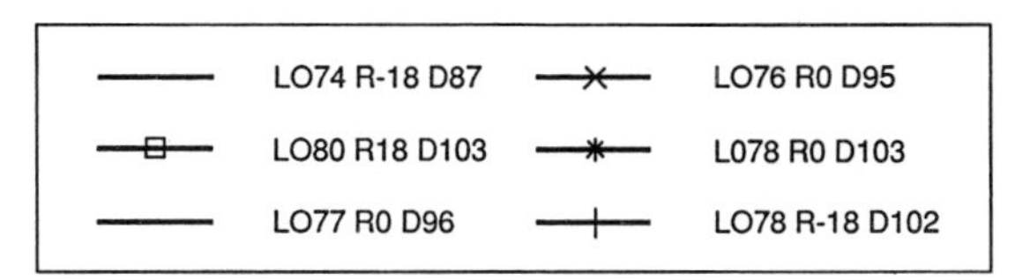

Figure VI.47

VERTICAL STRAIN VS TRAFFICKING
(SECTION 03, Initial Depths 345 & 545mm)

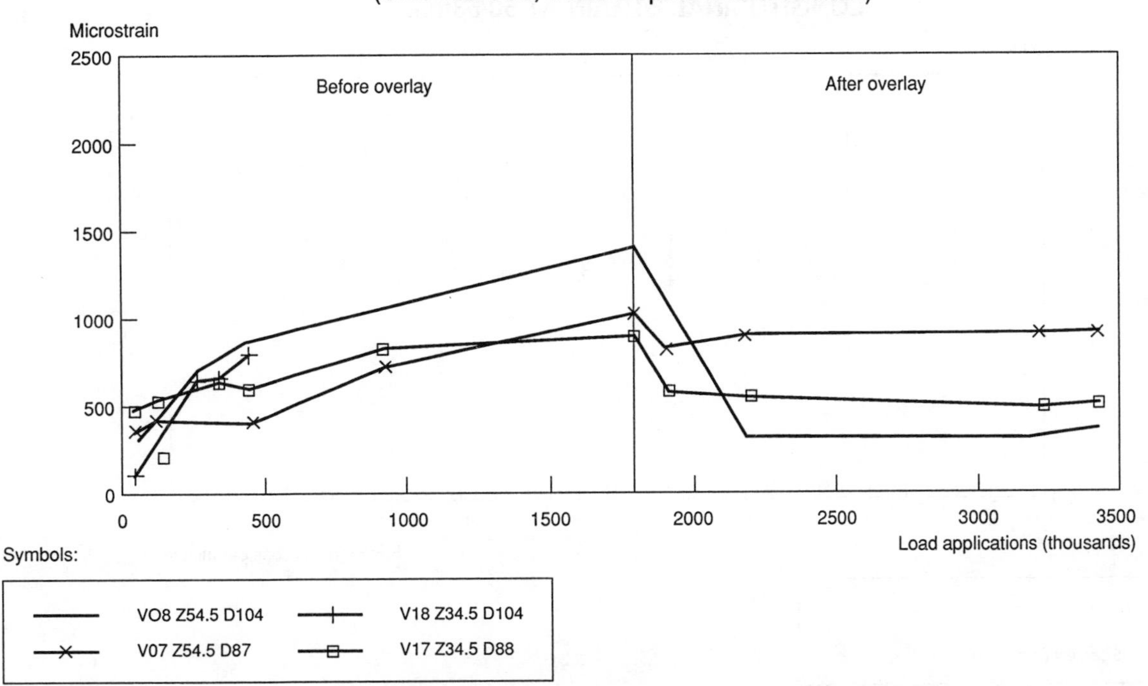

Figure VI.48

DEFLECTION AT SURFACE VS SPEED
(SECTION 03)

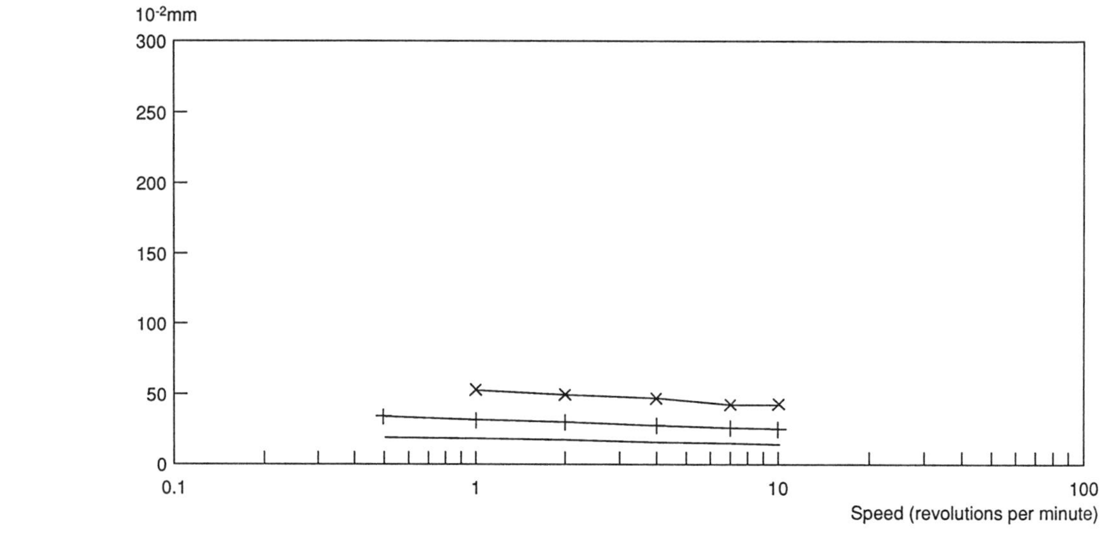

Symbols:

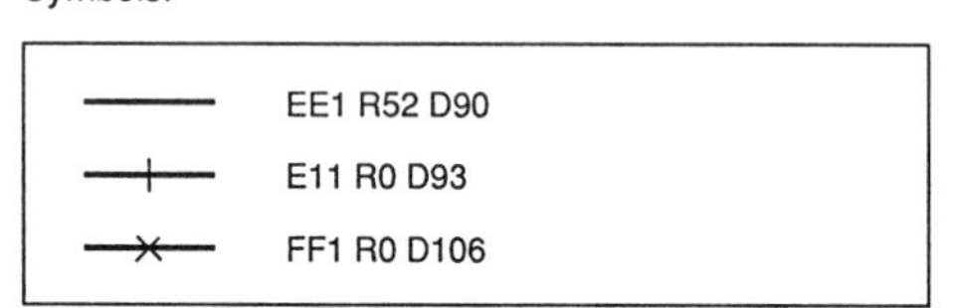

Figure VI.49

EFFECT OF SPEED — STRUCTURE I
LONGITUDINAL STRAIN AT 60/63mm

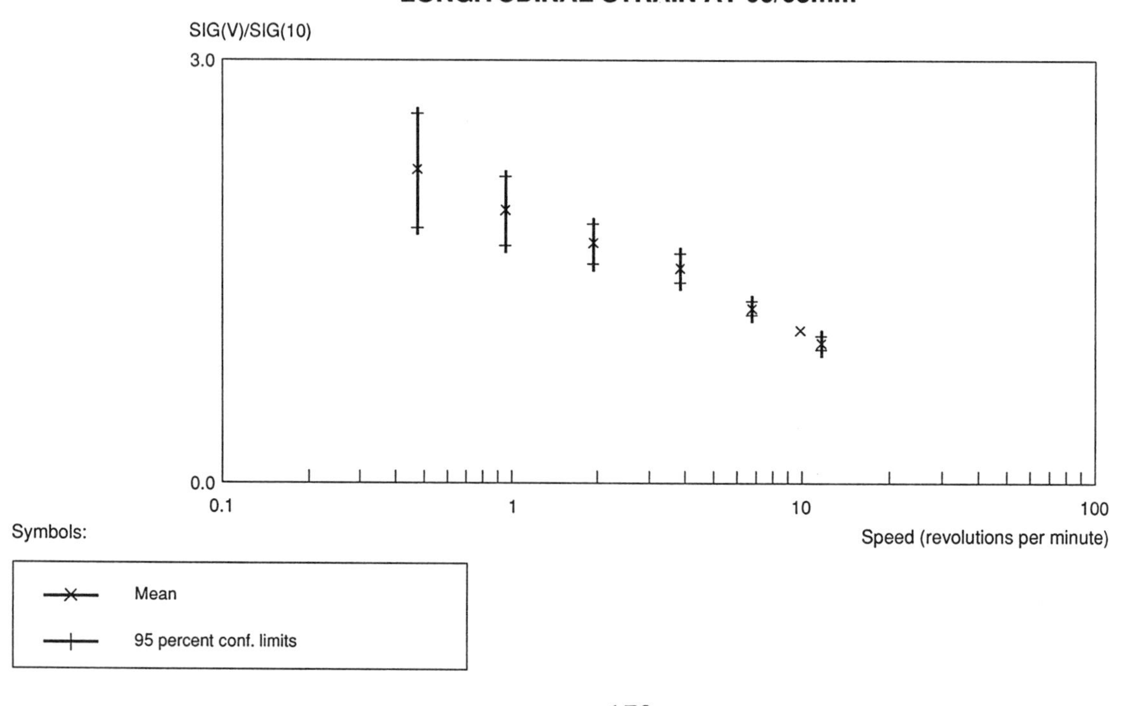

Figure VI.50

EFFECT OF SPEED — STRUCTURE II
LONGITUDINAL STRAIN AT 130/139mm

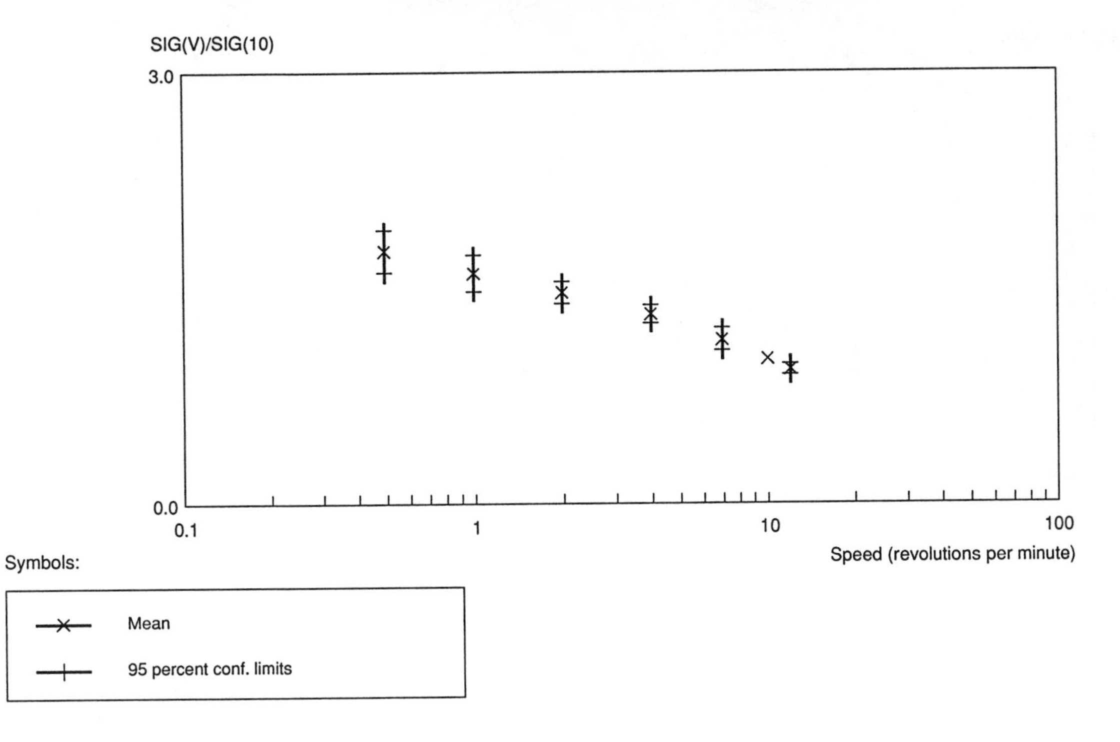

Figure VI.51

EFFECT OF SPEED — STRUCTURE III
LONGITUDINAL STRAIN AT 65/75mm

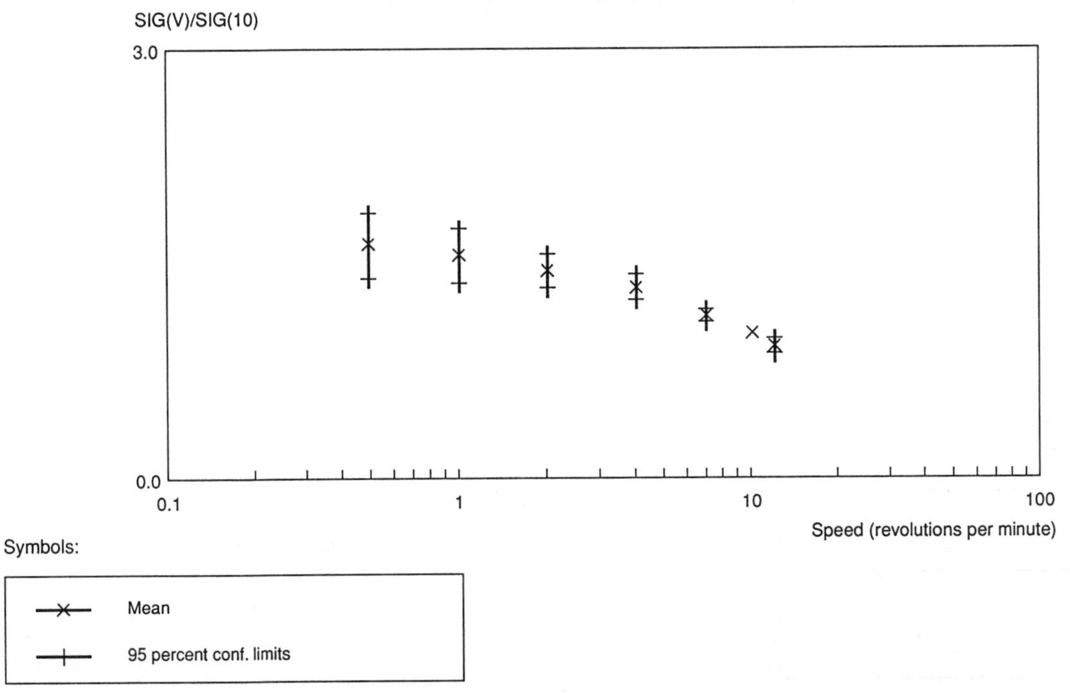

Figure VI.52

EFFECT OF SPEED — STRUCTURE I
VERTICAL STRESSES AND STRAINS IN SUBGRADE

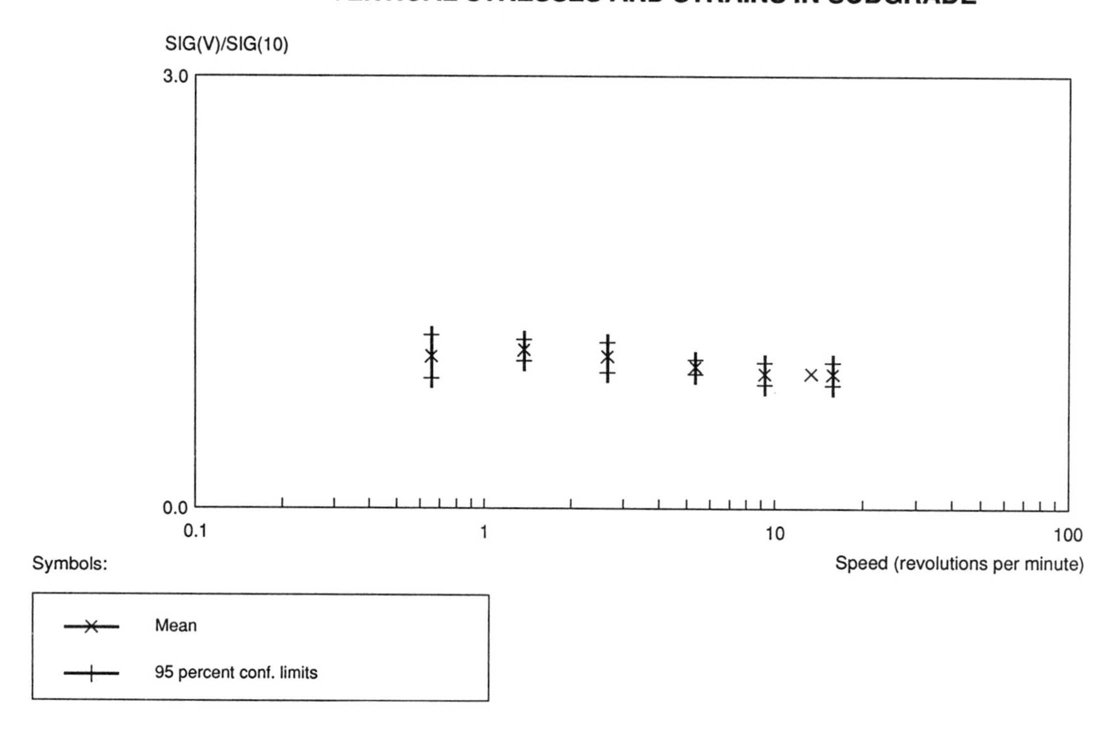

Figure VI.53

EFFECT OF SPEED — STRUCTURE II
VERTICAL STRESSES AND STRAINS IN SUBGRADE

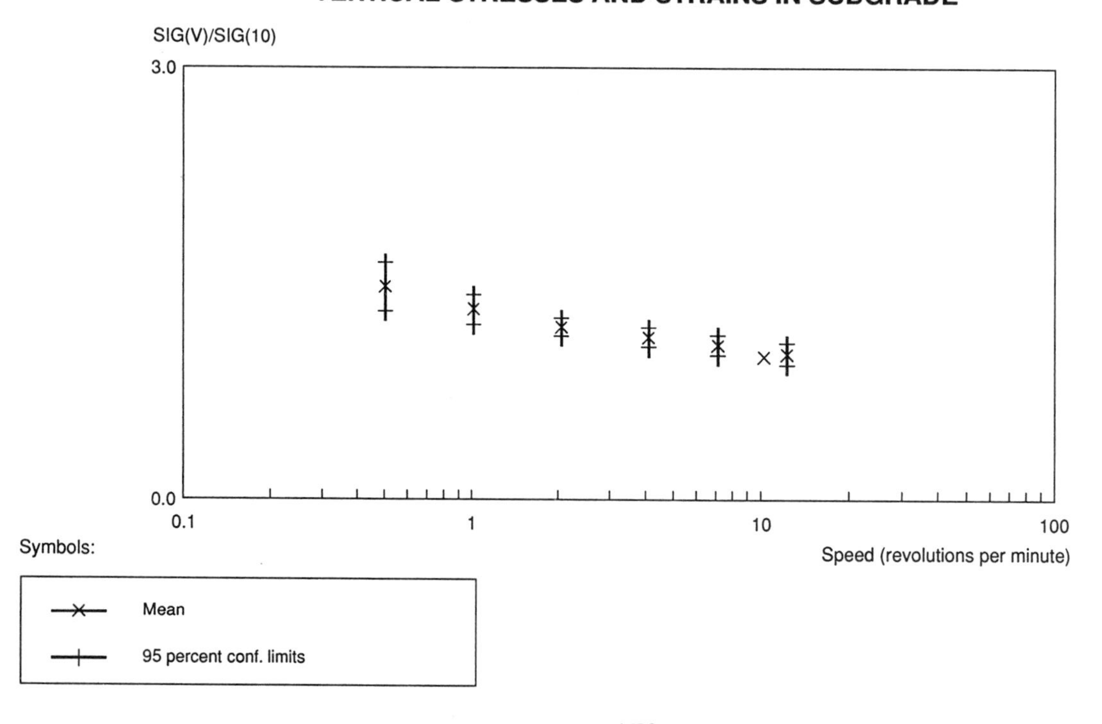

Figure VI.54

EFFECT OF SPEED — STRUCTURE III
VERTICAL STRESSES AND STRAINS IN SUBGRADE

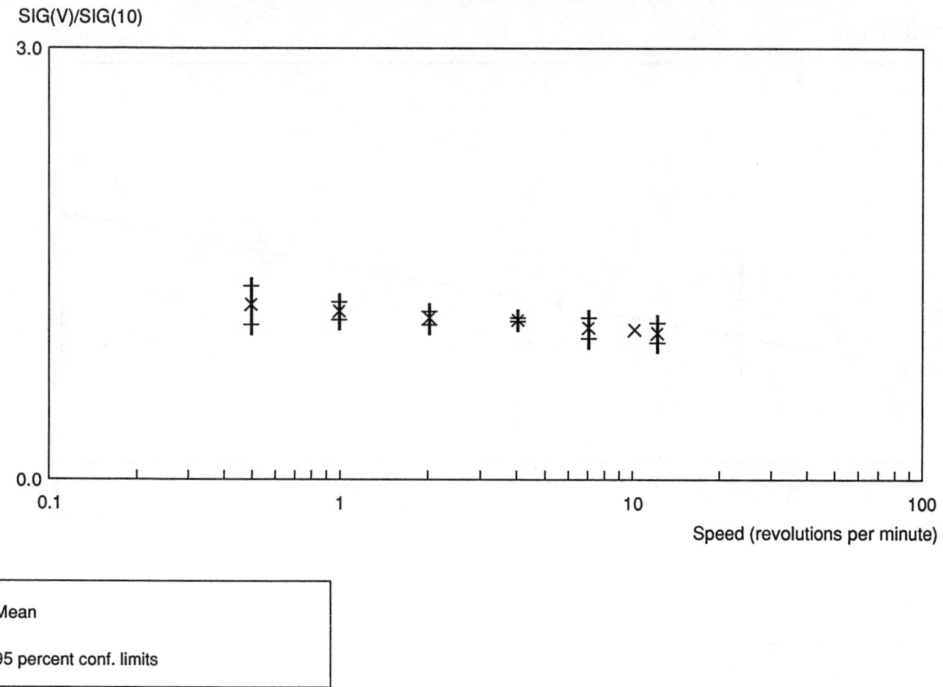

Symbols:

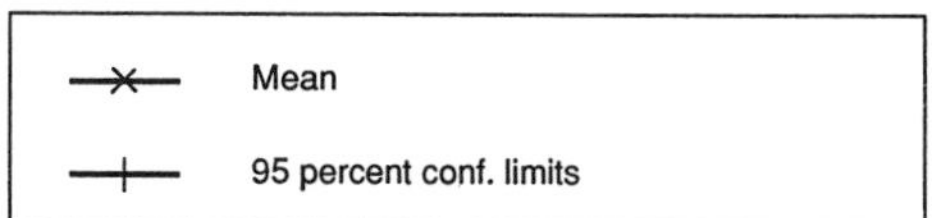

Figure VI.55

EFFECT OF LOAD — STRUCTURE I
LONGITUDINAL STRAIN AT 60/63mm

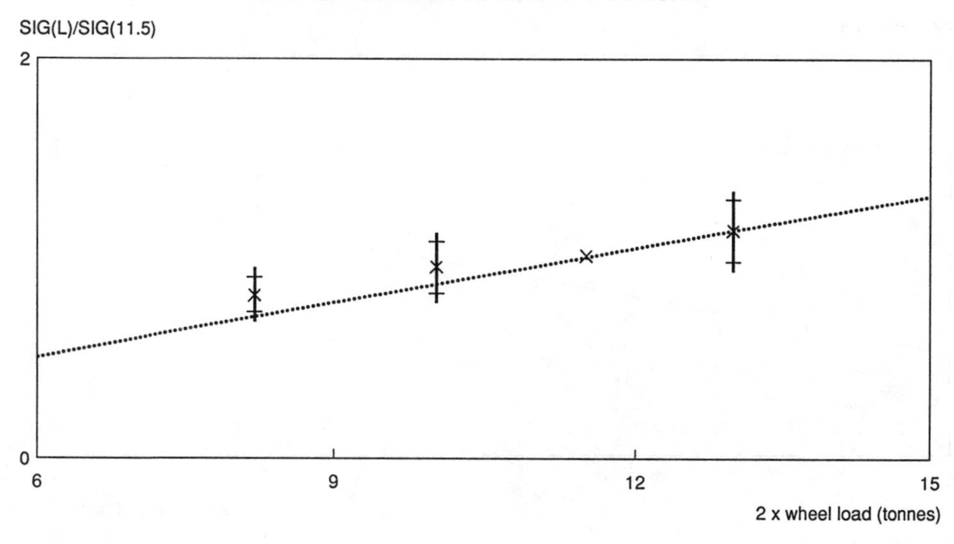

Symbols:

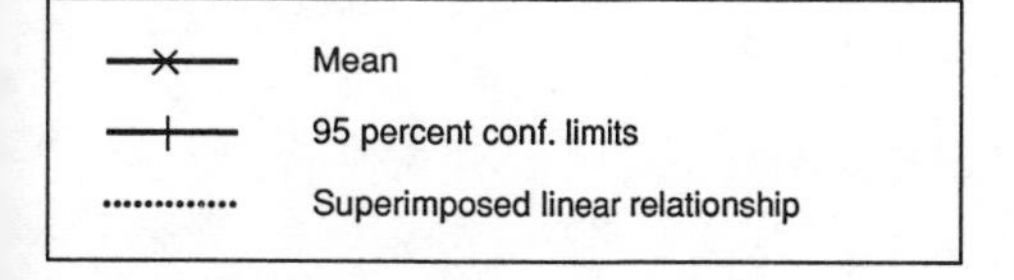

Figure VI.56

EFFECT OF LOAD — STRUCTURE II
LONGITUDINAL STRAIN AT 130/139mm

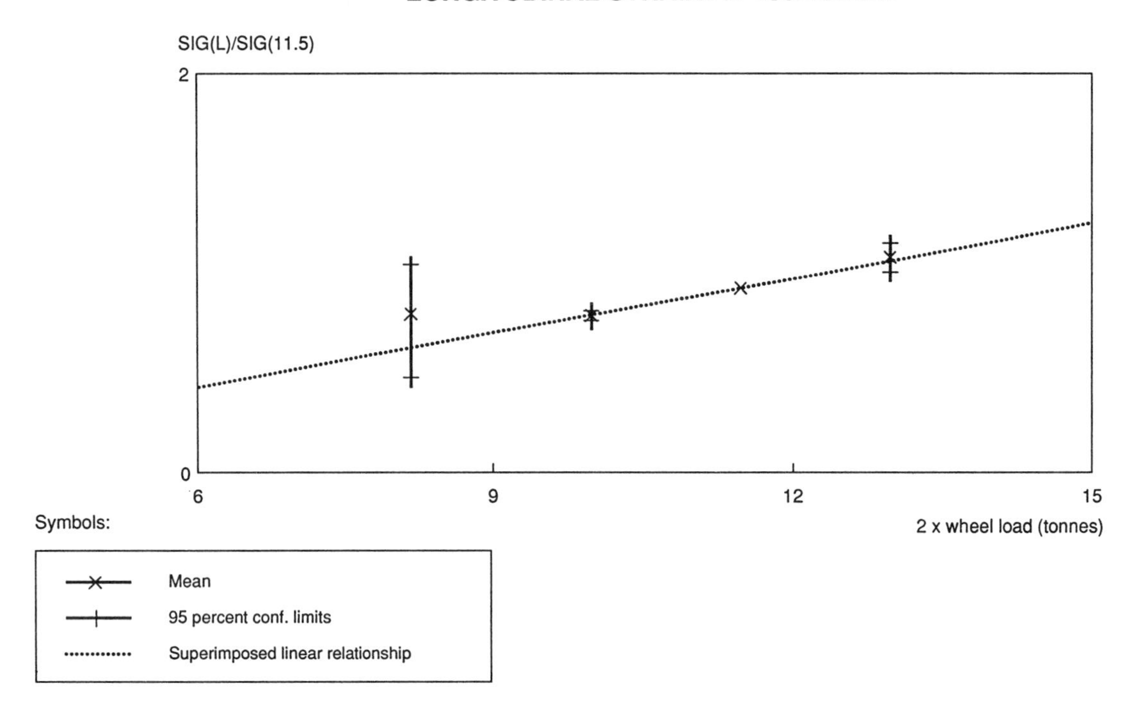

Figure VI.57

EFFECT OF LOAD — STRUCTURE III
LONGITUDINAL STRAIN AT 65/75mm

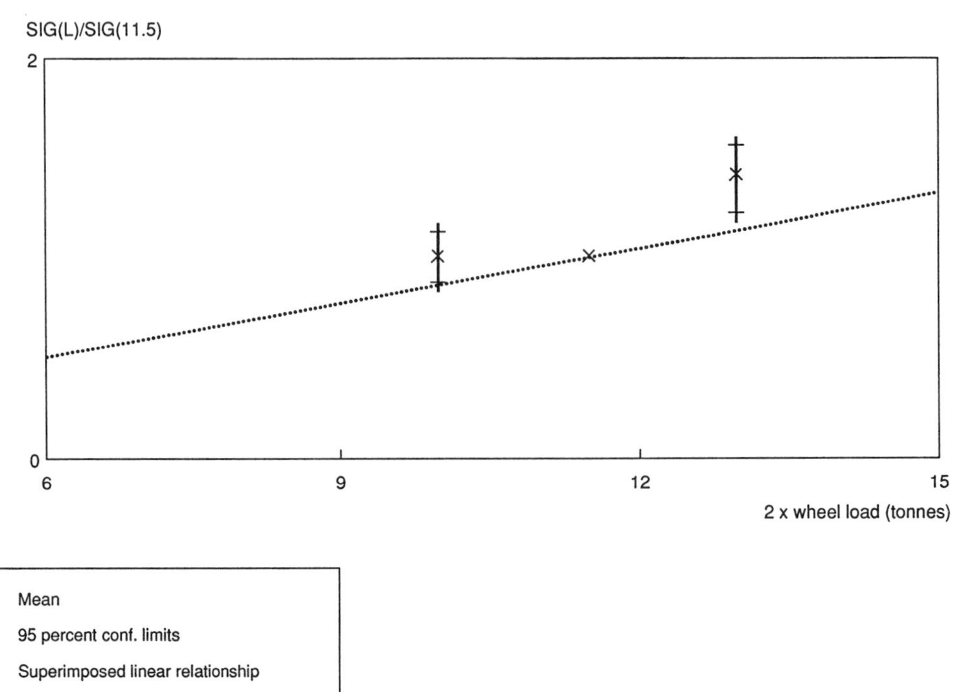

Symbols:

—×—	Mean
—+—	95 percent conf. limits
············	Superimposed linear relationship

Figure VI.58

EFFECT OF LOAD — STRUCTURE I
VERTICAL STRESSES & STRAINS IN SUBGRADE

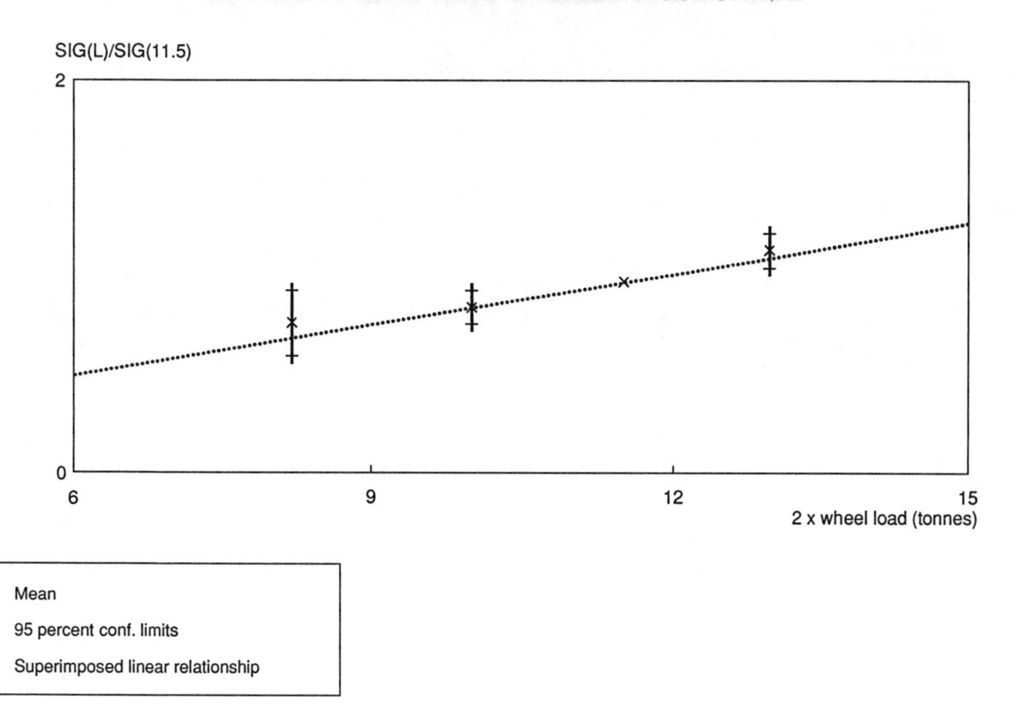

Figure VI.59

EFFECT OF LOAD — STRUCTURE II
VERTICAL STRESSES & STRAINS IN SUBGRADE

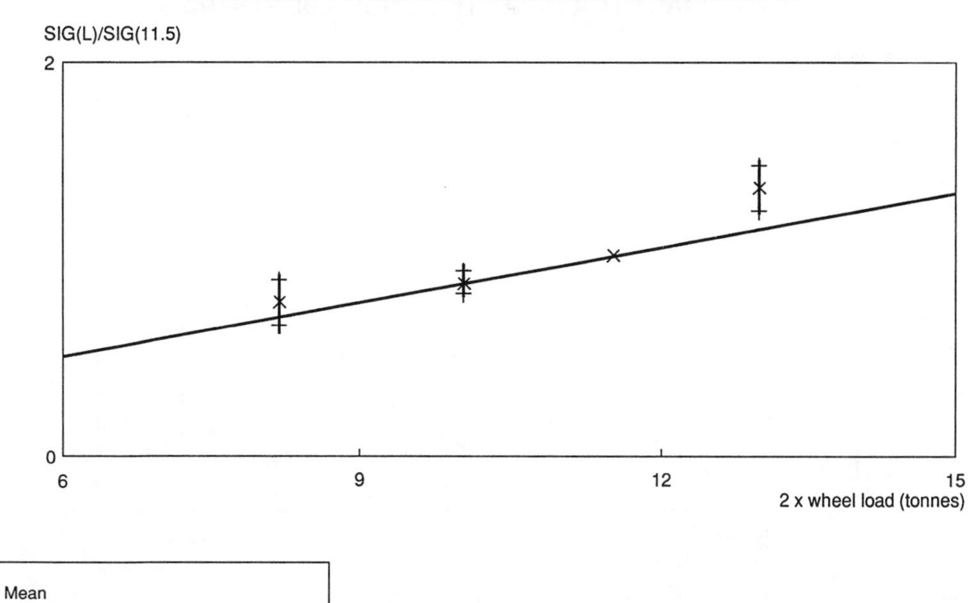

Figure VI.60

EFFECT OF LOAD - STRUCTURE III
VERTICAL SRESSES & STRAINS IN SUBGRADE

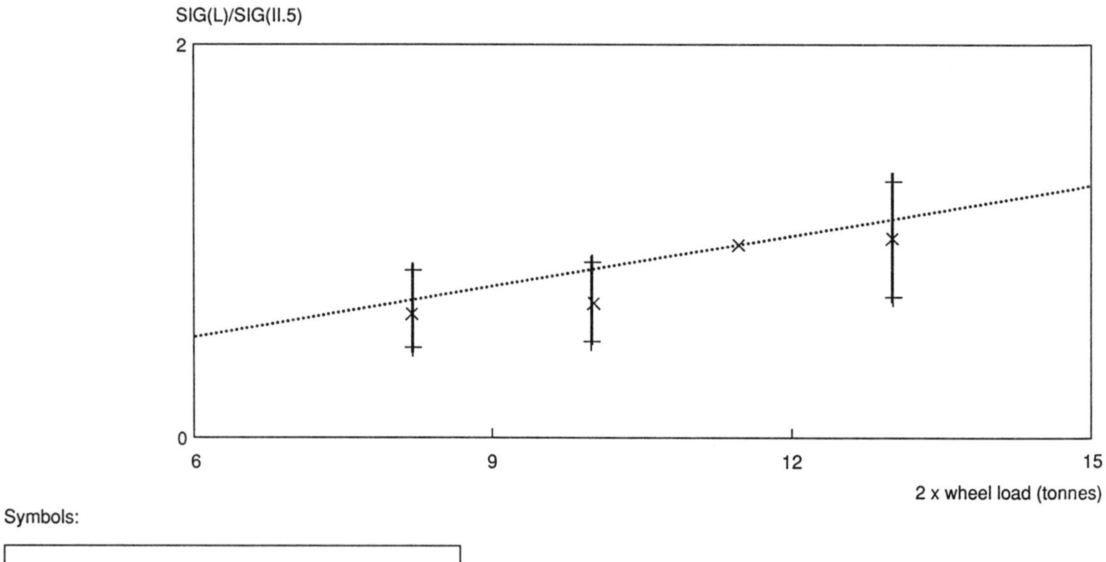

Symbols:

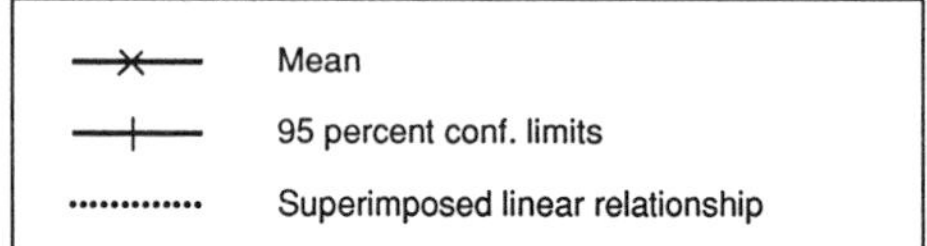

Figure VI.61

INITIAL SIGNAL LEVELS
LONGITUDINAL STRAINS AT THE UNDERSIDE OF BASE

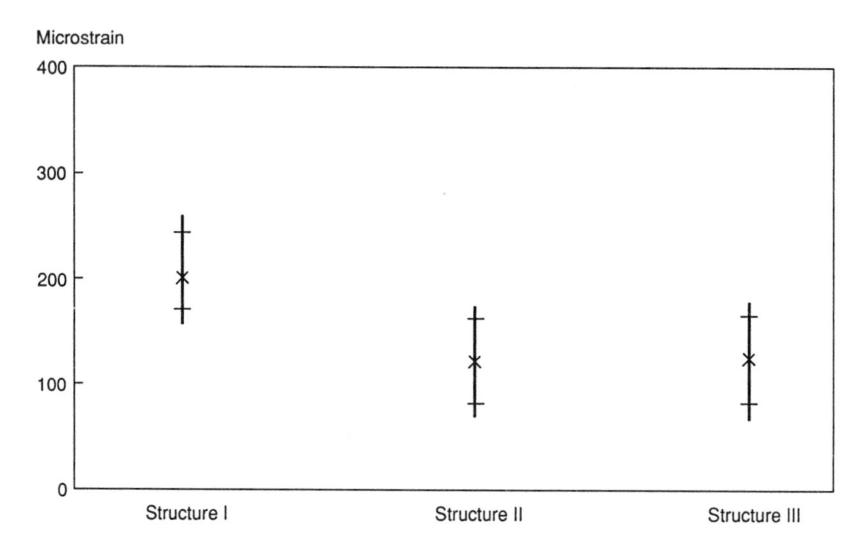

Symbols:

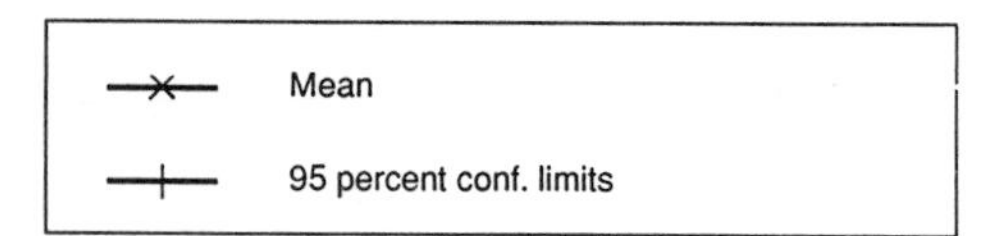

PART B -- USE OF MODELS

VI.4. REVIEW OF PAVEMENT BEHAVIOUR MODELS

VI.4.1. Introduction

The FORCE project generated enormous amounts of data. Pavement excitations in terms of load repetitions, temperature and moisture changes; and pavement response in terms of stresses, strains, deformation, cracks, and roughness are the major types of data collected. The central thrust of this experiment lies in the use of these data to provide a better understanding of intrinsic pavement performance and to further develop and improve pavement analysis and design procedures on an international basis.

Keeping in mind two general uses of pavement data, comparative and modelling, the OECD FORCE team addressed this issue and pursued the overall goals by a combined approach.

The comparative approach is most ideally suited to accelerated testing. The comparison of pavement performance of three different pavement structures under identical load excitations or the comparison of three identical pavement structures under different load expectations are typical examples of a comparative analysis of the experiment conducted herein. In addition, the cross testing program offers the opportunity to compare the performance of identical pavement geometries under different climates; however, with less probability of success because it would be impossible to isolate all of the other contributing factors affecting pavement performance.

The modelling approach on the other hand is suited to a variety of test programme types including in-service pavement experiments. It may be divided into two categories: (a) development or use of regression models, and (b) employment of mechanistic models to evaluate pavement performance and to calibrate the models for use in design on a local basis. The importance of this approach is illustrated by Figure VI.62, which shows the relationship between knowledge of the deterioration of a pavement and the costs of its construction and use. The development of the first category, however, is not so appropriate in these OECD experiments noting the lack of a sufficient

Figure VI.62

THE HDM MODEL — INTERACTION OF COSTS OF ROAD CONSTRUCTION, MAINTENANCE AND USE

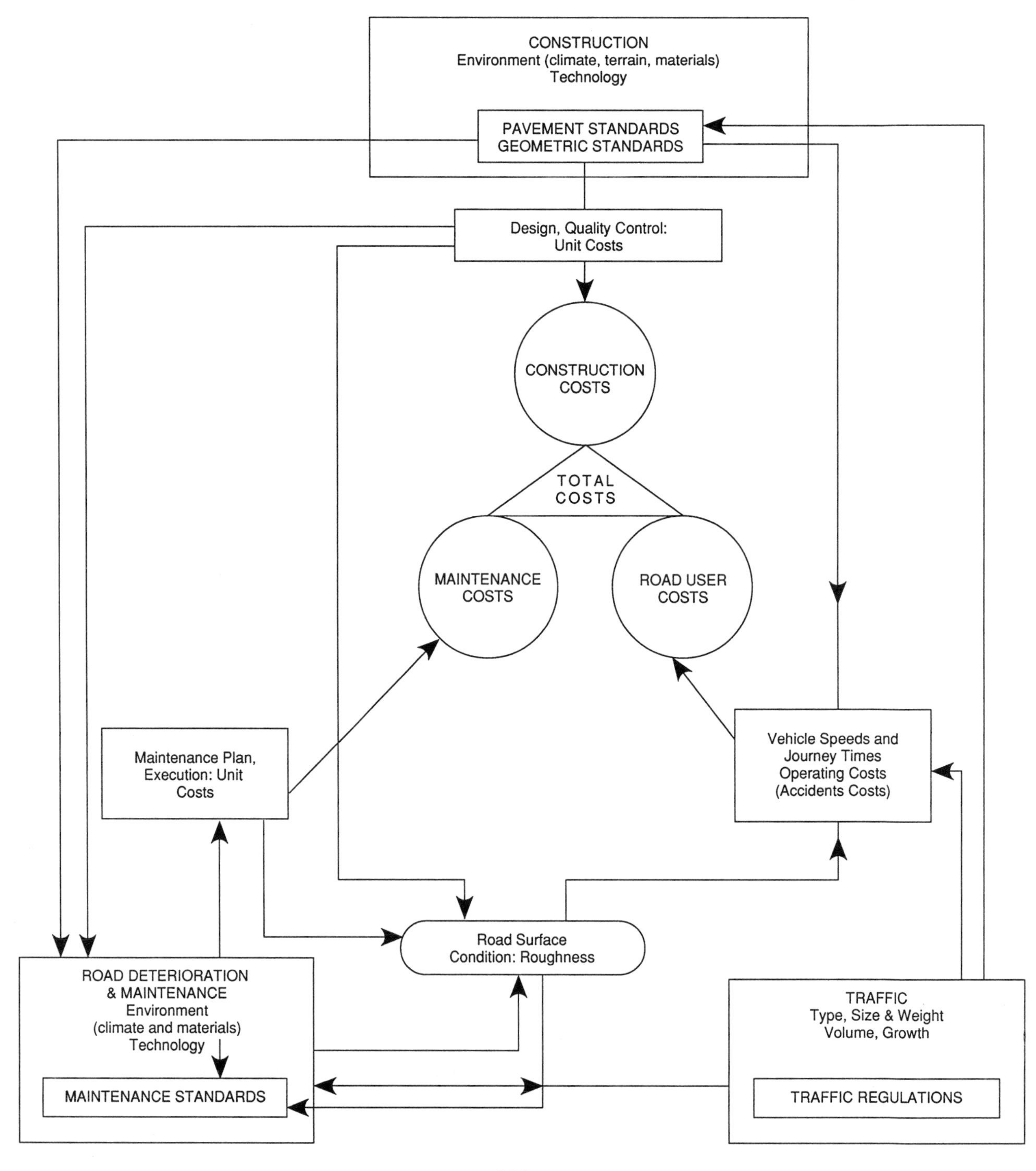

number of test replications to provide appropriate regression type models for use on an international basis. On the contrary, one should note the large number of test cells comprising the Strategic Highway Research Program (SHRP) experiments as well as the large number of replications of the American Association of State Highway Officials (AASHO) road tests.

In order to accomplish the goals of the OECD/FORCE project the participating Members have selected to pursue the modelling approach described above. In doing so, they have initially selected four specific structured systems, wherein each system comprises one or more pavement behaviour submodels. The structural systems selected represent a broad spectrum of different model types, but each having the potential to estimate one or more of the pavement responses discussed above.

The models selected represent the two major model types currently available viz: regression-type models and mechanistic models.

The regression model is usually developed from site specific data, wherein the data is used to fit a predetermined mathematical form. The coefficients so derived are, therefore, associated with those materials, environments and loadings used to generate the test data. One regression-type model recently developed from site specific data is the World Bank's Highway Design and Maintenance Standards Model (HDM). This damage model has the capability of estimating the three limiting pavement response measures, cracking, rutting, and roughness, however, it does not estimate the primary responses, stress, strain, and deflection. Because it can be used to estimate the limiting response measures, it was selected to represent the regression model type for this initial study phase.

Mechanistic models, however, do not rely on observed pavement data for their development. These models instead rely on the laws of physics and mechanics and on material component properties obtained from laboratory behavioural tests. Various versions of BISAR PC, VESYS, and MOEBIUS are the other three models selected for use in this study representing mechanistic model types. The primary response submodels of BISAR, VESYS and MOEBIUS are similar and are based on one form or other of linear elastic layer theory. The other submodels of VESYS, MOEBIUS, and BISAR are used to estimate various forms of pavement damage, and as such are called damage submodels.

There are four damage submodels comprising VESYS-cracking, rutting, roughness and present serviceability index (P.S.I.). MOEBIUS likewise contains two damage submodels-cracking and rutting, and BISAR PC contains one damage submodel- cracking. Amongst other sub-models HDM-III contains cracking, rutting and roughness submodels.

The intent of this review is to provide information on the makeup of these models and the submodels of each are presented under their appropriate classification e.g. primary response, cracking, rutting and roughness or P.S.I.

VI.4.2. Primary models

Primary response is defined herein as the stress, strain, or deflection occurring in the pavement due to the application of a single pass of a given axle or vehicle configuration. It may be of linear or non-linear elastic, viscoelastic, or viscoplastic behaviour. Most primary response models developed to date are formulated from continuum mechanics principles as it is applied to elastic or viscoelastic layer theory solutions.

Some important aspects of layer theory are noted here. First, it must be kept in mind that an elastic layer theory solution will not directly account for vehicle speed, i.e., the pavement responds similarly for all loading times and frequencies. On the other hand, a viscoelastic layer theory solution will account for vehicle speed. When a load is applied over a short time period (high speed) to a viscoelastic body, the primary deflection response is much smaller than it would be for the equivalent elastic case, however, when load is applied over a long period (slow speed), the deflection response gets bigger and approaches that for the equivalent elastic case.

It is also important to note the difference between a static and a dynamic layer theory solution. In a static layer theory solution, the inertia term is omitted from the equations of motion and thus the primary response is by definition independent of the particle mass accelerations. In a dynamic solution the inertia term is included and as a result, increased speed causes increased primary displacement responses. It has been shown, however, that this increase is so small for all practical vehicle speeds, that the inertia term can be neglected in the equations of motion.

All of the primary response models discussed here make use of either deterministic or probabilistic static elastic layer theory to calculate primary responses due to a uniformly distributed circular stationary load applied to the pavement surface (stationary is used here to imply that the load is fixed and that it is not moving up or down or laterally on the pavement surface). The solutions for all models represent the pavement by a system of layers of homogeneous and isotropic materials possessing linear stress-strain relationships. The layers are of uniform thickness, infinite in horizontal extent, and overlying a semi-infinite subgrade of homogeneous and isotropic material.

In all models, the pavement is subjected to a uniformly applied circular stationary load at the surface, and all materials possess a linear stress-strain relationship. The following list summarizes the attributes of the primary submodels of selected versions of VESYS, BISAR, and MOEBIUS.

The primary response submodels of each structural model require in all cases the modulus of elasticity of each layer. There are however different ways of determining this value and thus solutions naturally yield slightly different results. Material input properties are:

VESYS - Normally any method one chooses could be used, however, the VESYS manual suggests using the bituminous concrete (BC) modulus obtained from 0.1 second on -0.9 second off repeated load tests or from the inverse of the creep compliance at a 0.03 second loading time creep test. Any specimen shape is allowed as long as the laboratory data are calibrated internally to local in-service roads. The repeated load test is, however, recommended for the other layer materials including aggregate base and subgrade.

MOEBIUS - Here the elastic modulus of the BC is obtained using a test called the Dynamic Stiffness Modulus test. It is synonymous to the dynamic modulus test or the complex modulus test. Load is applied using a ten cps sinusoidal controlled strain wave. Ratio of peak to peak stress to peak to peak strain determines the modulus.

BISAR - The BISAR PC user manual suggests using BAND's suite of programs. Knowing various asphalt properties, a set of nomographs are used to determine the elastic modulus which is called the stiffness modulus of the BC mix.

VI.4.3. Rutting submodels

MOEBIUS Rutting

Vertical stress σ_v acting at each bituminous sublayer interface below the load axis and one-half of the average of the horizontal stress state acting at these same bituminous interface points are used in the calculation of rut depth. The two radial and two tangential stresses acting on opposite sides of each interface are used to obtain the average horizontal stress (the authors assume that the peak stress under a moving load is one half the static stress).

Two choices exist for calculating rut depth (RD). Each assumes accumulation of permanent deformation in accordance with equations VI.3 AND VI.4 below. Predetermined coefficients developed from regression analysis on results of numerous laboratory repeated load tests of bituminous concrete are also available. In the test, called a "dynamic creep test," a cylindrical specimen is subjected to a 10 cps sinusoidal compressive loading under a small compressive prestress. Accumulative permanent strain e_a is measured over time t in seconds (N repetitions = 10t). The permanent strain curve is represented by two separate regression equations:

$$\varepsilon_a = \alpha\, t^{\beta} \qquad \text{Eq. VI.3}$$

$$\varepsilon_a = A\, t \qquad \text{Eq. VI.4}$$

where α, ß and A are functions of temperature T, horizontal stress σ_H and vertical stress σ_v,

$$\beta = b_1 + b_2\, T + b_3\sigma_v + b_4\ (1/\sigma_H+1) \qquad \text{Eq. VI.5}$$

$$\alpha = \varepsilon_a\,(\infty)\ 10^{-6\beta} \qquad \text{Eq. VI.6}$$

$$\log\ A = A_1 + A_2\, T + A_3\, \sigma_H + A_4 \log \sigma_v \qquad \text{Eq. VI.7}$$

where $\varepsilon_a(\infty)$ is a constant representing the permanent strain after 1 000 000 sec or 10^7 repetitions.

Taking time derivatives of Eq. VI.3 and Eq. VI.4 yields:

$$\delta\varepsilon_a/\delta t = \ \beta\, t^{\beta-1} \qquad \text{Eq. VI.8}$$

$$\delta\varepsilon_a/\delta t = \ A \qquad \text{Eq. VI.9}$$

Note that the rates of accumulation of permanent strain in Eq. VI.8 is a linear function of t (N) and that in Eq. VI.9 the permanent strain rate is independent of t (N). The authors have used these two forms to represent the initial and linear stages as shown in Figure VI.63. The user can select the full representation. The program switches back and forth between the linear and non-linear forms.

Figure VI.63

PRINCIPLE OF RUT DEPTH COMPUTATIONS

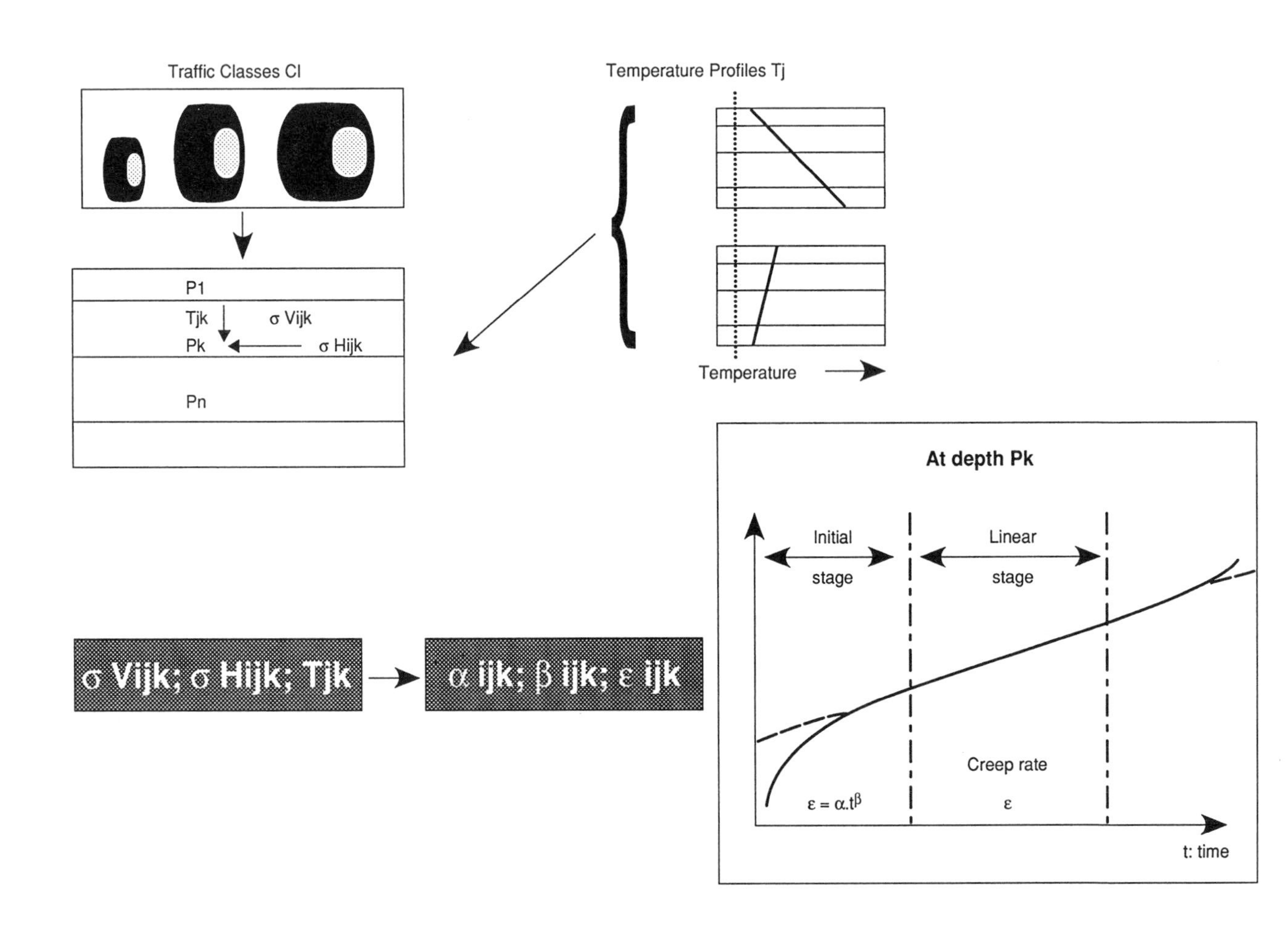

Rut depth in the bituminous layer is calculated and by summing the incremental permanent deformations calculated for each sublayer:

$$RD = \sum_{k=1}^{n} \varepsilon_{ak} H_k \qquad \text{Eq. VI.10}$$

where:

n = number of bituminous sublayers
H_k = sublayer thickness
ε_{ak} = permanent strain for BC sub-layer k per million cycles.

HDM Rutting

Rut depth progression is given as

$$RD = \alpha N_s^{\beta} \text{ and} \qquad \text{Eq. VI.11}$$
$$\alpha = A^{a1}/SNI^{a2}$$

where:

N_s = number of equivalent axle loads
β = $a_3 + a_{/14}\ D + a_5\ E + a_6\ P\ (.62AC+.39WC)$
D = Benkelman beam deflection.
E = 1 overlay, 0 no overlay
P = precipitation
AC = area all cracking
WC = area of wide cracking
A = pavement age since construction.
SN = structural number
a_k = regression coefficients.

The HDM-III user manual includes two different regression equation forms for rutting, one for initial rutting following construction or rehabilitation and another to estimate incremental rutting during the analysis year. Equation VI.11 was developed from the simplified user manual for Rodeman where the two equations were apparently combined to form a single equation involving pavement age.

VESYS Rutting

Two mechanistic distress methods to estimate accumulation of permanent deformation in the pavement have been developed for VESYS depending upon which version of VESYS is used. The rutting model for VESYS 3 AM is a displacement-based approach called the "SYSTEM FORMULATION". VESYS 5 has included, in addition, a strain-based approach "LAYER FORMULATION" to calculate the rutting in each layer and through integration calculates total system rut depth.

The first method "SYSTEM FORMULATION" uses elastic layer theory and a laboratory permanent deformation law for each layer to calculate the accumulated permanent deformation (rut depth) RD_a due to N repetitions.

$$RD = \int_{1}^{N_j} U_p(N)\, dN \qquad \text{Eq. VI.12}$$

where:

- U_p = $U - U_{un}(N_j)$, increment of system permanent deformation due to repetition N_j
- U = $f[E]$, layer theory system displacement upon loading.
- U_{un} = $f[E_{un}]$, layer theory system displacement due to repetition N_j upon unloading.
- E, E_{un} = layer moduli during load application and load removal
- $E_{un}(N)$ = $N/(N^{\alpha} - \mu)$ and
- α,μ = layer rutting properties

The system rutting properties μsys and αsys are calculated and input to the system rutting equation above.

The second method "LAYER FORMULATION" estimates the permanent deformation in each finite layer (i) as the product of the elastic compression in that layer and the layer material permanent deformation law associated with that layer. It provides a closed form solution for tandem and triple axles and it is based upon the superposition of strain. The permanent deformation in the subgrade is given by the triple product in the first term of equation (6) and that of the finite layer is given in the second term:

$$RD = [U_s(\varepsilon_t/\varepsilon_s)qsub + \sum_{i=1}^{n=1} (U^{+} - U^{-})] \qquad \text{Eq. VI.13}$$

where:

- U_i = superimposed deflection at top and bottom of a finite layer due to all axles in tandem or triple axle group
- U_s = deflection at top of subgrade due to single axle loading
- ε_s = strain at top of subgrade due to single axle loading
- ε_t = superimposed subgrade strain due to tandem or triple axle group loading
- q = $(I/e)\ N^S$, laboratory permanent deformation law and I,S,e are laboratory permanent deformation properties for each layer

The ratio $\varepsilon_t/\varepsilon_s$ is a measure of the relative increase in the subgrade strain produced by inclusion of the other axles.

The user must input μ and α for each layer. The manual recommends that the user estimate these and to further calibrate these quantities internally using in-service pavements. A laboratory test, "the incremental creep test," on cylindrical or indirect tensile disks is recommended as an aid to a first estimate of the bituminous concrete modulus. Examples of the measured output from this test are shown in Figure VI.64. Another laboratory test also recommended for all layer materials is the repeatedly applied halfsine load for at least 40,000 pulses 0.1 seconds on and 0.9 seconds off.

VI.4.4. Cracking submodels

All of the mechanistic cracking submodels use a form of the well known fatigue equation

$$N_f = k_1 \ (1/\varepsilon)k_2 \qquad \text{Eq. VI.14}$$

Two of the models, VESYS and MOEBIUS also use a form of Miner's Law to estimate cracking Damage Index C:

$$C = \ \Sigma \ (n/N_f) \qquad \text{Eq. VI.15}$$

where k_1k_2 are laboratory developed fatigue coefficients, ε is the radial fatigue strain calculated from the Primary Response Model at the bottom of the bituminous layer, N_f is the number of load repetitions of the fatigue strain to failure, and n is the number of repetitions of the fatigue strain.

BISAR-PC Cracking

BISAR uses Eq. VI.14 to estimate fatigue life where:

$k_1 = 856 \ V_b + 1.8E^{-.36}$
$k_2 = 5$
V_b = percent bitumen by volume
E = mix stiffness

The mix stiffness is calculated in the MIX STIFFNESS module from a knowledge of percent aggregate by volume, percent binder by volume, percent voids and stiffness of the bituminous material using a rather complex regression equation built into the computer program. The BITUMEN STIFFNESS is calculated in BISAR PC in a specific module for a specific temperature and a specific loading frequency from a knowledge of the softening point and penetration index using an equation representing Van der Poel's nomograph. The fatigue life N_f is then calculated in the MIX FATIGUE module.

Figure VI.64

EXAMPLE OF MEASURED OUTPUT USING THE "INCREMENTAL CREEP TEST"

a. Stress strain of incremental static test series

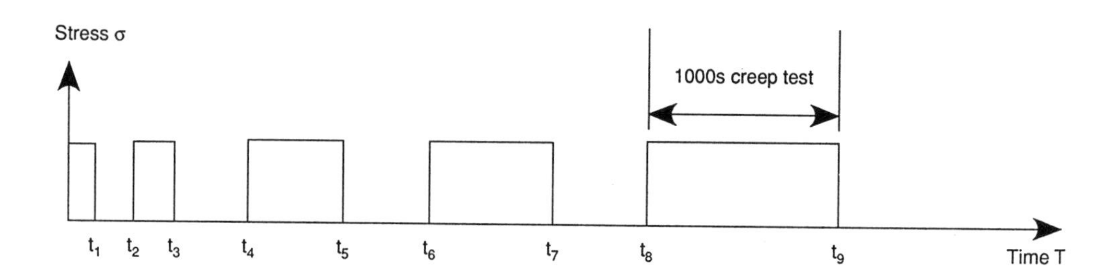

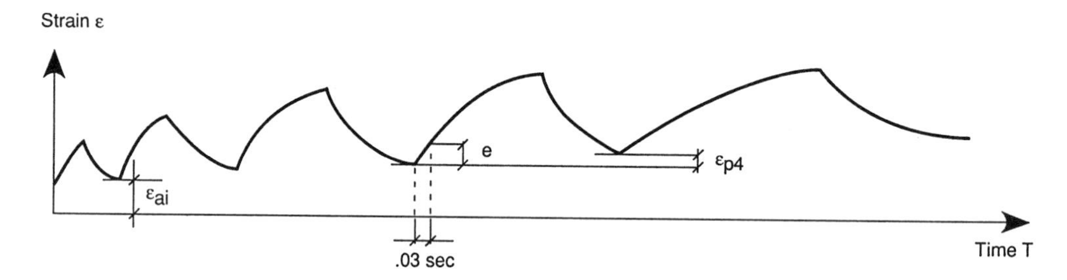

t_n = time at the beginning (n even) or end (n odd) of a step pulse in load

ε_{pi} = increment in permanent strain due to the ith load pulse where $i = 1 + \frac{(n-1)}{2}$ and n is an odd integer

ε_{ai} = total accumulated permanent strain due to i step pulse: $\varepsilon_{ai} = \sum_{j=1}^{i} \varepsilon_{pj}$

e = strain amplitude measured at .03 secondes for any load pulse

b. Permanent strain for bituminous concrete at 70°C using alternate procedure I.

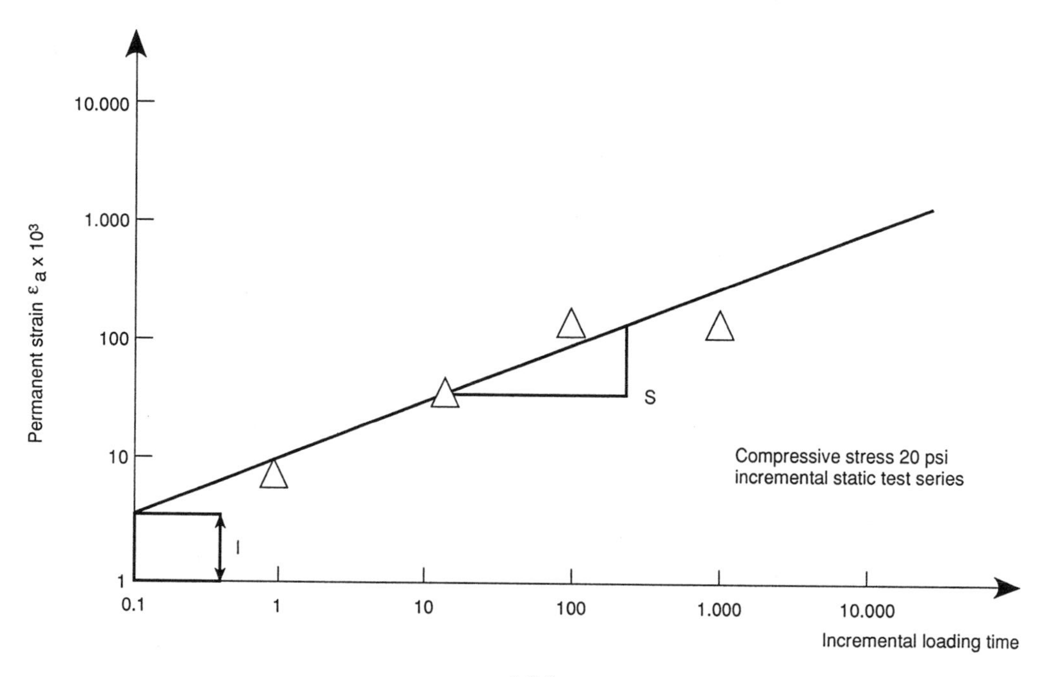

HDM Cracking

The World Bank cracking model describes crack manifestation in terms of "All Cracking," CA, and Wide Cracking, CW. All cracking includes both wide cracking and narrow cracking (1 to 3 mm width) and relates to alligator crack formations rather than to purely transverse or longitudinal cracks which are assumed in this report to be due mostly to environmental causes. Two types of rather complex regression equations are given in the literature for asphalt concrete pavements. The first type estimates the age, A, of the asphalt layer for "all cracking" and "wide" cracking at, respectively:

$$A_{CA} = g_1 \, e^{(g2 \; SN - g3 \; Ns/SN)} \qquad \text{Eq. VI.16}$$
$$A_{CW} = g_4 \, e^{(g5 \; Ns/SN)}$$

where:

g_i = regression coefficients
SN = modified structural number
N_s = Number of equivalent single axle loads

The second type estimates the change in percent cracking area during any year. It is a rather complex formulation involving many different factors including pavement type, deterioration factors, retardation factors, maintenance treatments, pavement age, etc.

VESYS Cracking

VESYS uses Eq. VI.14 to compute a closed-form expression for the mean and variance of the cracking damage index C.

In this formulation the expected cracking damage index E [c] is assumed to take on a normal distribution with variance Var[c]. The integral of the probability density function f(c) from C_o to infinity gives the probability P of C being greater than C_o:

$$P = \text{Prob}\,[c > C_o] = 1\text{-}F(C_o]$$

where F is the cumulative density function on C. Under Miner' hypothesis C_o = 1 and F(1) is the probability that a test specimen has not failed in fatigue. The expected area cracked per reference area A is

$$E\,[\text{Area Cracked}] = AP$$

MOEBIUS CRACKING

In MOEBIUS, Miner's equation is used to calculate the fatigue damage index C wherein N is given by

$$N = 10^{-(A+BT)} \, 1/\varepsilon_o^{-(C+DT)}$$

where: T = temperature
ε_o = initial strain
ABCD = laboratory regression constants.

The coefficients A, B, C and D for two different mixes are given in the program. They were determined from controlled stress or strain fatigue tests under a 10 Hz sinusoidal loading (no rest period).

An adjusting factor called k_4 or k'_4 is introduced in order to account for differences in laboratory and field fatigue cracking histories. An additional feature in MOEBIUS is a subroutine to simulate crack propagation sequentially from the bottom of the bituminous concrete layer to the top where the bituminous concrete is divided into a number of elemental layers. The following law is used for each elemental layer:

$$dL/dN = A\sigma^m$$

where dL/dN is rate of change of crack length, A and m are material crack propagation constants, and σ is tensile stress at the bottom of an uncracked layer.

VI.4.5. Roughness submodels

HDM Roughness

HDM calculates for each year the roughness variation δR. The roughness value R is measured using the QI (Quarter car Index as related to Maysmeter) or the BI (related to Bump Integrator) and can be expressed in IRI (International Roughness Index). In the model δR is a function of different parameters:

$$\delta R = f(A, SNM, N_{st}, \sigma_r, CA, P, R_0)$$

where: δR = roughness variation
A = pavement age
SNM = structural number
N_{st} = equivalent standard axle load
σ_r = standard deviation of rut depth
CA = State of deterioration, including all types of cracking and in particular wide cracking
P = area patching
R_0 = Initial roughness value

VESYS Roughness

VESYS calculates roughness in terms of mean (E[SV]) and variance (Var[SV]) of slope Variance SV. It is derived by taking approximate moments of the second partial derivation of the spatial auto correlation function of the pavements surface deformation along the wheel path:

$$E[SV] = 2B/C^2 \sigma_d^2 (Var[R] + (E[R])^2$$
$$Var [SV] = 4 B/C^2 \sigma_d E[R]^2 Var [R]$$

VESYS also calculates present serviceability index (P.S.I.), using the three modes-cracking, rutting and roughness as well as the AASHO P.S.I. equation.

VI.5 USE OF VESYS 3AM

VI.5.1. Application of VESYS 3AM to model early life performance of FORCE pavements

VESYS 3AM is a probabilistic elastic predictive model, capable of describing pavement performance and behaviour over lengthy periods of time. The version selected, 3AM, is also capable of dealing with several different environmental conditions and loading ranges, as well as a wide range of material properties. It is a very efficient program, able to be run on a PC, permitting a large number of calculations to be made in a short time

Structure 01 was first selected for the trials of the model. This section failed relatively early, as planned. The VESYS analysis indicated different behaviour before and after overlaying. It was suspected that the excessive pavement damage was caused either by conditions not considered in the 3AM version of VESYS, or that the available input data were insufficient. Layer separation or excessive wetting of the subgrade, for example, were not considered in the test runs. For these reasons, and because Structure 02 gave a more consistent performance throughout the trafficking period, it was used for subsequent analysis with VESYS.

VI.5.2. Input data

The pavement geometry and loading data were readily available from earlier measurements. The layer thicknesses used were those indicated by the Penetradar measurements carried out at the beginning of the experiment. The assumed traffic load for the program was 11.5 tonne; the relatively small number of passes with the 10 tonne axle load (10 000) were ignored. The number of seasons considered was increased to twelve rather than the usual four, because comprehensive temperature data were available. The rate at which loads were applied also varied with time, and therefore temperature, so that this was a desirable improvement to the input conditions.

At the time of the analysis, no data were available with which to characterise the temperature of the bituminous layer in the structure; the air temperature data were therefore used for this purpose, and an estimate made of the corresponding temperature in the bituminous material. The stiffness moduli of the bituminous material were estimated from the initial FWD measurements, and these values were extrapolated for the assumed temperature range. In the absence of relevant data, the base and subgrade moduli were kept constant throughout the selected seasons. Again, because the analysis was undertaken at an early stage in the experiment, no measured materials properties were then available, and estimates based on AASHO test data, and on previous experience of similar materials, were used. As measured data for the materials actually used become available, the analysis can be repeated.

Two trafficking rates were used; i) the actual accelerated trafficking rate of the Nantes facility, and ii) a rate that might apply to a normally trafficked road in service (2000 axles/day).

VI.5.3. Data requirements

The VESYS program requires input data in the form of tabulated values, reflecting the conditions and circumstances of the FORCE experiment, and their accurate completion is essential to a successful analysis of the performance of the pavement with the program.

VI.5.4. Comparison of accelerated and normal trafficking

For the purpose of the analysis, pavement performance under the different trafficking conditions is examined in terms of:

(i) A damage index which is a measure of the dissipated fatigue life of the pavement. When the damage index has attained a value of 1, all the fatigue life has been consumed and a crack is initiated at the bottom of the base layer.

(ii) Rut depth i.e.the accumulated permanent deformation over the period of the analysis. It is a function of the pavement response to loading, and the permanent deformation parameters of the pavement system.

(iii) Pavement serviceability, expressed in terms of the Present Serviceability Index (P.S.I.).

The results of the VESYS calculations are presented in Figures VI.65 and VI.66, which show the variation of the performance parameters as a function of number of passes, elapsed days of the experiment, and temperature. Since the results of the experiment have become available later, these can be compared with the development of measured relevant parameters described in this and earlier Chapters. The following general remarks apply only to the comparison of different loading rates under investigation.

According to the VESYS analysis, rutting occurs almost only in warm periods, while cracking develops only under cold conditions. Thus trafficking during warm periods tends to produce only rutting, with little effect on cracking performance, the reverse being the case for cold periods.

Rut development under the two different loading rates is quite similar, particularly when the rate of rutting (deformation per unit load) is considered. Differences are apparent, however, when the time at which loads were applied by each of the loading mechanisms considered is taken into account.

The damage index increases during periods of cold temperatures for both conditions of loading, but at a very low rate, becoming even lower as temperatures rise. Given the low absolute level of the damage index, the difference between the two modes of loading may be significant.

The P.S.I. combines several indicators of pavement performance, and the plotted results therefore reflect the characteristics described above.

VI.6. PAVEMENT ANALYSIS WITH ESSO MOEBIUS SOFTWARE

Rather than being a predictive model, MOEBIUS (7) is primarily an analytical tool with which it is possible to investigate the effect of varying structural parameters, temperatures and traffic loads. It also allows an interpretation of the stresses and strains generated in a pavement in terms of pavement performance. This is achieved through the calculation of so-called "Performance Indicators". Each Performance Indicator addresses a particular type of pavement distress and relates calculated stresses and strains to the behaviour of the materials as established in the laboratory. In addition to a Fatigue Index, and Rut Depth computations, the program also gives estimates of the risk of failure, and of pavement performance over time to allow various maintenance strategies to be investigated.

Two of these performance indicators were selected for use in this study:

-- FATIGUE INDEX which is the fatigue damage undergone by a certain layer after a given period of time. This damage is derived from the calculated tensile stresses or strains and the laboratory-established fatigue curve of the material which is assumed to follow Miner's rule. The fatigue index alone is therefore used to investigate comparisons between different variables, and not to predict the actual fatigue life of the pavement.

Figure VI.65

RESULTS OF VESYS CALCULATION - RUT DEPTH AND DAMAGE INDEX

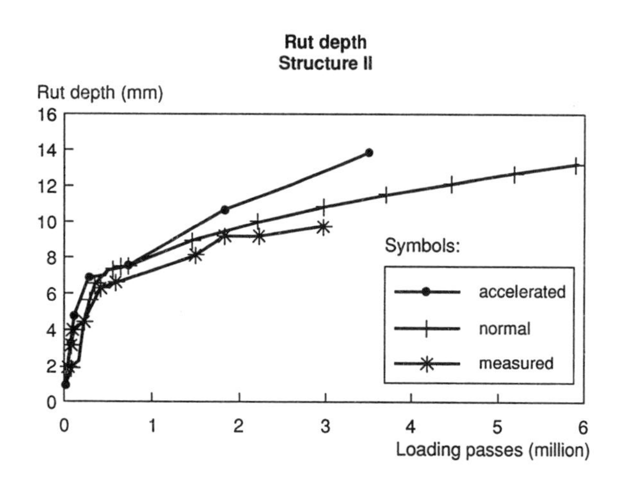

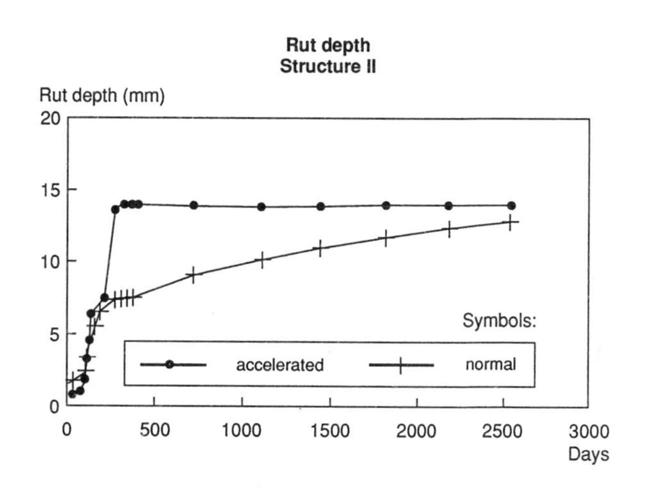

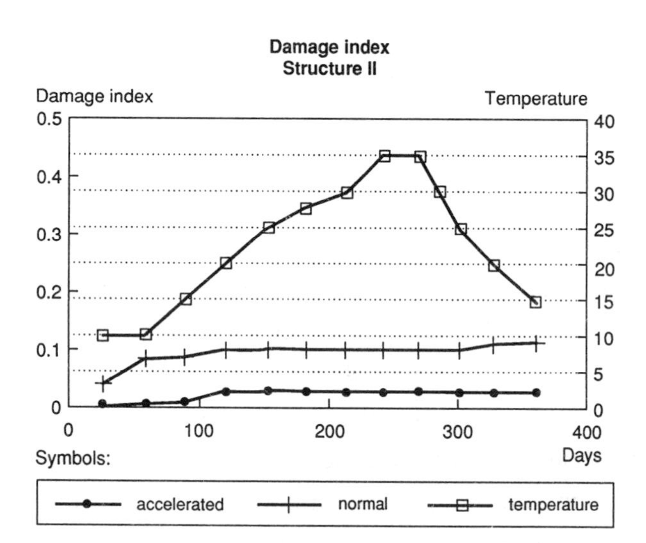

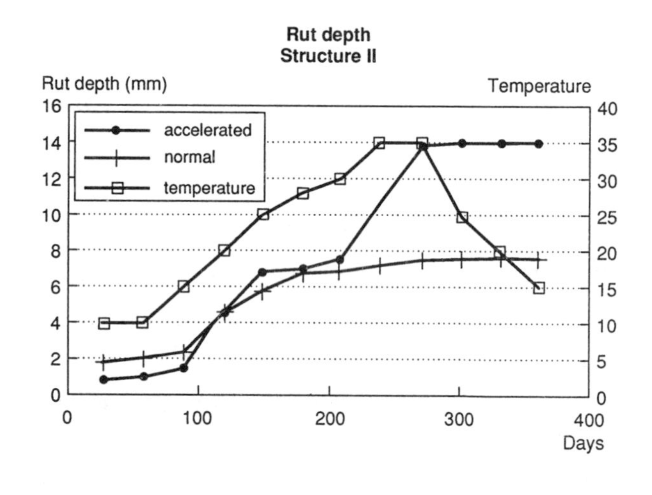

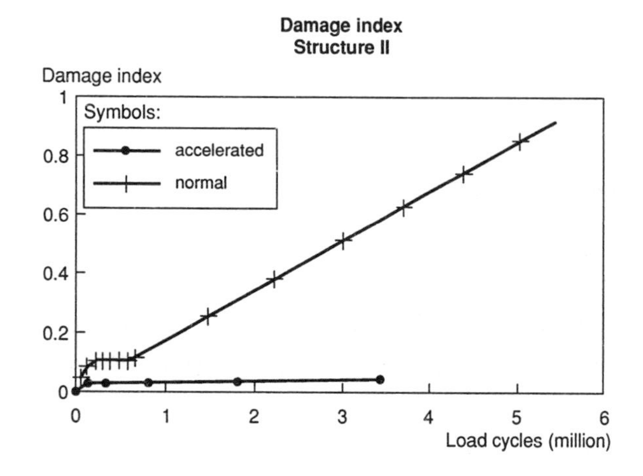

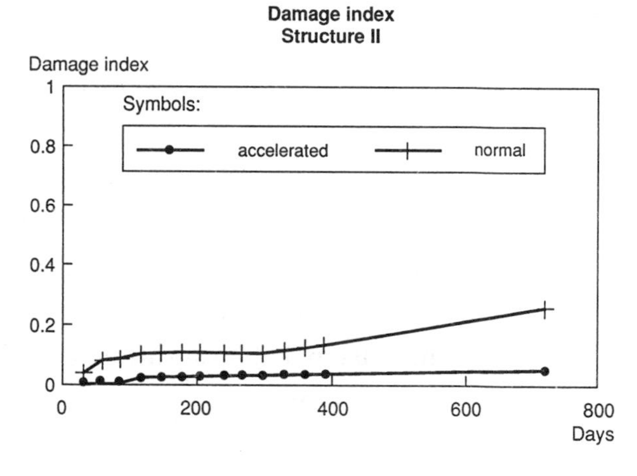

Figure VI.66

RESULTS OF VESYS CALCULATION - SERVICEABILITY

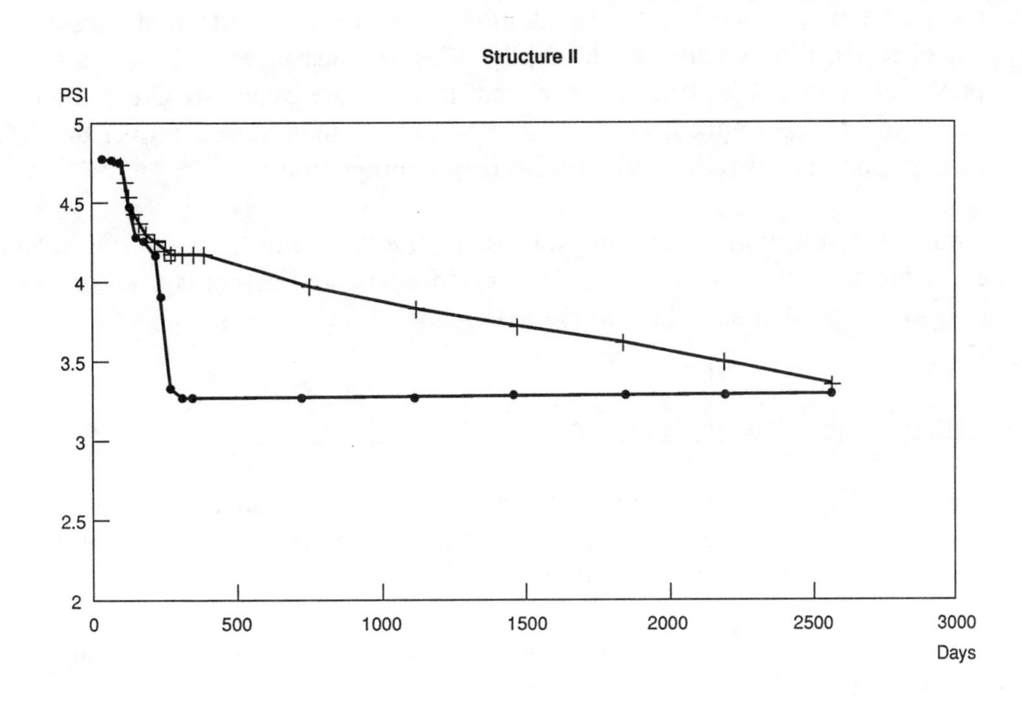

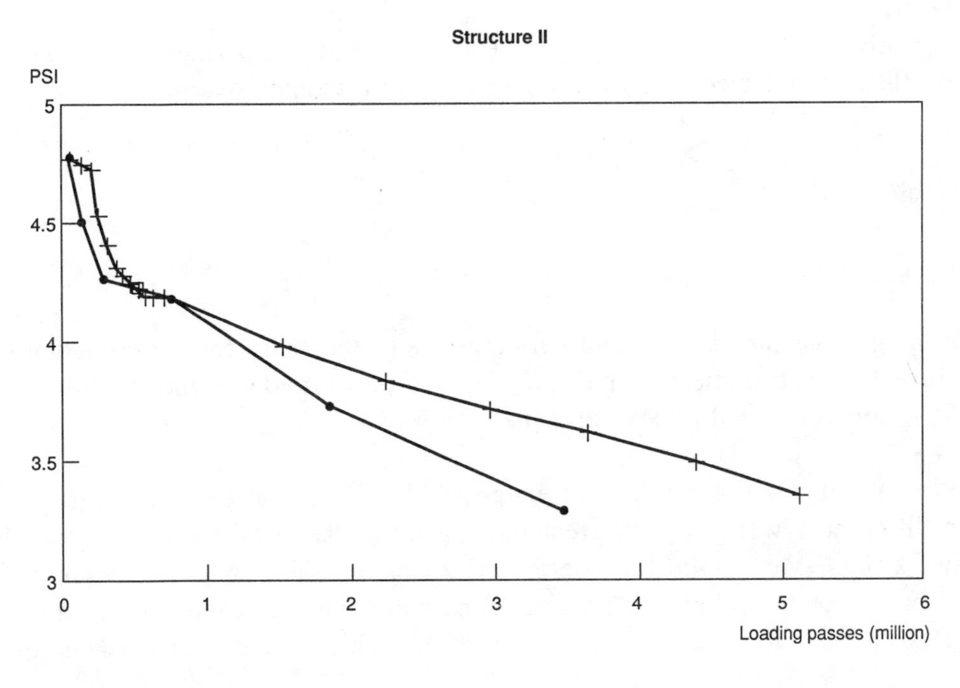

Symbols:

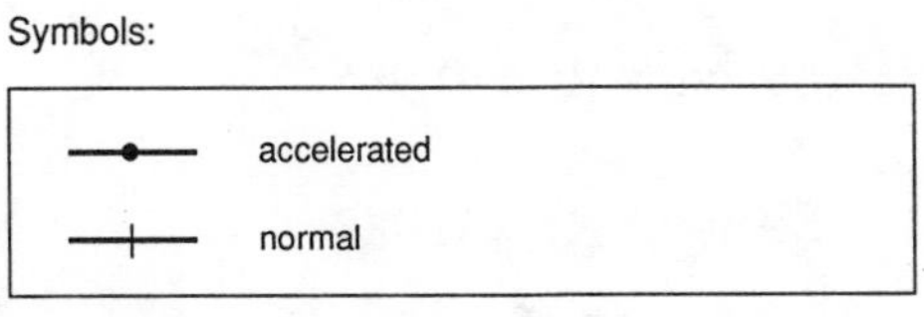

-- RUT DEPTH computations are based on the dynamic creep characteristics of bituminous materials as established through the Simplified Dynamic Creep Tester (8). This machine allows the permanent deformation of the material to be related to a pulsing compressive axial stress, a constant lateral stress and temperature. Rut depth computations are based on the calculation of vertical and horizontal stresses under the wheel loads, through the whole depth of bituminous layers. These stresses and the prevailing temperatures are then related, through the materials Creep Damage Law, to "elemental" permanent deformations which are then summed over depth, and the time period considered, to yield a rut depth computation.

A complete description of the analysis is reported elsewhere; what is presented here describes a part of the analysis in which one of the performance indicators is used to compare the effects of loading with 10 tonne and 11.5 tonne axle loads.

VI.6.1. Introduction to the calculations performed with MOEBIUS

For the FORCE experiment, Fatigue Index calculations and analysis were performed for test sections 01 and 11 over a period from the start of trafficking (end of December 1988) to the end of May 1989. These computations include studies of:

-- Comparison of 10 tonne axle loads (section 11) and 11.5 tonne axle loads (section 01).
-- Sensitivity of the calculation to stiffness moduli of subgrade and unbound granular layer.
-- Sensitivity to temperature data: mean pavement temperatures versus temperature profiles as indicated by measurements at strain gauge positions.

VI.6.2. Temperature and traffic data

Temperature Data

A thorough analysis of pavement temperatures is necessary for the computations, which are very sensitive to this parameter. The analysis was performed for the months of March to September, 1989, and conducted in several steps.

The initial temperature readings of gauges S2,S3,S4,S8 and S9 were averaged over time periods where differences were not too great (e.g. readings taken at 5 min. intervals have been averaged to give a single value valid for a period of one or several hours). The readings for gauges S2 and S3 had been found unreliable from early June and have thus been estimated from a linear regression analysis applied to the data from March to May which led to the following relationships:

$$S2 = -0.573 + 0.398 * S4 + 1.073 * S8 - 0.427 * S9 \text{ with } R^2 = 0.985$$

$$S3 = -0.246 + 0.504 * S4 + 0.841 * S8 - 0.271 * S9 \text{ with } R^2 = 0.989$$

To further reduce the number of different temperature profiles, linear regression analysis was used. Having defined "homogeneous" time periods (several days to a few weeks) for which the daily temperature pattern was consistent, the daily temperature variations could be described by a 4th degree polynomial function of time (hours). This led to a standard subdivision into 11 "hourly" profiles. This was done whenever possible (June to August). When temperature data were not consistent enough for such a regression (e.g. March to May), the profiles corresponding to the loading periods were directly estimated from the measured values. When possible, profiles close to each other were again averaged.

Traffic Data

The traffic data corresponding to a given temperature profile were obtained by summing the relevant number of loadings for the whole period covered by the profile. For example, the first profile in March (MR1) is applicable to 6 different hourly periods (March 6 -9.30 to 12.00 ; March 8 - 12.00 - 15.00). The total number of loadings corresponding to MR1 is thus the sum of the loadings for these 6 time spans.

The same principle was applied to the profiles obtained through regression analysis. Thus, for profile JU1-4 (June 1 to 16/10.00-12.00) the number of loadings is the sum of all the loadings occurring between 10.00 and 12.00 from June 1 to June 16th.

Temperature and Traffic Data Prior to March 6, 1989

Temperature gauge readings were not available before March 6th, 1989. However, Fatigue Index computations do take into account the loadings prior to this date. For this early period, mean bituminous temperatures were estimated from the recorded mean air temperatures using a formula derived by WITZCAK abacuses (9). This gave the following mean pavement temperatures (°C) for sections 01 and 11 :

Week	Air °C	Pavement °C
51 (1988)	9.6	14.9
1 (1989)	5.8	10.3
6 (1989)	7.9	12.8
7 (1989)	9.5	14.7
8 (1989)	7.1	11.9
9 (1989)	9.5	14.7

All the procedures and data noted in the preceding paragraphs are reported elsewhere.

VI.6.3. Modelling of the axle loads

The stress/strain program used within MOEBIUS models a dual-wheel load through 2 circular load imprints. The distance between the vertical axes of the two wheels is assumed to be 3 times the radius of the imprint (see Figure IV.2 which gives the true distance). The following values were adopted for the various axle loads used in the MOEBIUS computations :

Axle Load (tonnes)	**Contact Pressure (MPa)**	**Imprint Radius (cm)**	**Imprint Surface (cm x cm)**
13	0.662	12.5	491
11.5	0.525	13.2	548
10	0.456	13.2	548
8.2	0.374	12.0	548

All stresses and strains were calculated under the axis of one of the dual wheels. Lateral distribution of the wheels (which took place during the trafficking at Nantes) was not taken into account by the calculations. How this may affect the final result is discussed separately.

VI.6.4. Fatigue index computations

Principle of Fatigue Index Computations

For the FORCE experiment, the fatigue characteristics of the bituminous material were expressed as a function of strain, as described below. The Fatigue Index computation uses the maximum principal strain (corresponding to the longitudinal strain gauges) calculated on the axis of one wheel at the bottom of the bituminous layer.

The calculation assumes Miner's law to be applicable; in particular, this means that the "order" in which axle loads pass over the pavement is of no importance. Thus, heavy axles passing before lighter ones lead to the same overall damage as if they were passing afterwards.

Modelling of the Structure

The structural parameters used for section 01 and 11 are shown in Table VI.7.

Table VI.7.

STRUCTURAL PARAMETERS SECTIONS 01 AND 11

LAYER	THICKNESS (cm)	STIFFNESS MODULUS (MPa)	POISSON RATIO (0< <=0.5)	INTERFACE CONDITION (-1 or +1)	NUMBER OF SUBDIVISIONS
(2)	6.0	Variable	0.35	-1	1
(1)	28.0	200	0.35	-1	1
(0)		50	0.45		1

Mechanical Characteristics of the Bituminous Materials

Stiffness. In order to be consistent with the selected fatigue characteristics, the stiffness data measured by the Delft University of Technology on a four-point-bending apparatus were used (see Chapter V). Results are expressed in the form of a mathematical equation relating Log E to temperature T and frequency (10Hz).

For the MOEBIUS calculations, a frequency of 10 Hz was employed as this was thought to be realistic for both tracks. Moreover, the stiffness measurements show relatively small changes between 10 Hz and 30 Hz. The Delft equation for stiffness E was thus converted to relation compatible with MOEBIUS:

$$\text{Log } E = a + b.T + c.T^2$$

a, b and c being constants.

Example values for stiffness at 10 Hz are shown below:

Temperature (°C)	-10	0	10	20	30	40
Stiffness (MPa)	24000	16500	9850	5130	2330	920

Fatigue. The four-point-bending fatigue testing carried out by Delft on specimens from the FORCE experiment employ a constant deflection in the middle of the beam while recording the force applied. Fatigue life can be expressed as a function of temperature and initial strain amplitude at the bottom of the beam. Such a flexural test appears to be of special interest in this particular case as it is made on rectangular beams whose dimensions are 450 x 50 x 50mm. The thickness on sections 01 and 11 being 60 mm, the test approximates very closely a "full-scale" laboratory simulation of the fatigue behaviour of the whole bituminous layer.

This test is therefore perhaps better suited to a comparison with the real behaviour of sections 01 and 11 than other types of fatigue tests used elsewhere. The results obtained by Delft (see Chapter V) were processed through linear regression analysis to give a Fatigue Law compatible with the MOEBIUS program. The relationship used in the software is as follows:

$$\log N_f = - (A + B.T) - (C + D.T).\log \ EPSo$$

where: EPSo = initial strain

N_f = number of cycles for failure,

T = temperature (°C).

A,B,C,D = constants

A comparison between measured data and values predicted from the regression analysis is shown below.

Temperature (°C)	Initial Strain (10^{-6} m/m)	Actual Value (cycles)	Predicted Value
0	262	1026	1116
0	219	5220	3404
0	167	21500	9112
0	158	19870	26049
0	132	95040	79894
10	260	2720	3631
10	222	6498	8042
10	201	6858	13262
10	183	13140	21265
10	159	32400	43145
10	145	51624	68610
20	310	3060	5754
20	267	12528	10197
20	236	34200	16364
20	220	30132	21415
20	206	43380	27551

VI.6.5. Effect of axle load - comparison 10 tonnes vs. 11.5 tonnes

This was performed on the structure defined in Table VI.7. The development of fatigue damage under the traffic loadings calculated as described earlier is shown in the table overleaf.

Development of Fatigue Damage for Sections 01 and 11

Data are presented in Figure VI.67 where the length of each time period is proportional to the number of loadings. Figure VI.68 shows a comparison between Section 01 and Section 11 during the month of April with damages starting at the same origin. During this period, Section 01 has been trafficked by only the 11.5 tonne axle whereas Section 11 has seen only the 10 tonne axle. Figure VI.68 therefore shows a true comparison between the two axle loads.

Comments

The following comments concerning the comparison can be made:

-- Section 01, due to a short period of early loadings with the 13 tonne axle has already undergone some significant damage by the beginning of March.

-- Calculated fatigue damage is the same for Section 01 and Section 11 at the end of their actually observed life. This is a very important result as it shows that calculated lives are consistent with observation.

-- Calculated damage at the end of the observed life is higher than the theoretical value which should have been 1. Although in this case we are probably as close as possible to "ideal" knowledge of parameters, this can still be attributed to the discrepancy between theory and practice. This may be due to differences between computed and measured strains, to possible effects of transverse distribution of the wheel loads in the experiment, or to a sensitivity to some design parameters.

-- The development of damage is quite linear over the months of March and April for both Sections which suggests that there is no significant effect of temperature.

-- The slope of the Damage/Number of Loadings line is lower in May for Section 11. This corresponds to the higher average pavement temperatures observed in this period (24.9 °C versus 15.9 °C in April and 14.6 °C in March).

	Section 01		Section 11	
Period	**Damage**	**Cumulative**	**Damage**	**Cumulative**
Week 51	0.296			
Week 1	0.246			
Week 6	0.0325		0.0168	
Week 7	0.200		0.107	
Week 8	0.282		0.236	
Week 9	0.0677	1.12	0.0362	0.396
March	1.812		0.902	
April	3.103		1.615	
May	0.124	5.04	2.709	5.22
TOTAL		**6.16**		**5.62**

By comparing the damages generated in April, one may define the factor corresponding to the "fourth power law". It may be obtained from the usual equation :

$$\frac{P_x}{P_y} = \left(\frac{S_x}{S_y}\right)^n$$

where P_x and P_y are axle loads and
S_x and S_y are the slopes of the corresponding Damage/Number of Loadings lines.

In the present case :

$P_x = 11.5$
$P_y = 10$
$S_x = 3.103 / 141734$
$S_y = 1.615 / 141734$

Thus: $1.15^n = 3.103/1.615$
Hence: $n = 4.67$

This value may be compared with the values derived by other means in earlier sections of this Chapter.

Figure VI.67

EVOLUTION OF FATIGUE DAMAGE FOR SECTIONS 01 AND 11

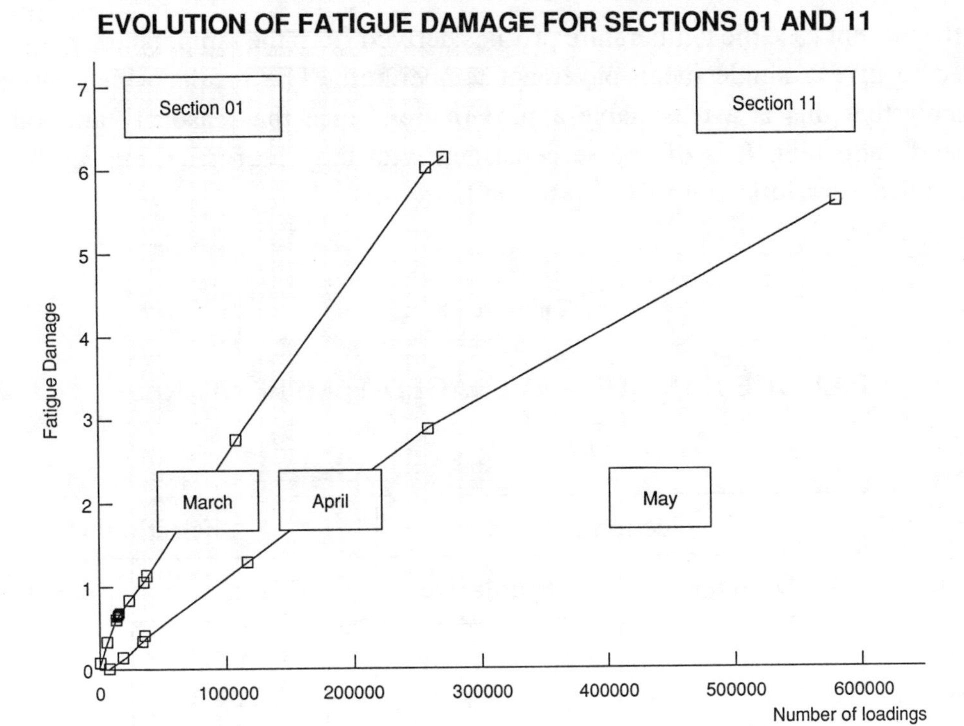

Figure VI.68

FATIGUE DAMAGE — COMPARISON OF 10 TONNES VS 11.5 TONNES
(April 1989)

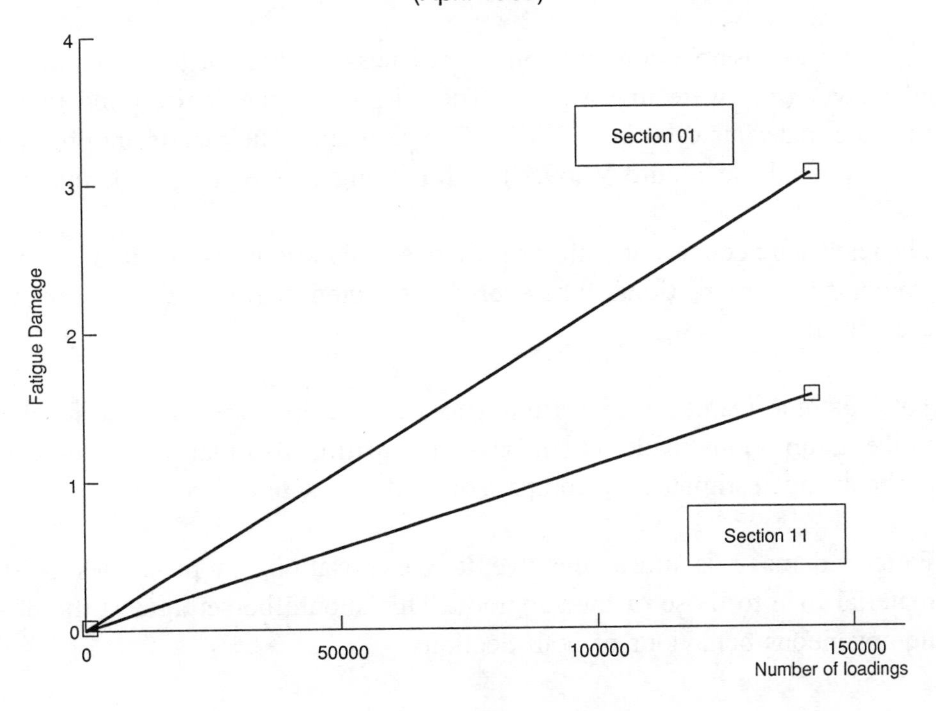

VI.6.6. Sensitivity to temperature assumptions

In the present case the temperature profiles derived from the temperature gauge recordings were averaged to give a single mean pavement temperature. The results which are gathered in Table VI.8 show that this is a reasonable approximation since the seasonal variation of fatigue damage is clearly apparent. It is of course consistent with the observation that in this thin layer temperatures varied very little from the top to the bottom.

Table VI.8.

FATIGUE DAMAGE - AVERAGED TEMPERATURES

	Section 01		Section 11	
Period	**Damage**	**Cumulative**	**Damage**	**Cumulative**
JAN./FEB.	1.131		0.393	
MARCH	1.753		0.914	
APRIL	2.941		1.599	
MAY	0.117		2.593	
		5.94		5.50

VI.6.7. Sensitivity to stiffness of subgrade and granular layer

Finally, several possible combinations of stiffness moduli for the subgrade (E0) and the unbound granular layer (E1) were investigated. The stiffness values correspond to the estimated possible range for the materials used in the FORCE experiment. The results are presented in Table VI.9 and shown graphically in Figure VI.69. The following comments can be made.

-- The results are consistent with the previous calculations. Total fatigue damage remains similar for both sections, whatever the selected stiffness values for subgrade and granular layer.

-- Total Fatigue Damages vary from 1 to 12. This indicates that the result is sensitive to the assumptions made on stiffness. It confirms also that the calculated Damage is probably overestimated by comparison with the actual damage.

-- Fatigue damage is more sensitive to the variations in properties of the granular material than to those of the subgrade. This should be set against the observed non-homogeneous behaviour of both Sections.

Table VI.9.

FATIGUE DAMAGE AS A FUNCTION OF SUBGRADE AND GRANULAR LAYER

SECTION 01 (11.5 TONNES)

	Week 51	Week 1	Week 6	Week 7	Week 8	Week 9	March	April	May	SIGMA
E1=150 EO= 50	0.570	0.477	0.064	0.393	0.550	0.133	3.58	6.17	0.24	12.2
E1=300 E0= 50	0.100	0.082	0.011	0.065	0.092	0.022	0.586	0.992	0.041	2.0
E1=150 E0=100	0.443	0.346	0.047	0.301	0.405	0.102	2.65	4.63	0.22	9.1
E1=300 E0=100	0.086	0.066	0.008	0.055	0.074	0.019	0.478	0.823	0.042	1.65
E1=150 E0=150	0.388	0.293	0.041	0.261	0.344	0.088	2.27	4.01	0.21	7.9
E1=300 E0=150	0.078	0.057	0.008	0.050	0.066	0.017	0.424	0.738	0.042	1.48

SECTION 11 (10 TONNES)

	Week 51	Week 1	Week 6	Week 7	Week 8	Week 9	March	April	May	SIGMA
E1=150 EO= 50			0.033	0.210	0.460	0.071	1.79	3.21	5.17	10.9
E1=300 E0= 50			0.005	0.035	0.078	0.012	0.29	0.516	0.923	1.86
E1=150 E0=100			0.024	0.161	0.339	0.054	1.33	2.42	4.27	8.6
E1=300 E0=100			0.004	0.029	0.063	0.01	0.238	0.430	0.842	1.62
E1=150 E0=150			0.021	0.140	0.289	0.047	1.14	2.10	3.88	7.6
E1=300 E0=150			0.004	0.027	0.056	0.009	0.211	0.386	0.799	1.49

Figure VI.69

FATIGUE DAMAGE AS A FUNCTION OF SUBGRADE AND GRANULAR LAYER

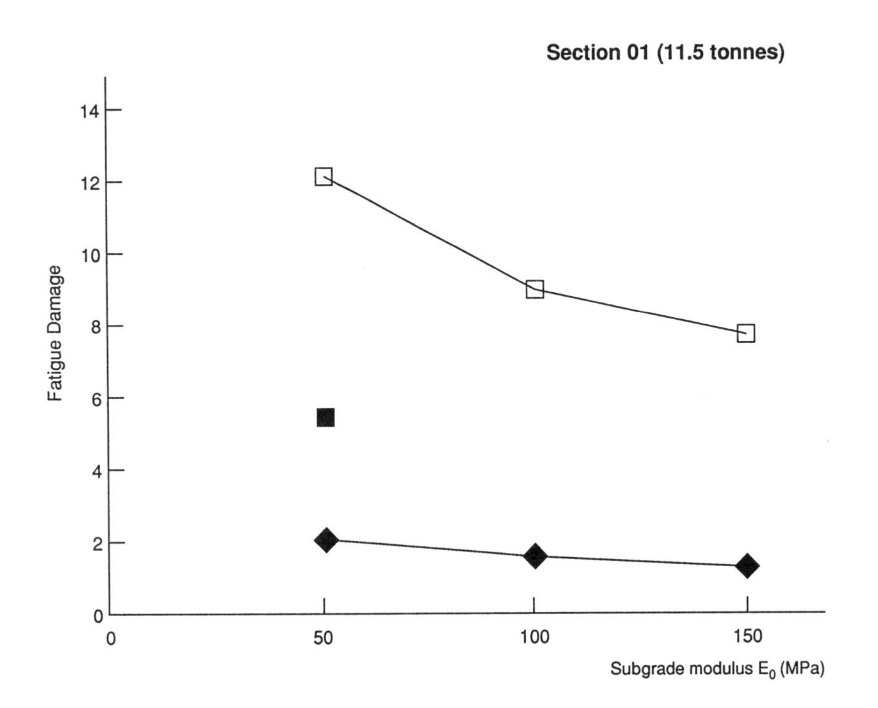

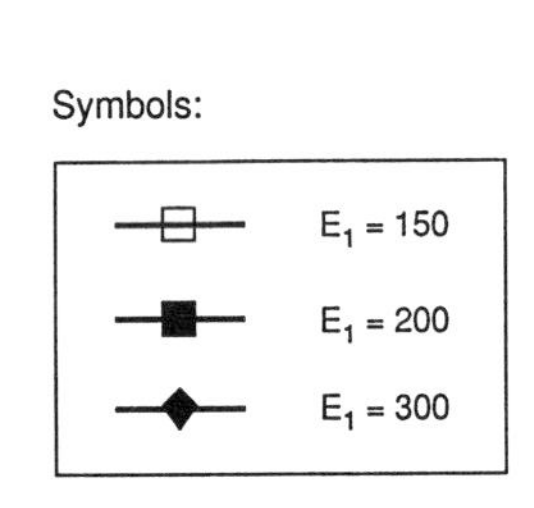

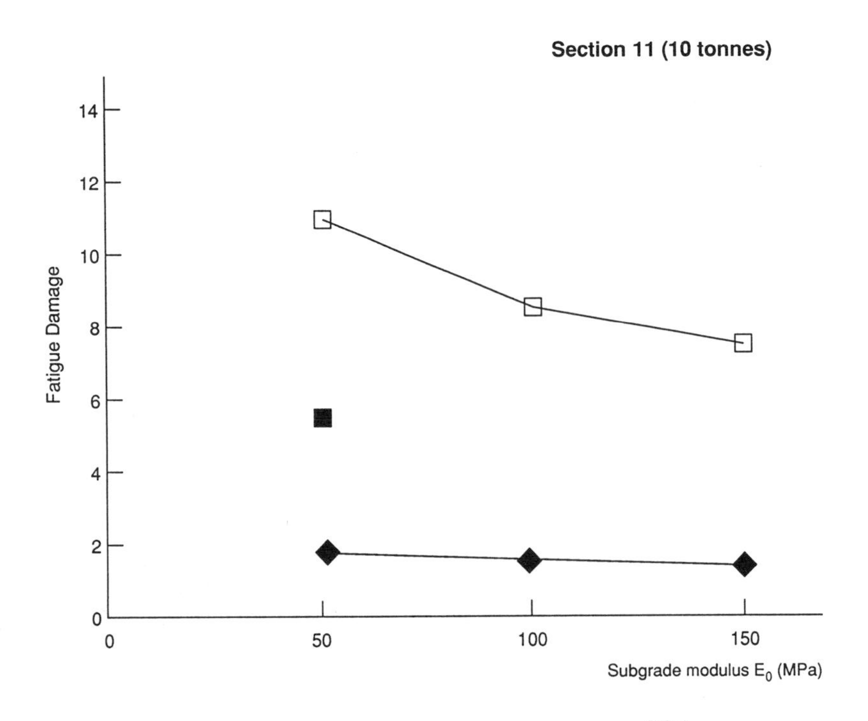

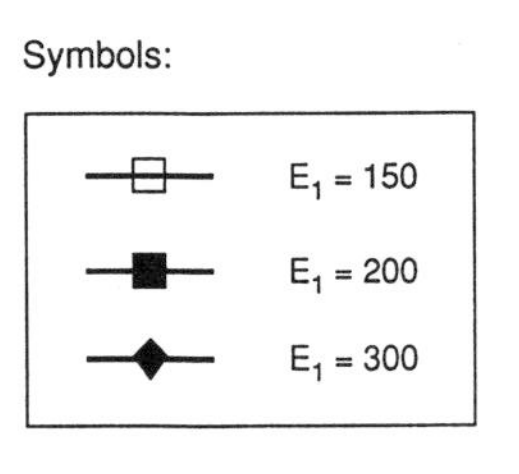

Chapter VII

CROSS TESTS

In the general context of cross tests, this Chapter presents a brief review of the tests undertaken on other fatigue pavement research facilities -- different from the Nantes circular test track -- involving comparable structures analogous to those defined for the FORCE test. The tests in question are hence carried out on facilities with different characteristics -- mechanical, climatic, materials -- from those used for the common test. Despite research efforts to obtain the same materials -- including the subgrade -- it will never be possible to reproduce identical conditions from one facility to another.

The description of the tests, the results of which have yet to be fully analysed, is intended primarily to highlight some of the general problems of cross tests and to propose certain comparisons with the results obtained from the Nantes manège.

VII.1 THE PROBLEM

Although the conduct of cross tests involving different manèges and test facilities is a very attractive idea in order to evaluate the accuracy of the tests and to establish the basis for joint research projects into optimising the operations of such facilities, the practical difficulties at present are quite considerable.

If direct comparisons are to be made of the data relating to the responses of comparable pavement structures, built with the same materials and the same techniques and subject to similar patterns of loading, the following aspects of each installation must be made identical:

- Conditions of load application: load (tonnes), configuration of axle (and wheels in a half-axle), contact pressure of tyres, speed, transverse distribution of load, system of suspension, etc.;

-- Climatic conditions during the testing, especially temperature variations, sunshine, rainfall and water content in the different courses of the pavement and subgrade;

-- The bearing capacity of the subgrade.

As things stand at present, it is practically impossible to meet all these conditions. Obtaining identical loading conditions would necessitate major design changes in each test track facility. It is impossible to achieve identical climatic conditions for any open-air installation (though covering the test sections could be a partial answer). Last, guaranteeing an identical subgrade would require the construction of a concrete casing (as exists in some installations) as well as the same type of filling material and the same conditions regarding water content and compaction.

It is however feasible to compare the results of tests made on different test facilities, on a quantitative rather than a qualitative basis. The aim would be to make studies of the relative behaviour of pavements and of the detailed characteristics of the materials used in building the pavement sections tested in other facilities. A better term than "cross tests" would hence perhaps be "comparative cross tests". Tests carried out so far should be placed in this latter category.

VII.2. COMPARATIVE CROSS TESTS

VII.2.1. Tests scheduled

A number of countries have expressed their intention to conduct comparative cross tests on one or several test sections similar to those used in the FORCE project in Nantes. At the time of writing these are: Germany, Italy, the Netherlands, the United Kingdom and the United States. Finland, Spain and Switzerland ave carrying out tests and the first results from Spain and Switzerland are already available and will be presented in detail in the reports published by the relevant centres. As examples, some of the main data on the comparative cross tests carried out in these three countries are presented. More comprehensive data will be found in the study reports to be published.

VII.2.2. Tests carried out in Spain

The tests carried out so far in Spain on the test track at the Centro de Estudios y Experimentación de Obras Publicas (see in Figure VII.1) focused on the study of the behaviour of two structures similar to the "thick" structure in the FORCE tests though with a slightly thicker bituminous layer (145 and 155 mm as against 130-140 mm) and with two variants of subgrade thickness (250 and 500 mm as against 280 mm for FORCE). The subgrades are in crushed gravel. The test sections are each 25 m long and were subjected to 500 000 loadings equivalent to a 13-tonne axle (6.5 tonne half axle). The main characteristics of the test sections are summarised in Table VII.1.

Figure VII.1

CENTRO DE ESTUDIOS Y EXPERIMENTACION DE OBRAS PUBLICAS (CEDEX) FATIGUE TEST TRACK, MADRID, SPAIN

Year of construction: 1987
Configuration: Mixed (linear and circular)
Total length: 304m
Load characteristics:
— Configuration: half axle and twin wheel
— Load value: 6.5 tonnes
— Transversal displacement: +/-400mm
— Speed: 40km/h
— Suspension system: pneumatic
Characteristics of the test sections:
— Total number: 6 per test
— Length: 25m
— Width: 8000mm
— Supporting devices: basement in cement concrete
Observations:
— Test sections covered
— Entire automatism (work 24h/24h and automatical gauge data collection)

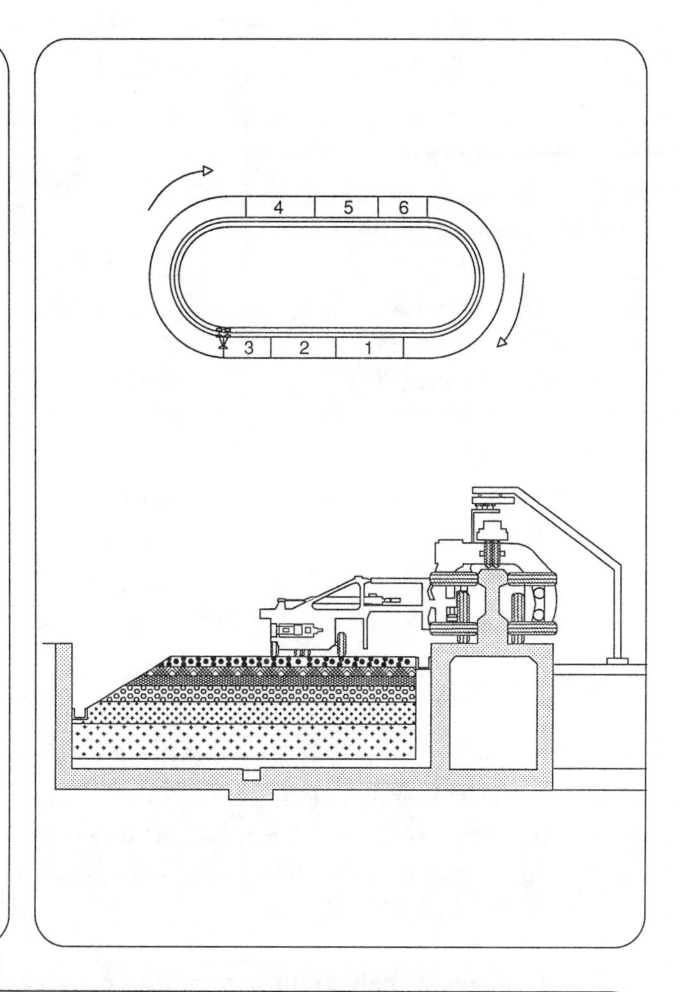

Table VII.1

COMPARISON OF CERTAIN FEATURES OF THE SPANISH TESTS WITH FORCE

Test section	Spain 1	Spain 2	Force: Structure II
Bit. thickness (mm)	145	155	130-139
Sub-base thickness (mm)	250	500	280
Dynamic modules of bit. materials at 25°C	4500 MPa	4500 MPa	
CBR of sub-grade (%)	10	10	-30
Initial deflection under Benkelman Beam (20°C)	50/100mm	68/100mm	70/100mm

The test for which different measuring, instrumentation and analytical techniques were used, and for which details are given in the corresponding research report, studied types of pavement behaviour presented in Figures VII.2, VII.3 and VII.4 (rutting, cracking and deflections).

VII.2.3. Tests carried out in Switzerland

Using the circular manège of the Zurich Federal University of Technology -- see (4) for description --, tests were carried out in 1989-90 on a structure corresponding to the "thin" structure of the FORCE test, loads being equivalent to a 10-tonne axle (first phase) and an 11.5-tonne axle (final phase). There, too, the loads were applied on a half-axle. The specifications of the structure are presented in Table VII.2.

Changes in behaviour are indicated by changes in the PSI, rutting and deflections (see Figures VII.5, VII.6 and VII.7). No cracking was observed. This test will also be dealt with in detail in a report published by the Centre.

VII.2.4. Tests carried out in Finland

Circular test track of Neste Oy

The cross test is done in two stages (see (4) for description of test facility). First, structures II (bituminous layers 140mm) and III (cement treated base course) were constructed and after one of these is deteriorated, it will be removed and structure I (bituminous layers 60mm) will be constructed. The test will be run until both structures are deteriorated. The structures are as similar as possible to the Nantes test with some exceptions, for example the subgrade is in fine sand (CBR 8).

Figure VII.2

DEFLECTIONS WITH THE BENKELMAN BEAM
(Temperature 20°C)

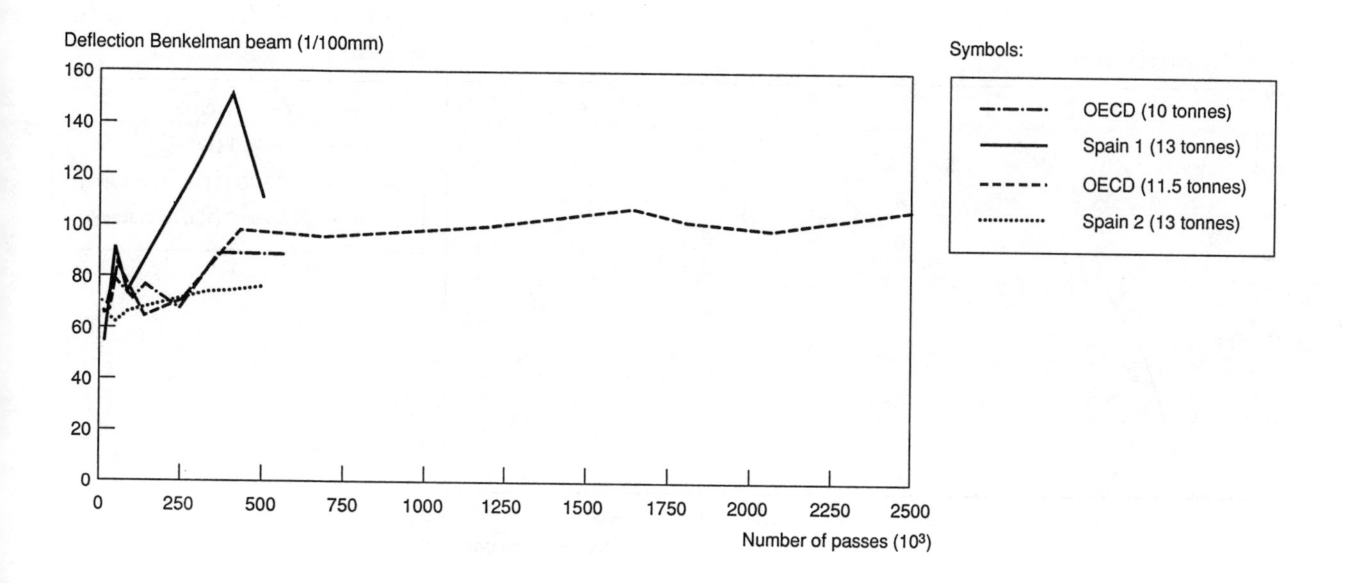

Figure VII.3

DEVELOPMENT OF RUTTING

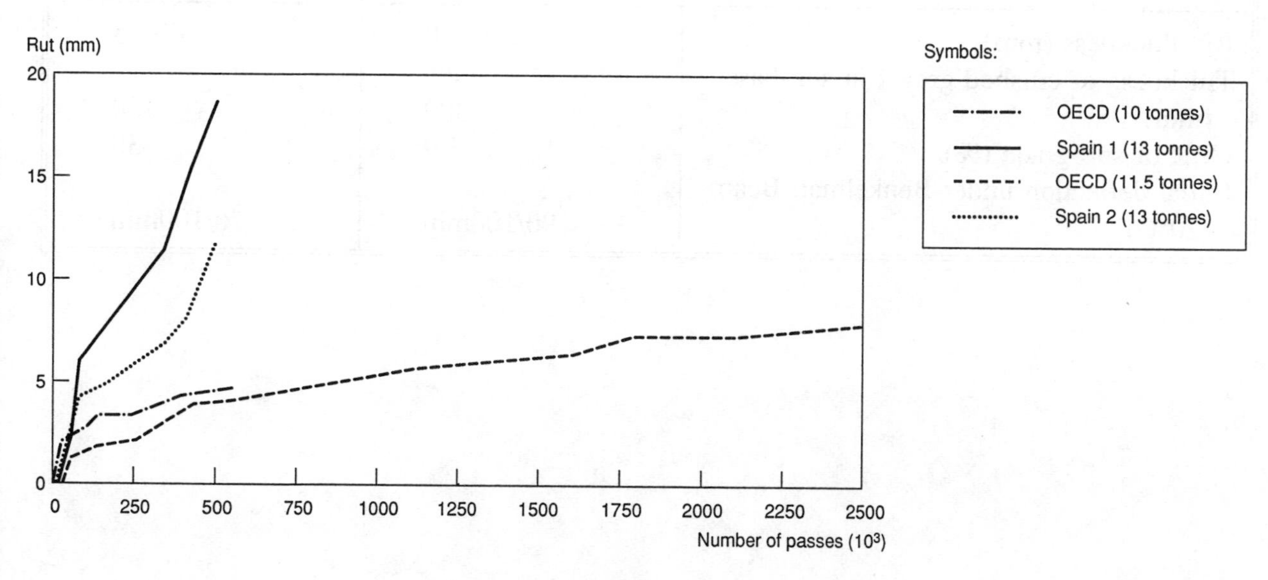

Figure VII.4

DEVELOPMENT OF CRACKING

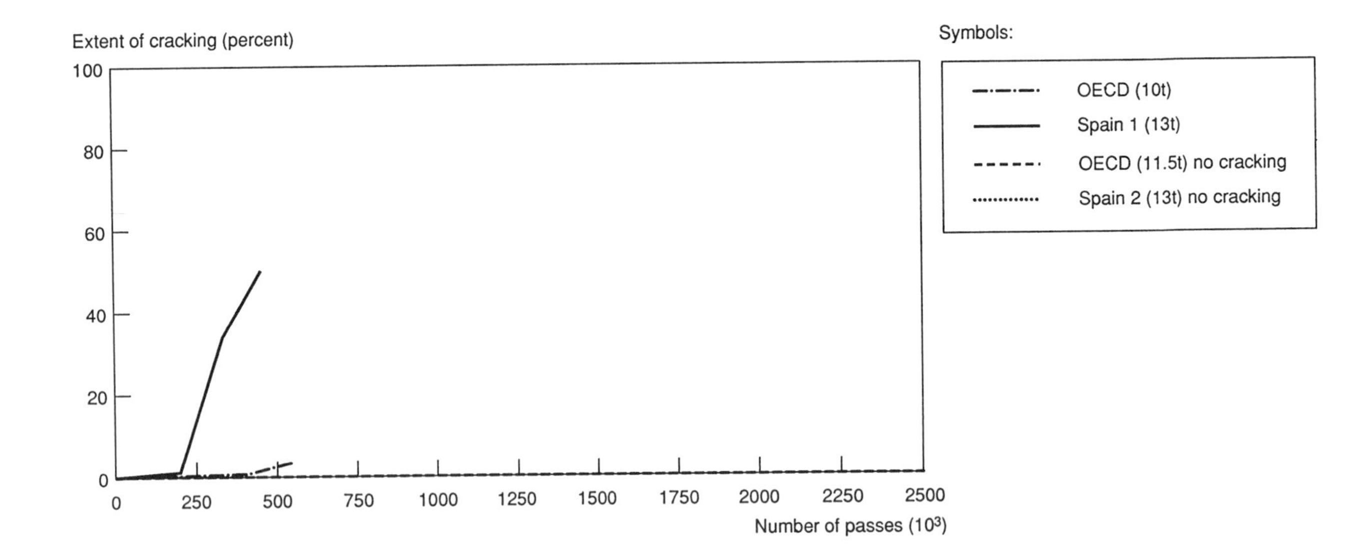

Table VII.2.

COMPARISON OF CERTAIN FEATURES OF THE ZURICH TEST AND FORCE

Test section	Zurich	FORCE: Structure II
Bit. thickness (mm)	60	60-63
Thickness of crushed gravel in sub-base (mm)	300	280
CBR of sub-grade (%)	5-9	-30
Initial deflection under Benkelman Beam (20°C)	90/100mm	70/100mm

Figure VII.5

EVOLUTION OF THE PSI SERVICEABILITY INDEX, TEST OF ZURICH

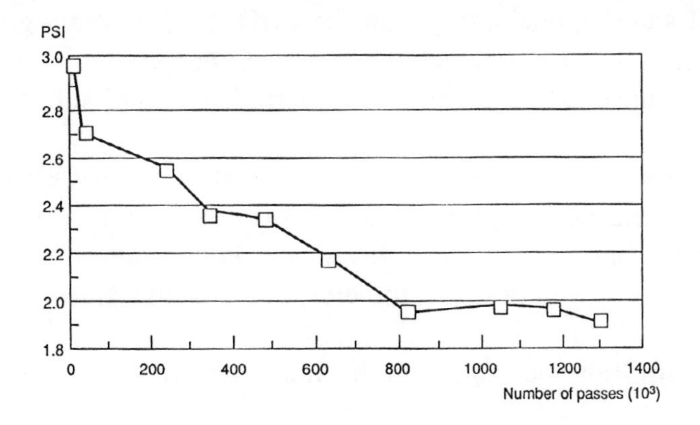

Figure VII.6

DEVELOPMENT OF RUTTING, TEST OF ZURICH

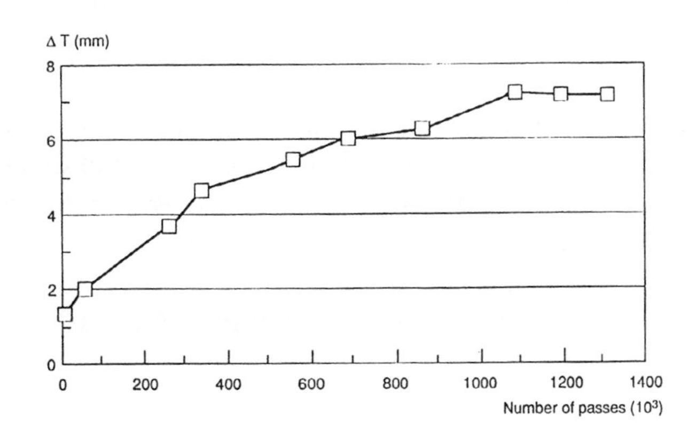

Figure VII.7

DEVELOPMENT OF DEFLECTIONS, TEST OF ZURICH

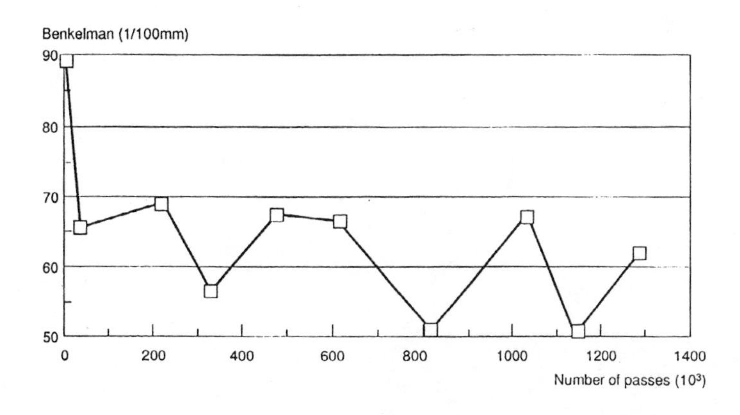

The track is instrumented by the Road and Traffic Laboratory of the Technical Research Centre (VTT). The strain gauge instrumentation for both sections includes three transversal and longitudinal strain gauges at the bottom of the bituminous or cement treated layers and three longitudinal, transversal and diagonal gauges on the surface. The strain gauges are of the type as VTT used in the common OECD Force test at Nantes. Other instrumentation includes deflection gauges and three stress gauges at two levels in unbound layers and subgrade.

The variables used in "point zero" measurements are the effect of speed (5, 15 and 30 km/h), axle loads (30, 50 and 60 kN), transversal position and temperatures from +0°C to 30°C. The temperature (+10°C) and water table level are kept constant during the test. Other measurements included falling weight deflectometer, profiles and plate bearing tests.

More than four million loadings have been applied by November 1990, some rutting but no cracking has been found. The test continues.

The Virttaa test site

All the three FORCE structures were constructed in a test pit where the watertable level can be regulated. The structures are similar to the Neste Oy. The length of each structure is 10 meters. In order to find out the possible effect at the bottom of the test pit, another structure I was constructed outside.

The test structures were instrumented with longitudinal and transversal strain gauges at the bottom of the bound layers and with longitudinal, transversal and diagonal strain gauges at the surface. Pressure cells were installed at two levels in the unbound layer and subgrade and a deflection gauge in each structure.

The structures were constructed during the summer season 1990. Response measurements will be made in 1991.

Chapter VIII

CONCLUSION AND OUTLOOK

The main conclusion from the policy point of view and the most positive achievement of the this joint project is the actual proof that multilateral co-operation in pavement research can be carried out effectively and with concrete results. These should be of particular significance to highway policy makers and research managers.

VIII.1. INTERNATIONAL SCIENTIFIC CO-OPERATION

Although over many years, significant efforts have been made in this sector by a number of international organisations, these tend to be placed in the more comfortable context of expert group meetings and take the form of exchanging technical documents and drafting of synthesis reports. While no-one would question the benefits derived from such collaboration, in the end, it is clear that a benchmark proof of international co-operation exists only in the conduct and completion of substantive joint research work. This is especially important in a domain where the economic stakes are of considerable significance and where direct co-operation and personal involvement at all levels are required, with all the risks that such field research entails, including human behaviour, matters of prestige, etc.

The success of a joint venture of this type depends on the total openness of ideas and access to existing research and human capacities. Such an experiment also leads, by its very nature, to intensive personal commitment of all the participants. This, in fact, is the only guarantee of ultimate success. From this point of view, the FORCE project can be considered to be a complete success.

The aptitude of the OECD Road Transport Research Programmes's structures to set up, manage, conduct and conclude such a test has been clearly demonstrated. The organisation adopted -- in particular an independent project manager on site -- worked well. It can be highly recommended for future experiments of a similar nature. To be recommended also is the hiring of a specialist responsible for analysing the test results and this on a full-time basis for a specified period of time.

International co-operation, in the case of the FORCE project, took on a very specific form with quite practical implications. In fact, the organisational scheme included on-site participation involving, at times simultaneously, research personnel from various countries and organisations and amounting to some 420 man-days - a figure which in itself is indicative of the need to conduct such a test. This working method offered all participants the unique opportunity of gaining first-hand experience which could not have been gained by any other channel.

VIII.2. OVERALL SCIENTIFIC CONCLUSIONS

VIII.2.1. Comparison of the effect of 10 and 11.5 tonne axle loads

A comparison of the performance of pavements under 10 and 11.5 tonne axle loads was a principal aim of the experiment. The results show that the 4th power law constitutes only a general description and approximation of the relative pavement damaging power of axle loads. It must be noted that wide variations to this general rule were found to apply changing continuously with powers from 2 to 9 depending on the degree of pavement deterioration, the criterion used for comparison and the condition of the pavement at the time when the comparison was made. Because of the lack of deterioration in the cement treated pavement structure, only the flexible pavements investigated are covered by this conclusion. Any comparison that one might make solely on the basis of observing the performance of the pavement before it began to deteriorate may be considered not relevant.

VIII.2.2. Experimental framework for future evaluations

The results obtained from the joint test may serve as a reference for all current and future cross testing projects to verify the possibilities of direct application of the results of research and road construction practices from other countries. Such a verification process would be all the more valuable if the cross test conditions were similar to the FORCE project conditions, as concerns the soil and the materials, including the quality of the test pavement construction as well as loading and climatic conditions. In areas where these aspects diverge substantially, a precise knowledge of the parameters will nonetheless enable a more in-depth interpretation of the results as well as clear and logical explanations for any possible differences.

VIII.2.3. Improving the use of measuring instruments (strain gauges)

From this angle, the FORCE project may be considered as a continuation of the co-operation initiated by the Group at the time of the Nardo test undertaken during the first phase of its activity (4). Alongside the detailed results described in this report, mention can also be made to the direct lessons learned in this intricate problem area by all the participants at the Nantes site. Temperature monitoring in the pavement structures was very important here also, whereas, as far as climatic factors, in general, are concerned, it is sufficient to rely on the information available at the neighbouring meteorological stations.

VIII.2.4. Enhancing data processing and communication methods

The collection and management of such large quantities of data is a problem that one does not encounter on a daily basis. A solution is all the more difficult to find, especially if there is a need, as was the case with the FORCE project, to use efficiently and economically the means provided and the personnel allocated within the framework of an activity involving the participation of various organisations. Consequently, it was necessary to allow all the participants access to all the data in order to encourage a greater sense of personal commitment, ensure sound progress with the project, allow individual studies of a general scientific nature to be conducted and specific analyses to be carried out within the framework of cross testing projects. The methods developed within the framework of this project in order to achieve the above-mentioned aims were successful and resolved the problem at hand to the general satisfaction of all concerned; these methods may be able to be used in the future for similar experiments.

VIII.2.5. Progress in the use of pavement performance models

The studies conducted on the use of computerised models for pavement stresses and performance were less comprehensive than planned. This was due to the long delay in having the models delivered, the amount of laboratory data required to make them work and the often incomplete character of certain models as concerns calculating and prediction capacity. Nonetheless, the studies undertaken and the further assessments are likely to provide additional evidence to show that full-scale research conducted under controlled test conditions is the best means of verifying or gauging the models.

VIII.2.6. Other on-going analyses

Next to the above-mentioned conclusions are certain other aspects of the project which are still inconclusive in character. These concern a number of scientific analyses, many of which are still being carried out in close co-operation and whose aim is to further develop and exploit the potential lessons to be drawn from the common test. As emphasized in the chapter on analysis, given the tight time schedule for this work, the results are only preliminary.

The complete results of the experiment have an immense research potential which is only just being exploited. In fact, there is nothing new about this. One only has to consider the example of the AASHO test of the 1950s which even today stimulates many researchers to continue to exploit the immense data pool in order to test new theoretical approaches towards solving problems associated with pavement design and performance. This is the reason why all the data obtained during this test will be made available to all those who wish to analyse them further.

VIII.3. POLICY AND ECONOMIC CONCLUSIONS

VIII.3.1. Improvement of the potential use of research facilities

The very fact that it was possible to implement and conclude such a test is a concrete example of the application of a rational approach in the use of large research facilities at an international level. The different lessons which may still be drawn from this test, either directly through the analysis itself or indirectly through the analysis of on-going or future cross tests, will improve further the potential for the rational use of facilities. Moreover, it should not be forgotten that beyond the setting up of technical bases to allow such a rationalisation, the FORCE project also demonstrated that it is possible to overcome human barriers which often lead to the failure of projects albeit scientifically valid.

VIII.3.2. Clear technical advice on the economic consequences of changing axle load regulations

Despite the fact that while the FORCE project was being conducted the EC had taken a decision towards the unification of the regulations regarding axle loads in international European traffic, discussions on the problem of the road damaging power of heavy trucks are likely to continue for some time. Nonetheless, one of the inferences of the FORCE project is that it supports the basic E.C. decision criterion in the context of present highway rehabilitation cycles. Hence, the basic orientation of the economic evaluations remains valid.

VIII.4. FUTURE DEVELOPMENTS

VIII.4.1. Continuing co-operation

The FORCE project demonstrated to all those involved the value of international collaboration in experiments of this complexity. The experience gained, the well-functioning working method and the exchange of information in the course of the experiment are the major results.

The success of the work of the Group was due to a large extent to the willingness of Member countries to participate in an active manner. Active participation in the project reached a level never attained before and gave proof of the availability of different research bodies for this type of project. As in other sectors, the risk of a potential slow-down of this willingness existed. It should therefore be considered how the active involvement -- in participating and financing -- of a great number of research agencies can be pursued. Future international collaboration should draw heavily on this experience so as to ensure effective and successful execution of experimental projects.

There is increasing interest in various aspects of vehicle/road interaction and work on these topics is proceeding in a number of countries. It is important that both vehicle engineers and highway engineers work closely together to ensure that national and international standards and legislation contribute to the benefits of both vehicle operators and road authorities. The FORCE experiment, its organisation, and the data recorded provide useful reference points for any co-ordinated work on, for instance, dynamic loading, suspension design and the influence of various types of tyres on pavement behaviour.

VIII.4.2. Results from on-going studies

As indicated earlier in this report, the analysis presented here includes consideration of the results available at the time of its drafting. Additional analysis work, based on the overall test results and on results deriving from additional special tests (e.g. gauges placed by individual teams) or from cross tests will continue to provide additional data, contributing to the general understanding and interpretation of the results of the test, reaching a step forward compared to the analysis contained in this report and to the presentation of the test at the occasion of the Conference of May 1991 in La Baule.

Similarly, one of the most successful aspects of the FORCE project was the collection and recording of extensive data on the performance of the pavements and pavement materials. The analyses presented in Chapter VI represent only a small fraction of the analytical work that could be carried out on the available data. It is to be hoped that both participants and non-participants in the experiment will continue to take advantage of the ready access to these data to carry out further analyses.

It is rather difficult, at this stage, to forecast the full potential of the scientific output deriving from these different studies. The availability of all the raw test data for further processing and analysis ensures that a more detailed assessment in the future is possible and should be pursued.

VIII.4.3. Recommendations deriving from the results of the FORCE Project

The results derived from the common test provide a firm and recommendable basis for future activities in a number of fields of application, including:

- -- The organisation and conduct of similar tests carried out in international co-operation;
- -- The organisation and conduct of cross tests on other full-scale test facilities;
- -- The implementation and joint analysis of other accelerated tests;
- -- The conduct of studies on pavement performance and the effects of different types of loadings (in terms of load value and configuration -- axle type and grouping, wheel configuration, tyre type and pressure etc.).

REFERENCES

1. OECD. ROAD TRANSPORT RESEARCH. Heavy Trucks, climate and pavement damage. OECD. Paris, 1988.

2. OECD. ROAD RESEARCH PROGRAMME, Accelerated methods of life testing pavements. OECD. Paris, 1972.

3. ISETH. International Colloquium Full-scale Pavement Tests. 27/28 May 1982. Mitteilung Nov 49. ETH Zurich (Federal Institute of Technology). Zurich, May 1982.

4. OECD. ROAD TRANSPORT RESEARCH. Full-scale pavement tests. OECD. Paris, 1985.

5. SWISS FEDERAL OFFICE OF HIGHWAYS/OECD ROAD TRANSPORT RESEARCH. Strain measurements in bituminous layers. Berne/Paris, 1985.

6. CAVELLIER, M, GODARD, JF and RETOUR, P. New methods developed in France for road network survey. Ann Arbor Conference. Ann Arbor, 1987.

7. ECKMANN B. ESSO MOEBIUS USER'S MANUAL, MSA B-0.350. June 1990.

8. AZIBERT, C, CELARD, B and LOMBARDI B. Machine d'essai de fluage - Machine de fluage dynamique pour enrobés bitumineux. Revue Générale des Routes et Aérodromes, no. 522. Paris, July 1976.

9. WITCZAK, M.W. Design of full-depth asphalt pavements. Third International Conference on the Structural Design of Asphalt Pavements. London, 1972.

Annex A

SPECIFICATIONS AND STANDARDS

A.1. SPECIFICATIONS FOR MATERIALS AND CONSTRUCTION STANDARDS OF TEST PAVEMENTS

The GNT (Grave Non-Traitée) O/31.5

A O/31.5 mm graded rock will be employed. Its aggregate content will be completely crushed. The contractor will reconstitute the rock in a mixer.

The responsible organisation will use a formula that will have been previously employed for the manufacturer of a O/31.5 rock for use on road-works. This formula, together with the associated references will be submitted for the approval of the administrative authority.

The responsible organisation will attempt to remain within the limits given in the following table.

Sieve size mm	Per cent passing	
	Minimum	Maximum
31.5	85	100
20	72	92
14	59	80
10	50	71
6.3	40	60
4	32	52
2	22	40
1	15	30
0.5	10	20
0.2	5	13
0.08	4	8

The sand equivalent for the O/2 fraction converted to 10 per cent of fines will be not less than 50.

The Los Angeles coefficient will be not greater than 25.
The wet MICRO DEVAL will be not greater than 2O.

The water content of the rock on manufacture must be within ±l per cent of the "Modified Proctor Optimum" MPO water content. In the case of a long transport distance, bad weather or a long storage time the responsible organisation must ensure that the MPO water content is maintained.

If the contractor is obliged to store the rock he must advise the administrative authority of the actions he proposes to take with regard to:

-- The preparation of the surface to be used for storage.
-- The prevention of segregation.
-- Maintaining the water content and cleanliness of the material.

Before making any arrangements for the delivery of part of the stock of rock the contractor must advise the administrative authority of the actions that he proposes to take with regard to:

-- The prevention of segregation.
-- Maintaining the cleanliness of the material.

A.2. SPECIFICATIONS FOR BITUMINOUS MATERIALS

A O/10 bituminous mixture will be employed. The aggregate will be completely crushed.

The sand equivalent for the O/2 fraction converted to 10 per pent of fines will be not less than 50.

The aggregates will have a Los Angeles coefficient of not more than 2O.

The contractor will supply the administrative authority concerned on request with a 1-litre sample of the binder being employed for each day of manufacture.

The responsible organisation will make up the mixture according to the NO 2 Maraîchères quarry formula. This formula is as follows:

6/10	43 per cent
2/6	15 per cent
0/2	40.5 per cent
Added fines (Noubleau)	1.5 per cent
Bitumen	60/70
Bitumen content	6.45 per cent

The contractor will apply a single layer surface dressing to all road bases before applying a layer of the bituminous mixture.

A.3. STANDARDS FOR LAYING THE ROAD BASE AND SURFACING

A.3.1. Road bases

The surface must have a slope of 2 per cent towards the centre of the circuit.

The heights with respect to the centre of the anchoring base of the central turret and at a radius of 17.5 metres from that centre must be as follows:

- Structure I: + 50 mm
- Structure II: - 10 mm
- Structure III: + 50 mm

These heights must be maintained to within ± 20 mm for at least 95 per cent of the points checked. The difference in height between any two points that will have been checked must not be greater than 20 mm. The cross section profiles must not deviate by more than 20 mm from the average slope.

The in-situ density of the pavement layers will be not less than 95 per cent of the modified proctor optimum density.

A.3.2. Surfacing

The surface of the bituminous concrete layer must form a plane inclined towards the centre of the circuit. The mean slope will amount to 2 per cent.

The height at a radius of 17.5m will amount to +O.11m. These dimensions are always to be measured from the centre of the anchoring block of the rotary test rig turret.

These dimensions must be correct to within ± 20 mm for at least 95 per cent of the points checked. The difference in height between two points must not be greater than 20 mm and the transverse cross sections must not deviate by more than 20 mm from the mean slope.

The in-situ density must be at least equal to the density obtained with the Gyratory Compaction Test. Thus, C60 for a 60 mm thickness = 94.7 per cent for at least 95 per cent of the measurements.

Annex B

TEST PHASES, MEASUREMENTS AND OVERLAYS

PROGRAMME GENERAL

DATE [aammjj]	HEURE [hhmm]	TOURS [nb]	TOURS CUMULES [nb]	CHARGE R=16 m [t]	CHARGE R=19 m [t]	CHARGES RELLES CUMULEES R=16 m [nb]	CHARGES RELLES CUMULEES R=19 m [nb]	VITESSE [t/min]	POSITION [1...11]	EVENEMENTS TRAVAUX	MESURES
881017	-	-	-	-	-	-	-	-	-	DEBUT PHASE 1	
881017	-	-	-	-	-	-	-	-	-	DEBUT DES TERRASSEMENTS	
881125	-	-	-	-	-	-	-	-	-	POSE BETON BITUMINEUX	
881222	-	-	-	-	-	-	-	-	-	MISE EN PLACE DU MANEGE	
881223	930	0	0	0.0	13.0	0	0	10	VAR		
	1010	331	331	0.0	13.0	0	1324	10	VAR		
	1325	570	901	0.0	13.0	0	3604	10	VAR		
	1415	512	1413	0.0	13.0	0	5652	10	VAR		
	1500	24	1437	0.0	13.0	0	5748	10	VAR		
890106	830	0	1437	0.0	13.0	0	5748	10	VAR		
	1030	301	1738	0.0	13.0	0	6952	10	VAR		
	1200	788	2526	0.0	13.0	0	10104	10	VAR		
890208	1000	0	2526	10.0	11.5	0	10104	3	6		
	1500	752	3278	10.0	11.5	1504	11608	3	6		
890213	1100	0	3278	10.0	11.5	1504	11608	2.5	6		
	1435	278	3556	10.0	11.5	2060	12164	7.5	6		
	1700	324	3880	10.0	11.5	2708	12812	7.5	6		
890214	1500	0	3880	10.0	11.5	2708	12812	10	VAR		
	1700	628	4508	10.0	11.5	3964	14068	10	VAR		
890214	-	-	-	-	-	-	-	-	-	FIN PHASE 1 - DEBUT PHASE 2	
890215	1530	0	4508	10.0	11.5	3964	14068	VAR	VAR		DEBUT DU POINT ZERO INTERNATIONAL
	1900	1579	6087	10.0	11.5	7122	17226	VAR	VAR		
890216	1500	0	6087	10.0	11.5	7122	17226	VAR	VAR		
	1900	1757	7844	10.0	11.5	10636	20740	VAR	VAR		
890217	900	0	7844	10.0	11.5	10636	20740	7.5	6		
	1200	162	8006	10.0	11.5	10960	21064	7.5	6		
890220	1000	0	8006	11.5	10.0	10960	21064	4	6		
	1100	273	8279	11.5	10.0	11506	21610	10	6		
	1200	517	8796	11.5	10.0	12540	22644	10	6		
	1530	0	8796	8.2	13.0	12540	22644	4	6		
	1645	282	9078	8.2	13.0	13104	23208	10	6		
	1800	474	9552	8.2	13.0	14052	24156	10	6		
890221	1400	0	9552	13.0	8.2	14052	24156	4	6		
	1540	782	10334	13.0	8.2	15616	25720	10	6		
	1550	97	10431	13.0	8.2	15810	25914	4	6		
	1610	86	10517	13.0	8.2	15982	26086	4	6		
890222	1100	0	10517	10.0	11.5	15982	26086	VAR	VAR		
	1200	1619	12136	10.0	11.5	19220	29324	VAR	VAR		
	1440	0	12136	10.0	11.5	19220	29324	VAR	VAR		
	1730	915	13051	10.0	11.5	21050	31154	VAR	VAR		
890223	945	0	13051	10.0	11.5	21050	31154	VAR	VAR		
	1130	1448	14499	10.0	11.5	23946	34050	VAR	VAR		
890228	1000	0	14499	10.0	11.5	23946	34050	3	6		
	1200	487	14986	10.0	11.5	24920	35024	3	6		
	1400	0	14986	10.0	11.5	24920	35024	3	6		
	1700	312	15298	10.0	11.5	25544	35648	3	6		
890302	1500	0	15298	10.0	11.5	25544	35648	VAR	6		
	1700	800	16098	10.0	11.5	27144	37248	VAR	6		
890306	930	0	16098	10.0	11.5	27144	37248	VAR	VAR		
	1200	938	17036	10.0	11.5	29020	39124	VAR	VAR		
	1300	0	17036	10.0	11.5	29020	39124	VAR	VAR		
	1600	1131	18167	10.0	11.5	31282	41386	VAR	VAR		
890307	900	0	18167	10.0	11.5	31282	41386	VAR	VAR		
	1200	1134	19301	10.0	11.5	33550	43654	VAR	VAR		
	1345	0	19301	10.0	11.5	33550	43654	VAR	VAR		
	1615	863	20164	10.0	11.5	35276	45380	VAR	VAR		
890308	900	0	20164	10.0	11.5	35276	45380	VAR	VAR		
	1200	843	21007	10.0	11.5	36962	47066	VAR	VAR		
	1400	245	21252	10.0	11.5	37452	47556	VAR	VAR		
	1500	429	21681	10.0	11.5	38310	48414	VAR	VAR		

890309	1000	0	21681	10.0	13.0	38310	48414	VAR	VAR		
	1100	310	21991	10.0	13.0	38930	49034	VAR	VAR		
	1200	310	22301	10.0	13.0	39550	49654	VAR	VAR		
	1400	0	22301	10.0	13.0	39550	49654	VAR	VAR		
	1515	310	22611	10.0	13.0	40170	50274	VAR	VAR		
	1630	308	22919	10.0	13.0	40786	50890	VAR	VAR		
890310	1000	0	22919	11.5	10.0	40786	50890	VAR	VAR		
	1200	246	23165	11.5	10.0	41278	51382	VAR	VAR		
890313	900	0	23165	11.5	10.0	41278	51382	10	VAR		
	1030	340	23505	11.5	10.0	41958	52062	10	VAR		
	1200	340	23845	11.5	10.0	42638	52742	10	VAR		
	1320	0	23845	11.5	10.0	42638	52742	10	VAR		
	1435	340	24185	11.5	10.0	43318	53422	10	VAR		
	1550	341	24526	11.5	10.0	44000	54104	10	VAR		
890314	900	0	24526	8.2	13.0	44000	54104	10	VAR		
	945	210	24736	8.2	13.0	44420	54524	10	VAR		
	1030	210	24946	8.2	13.0	44840	54944	10	VAR		
	1115	210	25156	8.2	13.0	45260	55364	10	VAR		
	1200	211	25367	8.2	13.0	45682	55786	10	VAR		FIN DES MESURES POINT ZERO OCDE
890314	.	.	.	.	.	.	.	.	.	FIN PHASE 2	
890321	900	0	25367	10.0	11.5	45682	55786	10	VAR	DEBUT PHASE 3	
	930	438	25805	10.0	11.5	46558	56662	10	VAR		
	1630	0	25805	10.0	11.5	46558	56662	10	VAR		
890322	700	7974	33779	10.0	11.5	62506	72610	10	VAR		
	1315	0	33779	10.0	11.5	62506	72610	10	VAR		
890322	.	.	.	.	.	.	.	.	.		FISSURATION 01
890323	800	11197	44976	10.0	11.5	84900	95004	10	VAR		
	1300	0	44976	10.0	11.5	84900	95004	10	VAR		
890323	.	.	.	.	.	.	.	.	.		FISSURATION 01
	2400	6338	51314	10.0	11.5	97576	107680	10	VAR		
890324	1130	0	51314	10.0	11.5	97576	107680	10	VAR		
	1600	2878	54192	10.0	11.5	103332	113436	10	VAR		
890328	.	.	.	.	.	.	.	.	.		FISSURATION 01 ET 11
890329	1130	0	54192	10.0	11.5	103332	113436	10	VAR		
	1200	351	54543	10.0	11.5	104034	114138	10	VAR		
890330	1030	0	54543	10.0	11.5	104034	114138	10	VAR		
	1600	1332	55875	10.0	11.5	106698	116802	10	VAR		
890404	1100	0	55875	10.0	11.5	106698	116802	10	VAR		
	1615	2941	58816	10.0	11.5	112580	122684	10	VAR		
890405	1200	0	58816	10.0	11.5	112580	122684	10	VAR		
	1630	2462	61278	10.0	11.5	117504	127608	10	VAR		
890406	1030	0	61278	10.0	11.5	117504	127608	10	VAR		
	1640	3668	64946	10.0	11.5	124840	134944	10	VAR		
890407	830	0	64946	10.0	11.5	124840	134944	10	VAR		
	1620	4406	69352	10.0	11.5	133652	143756	10	VAR		
890410	.	.	.	.	.	.	.	.	.		FISSURATION 01 ET 11
890414	830	0	69352	10.0	11.5	133652	143756	10	VAR		
	1635	4613	73965	10.0	11.5	142878	152982	10	VAR		
890417	900	0	73965	10.0	11.5	142878	152982	10	VAR		
	1625	4325	78290	10.0	11.5	151528	161632	10	VAR		
890418	930	0	78290	10.0	11.5	151528	161632	10	VAR		
	2245	7579	85869	10.0	11.5	166686	176790	10	VAR		
890419	930	0	85869	10.0	11.5	166686	176790	10	VAR		
890419	.	.	.	.	.	.	.	.	.		FISSURATION 01 ET 11
890420	800	13303	99172	10.0	11.5	193292	203396	10	VAR		
	1645	4295	103467	10.0	11.5	201882	211986	10	VAR		
890421	840	0	103467	10.0	11.5	201882	211986	10	VAR		
	1630	4309	107776	10.0	11.5	210500	220604	10	VAR		
890424	.	.	.	.	.	.	.	.	.		FISSURATION 01 ET 11
890424	800	0	107776	10.0	11.5	210500	220604	10	VAR		
	815	70	107846	10.0	11.5	210640	220744	10	VAR		
	1130	0	107846	10.0	11.5	210640	220744	10	VAR		
890425	810	12286	120132	10.0	11.5	235212	245316	10	VAR		
	1015	0	120132	10.0	11.5	235212	245316	10	VAR		
	1620	3600	123732	10.0	11.5	242412	252516	10	VAR		
890426	800	0	123732	10.0	11.5	242412	252516	10	VAR		
	1615	2692	126424	10.0	11.5	247796	257900	10	VAR		
890427	1600	318	126742	10.0	11.5	248432	258536	10	VAR	FIN PHASE 3	
890427	.	.	.	.	.	.	.	.	.		FISSURATION 01, 11 ET 13

890503	1345	0	126742	10.0	0.0	248432	258536	10	VAR	DEBUT PHASE 4
	1530	694	127436	10.0	0.0	251208	258536	10	VAR	
890505	900	0	127436	10.0	0.0	251208	258536	10	VAR	
	1135	1381	128817	10.0	0.0	256732	258536	10	VAR	
890509	1000	0	128817	10.0	0.0	256732	258536	10	VAR	
	1145	949	129766	10.0	0.0	260528	258536	10	VAR	
	1630	0	129766	10.0	0.0	260528	258536	10	VAR	
890511	800	23445	153211	10.0	0.0	354308	258536	10	VAR	
	845	0	153211	10.0	0.0	354308	258536	10	VAR	
	1500	3708	156919	10.0	0.0	369140	258536	10	VAR	
890512	800	0	156919	10.0	0.0	369140	258536	10	VAR	
	1200	1116	158035	10.0	0.0	373604	258536	10	VAR	
890512	-	-	-	-	-	-	-	-	-	FISSURATION 11 ET 13
890516	1635	0	158035	10.0	0.0	373604	258536	10	VAR	
890517	930	10146	168181	10.0	0.0	414188	258536	10	VAR	
	1640	0	168181	10.0	0.0	414188	258536	10	VAR	
890518	1400	4069	172250	10.0	0.0	430464	258536	10	VAR	
	1530	0	172250	10.0	0.0	430464	258536	10	VAR	
890519	930	10754	183004	10.0	0.0	473480	258536	10	VAR	
890519	-	-	-	-	-	-	-	-	-	FISSURATION 11 ET 13
	1630	0	183004	10.0	0.0	473480	258536	10	VAR	
890520	630	8442	191446	10.0	0.0	507248	258536	10	VAR	
	1700	0	191446	10.0	0.0	507248	258536	10	VAR	
	1630	643	192089	10.0	0.0	509820	258536	10	VAR	
890521	830	0	192089	10.0	0.0	509820	258536	10	VAR	
	900	78	192167	10.0	0.0	510132	258536	10	VAR	
	1800	4340	196507	10.0	0.0	527492	258536	10	VAR	
	1830	0	196507	10.0	0.0	527492	258536	10	VAR	
890522	830	8388	204895	10.0	0.0	561044	258536	10	VAR	
890522	-	-	-	-	-	-	-	-	-	FISSURATION 11 ET 13
890525	800	0	204895	10.0	11.5	561044	258536	10	VAR	
	915	508	205403	10.0	11.5	562060	259552	10	VAR	
890529	930	0	205403	10.0	11.5	562060	259552	VAR	VAR	
	1530	887	206290	10.0	11.5	563834	261326	10	VAR	
890530	830	0	206290	10.0	11.5	563834	261326	10	VAR	
	1700	4712	211002	10.0	11.5	573258	270750	10	VAR	FIN PHASE 4
890605	-	-	-	-	-	-	-	-	-	RENFORCEMENT PLANCHE 01
890605	-	-	-	-	-	-	-	-	-	DEBUT PHASE 5
890608	1600	0	211002	0.0	11.5	573258	270750	10	VAR	
	1630	201	211203	0.0	11.5	573258	271554	10	VAR	
890609	1000	0	211203	0.0	11.5	573258	271554	0.5	VAR	
	1100	68	211271	0.0	11.5	573258	271826	10	VAR	
890612	900	0	211271	0.0	11.5	573258	271826	10	VAR	
	1100	1225	212496	0.0	11.5	573258	276726	10	VAR	
890613	830	0	212496	0.0	11.5	573258	276726	10	VAR	
890614	830	14277	226773	0.0	11.5	573258	333834	10	VAR	
	900	0	226773	0.0	11.5	573258	333834	10	VAR	
890616	830	27031	253804	0.0	11.5	573258	441958	10	VAR	
890620	900	0	253804	0.0	11.5	573258	441958	10	VAR	
	2100	6969	260773	0.0	11.5	573258	469834	10	VAR	
890621	900	0	260773	0.0	11.5	573258	469834	10	VAR	
890622	530	11476	272249	0.0	11.5	573258	515738	10	VAR	
	1400	0	272249	0.0	11.5	573258	515738	10	VAR	
890623	1000	11100	283349	0.0	11.5	573258	560138	10	VAR	
	1620	0	283349	0.0	11.5	573258	560138	10	VAR	
890623	-	-	-	-	-	-	-	-	-	FISSURATION 03
890624	1400	11377	294726	0.0	11.5	573258	605646	10	VAR	
	1500	0	294726	0.0	11.5	573258	605646	10	VAR	
890625	1830	13915	308641	0.0	11.5	573258	661306	10	VAR	
890627	930	0	308641	0.0	11.5	573258	661306	10	VAR	
	1730	4304	312945	0.0	11.5	573258	678522	10	VAR	
890628	930	0	312945	0.0	11.5	573258	678522	10	VAR	
	1030	596	313541	0.0	11.5	573258	680906	10	VAR	
890629	1615	0	313541	0.0	11.5	573258	680906	10	VAR	
	1930	2148	315689	0.0	11.5	573258	689498	10	VAR	
890630	815	0	315689	0.0	11.5	573258	689498	10	VAR	
890703	815	41899	357588	0.0	11.5	573258	857094	10	VAR	
890703	-	-	-	-	-	-	-	-	-	FISSURATION 03
	945	0	357588	0.0	11.5	573258	857094	10	VAR	

890704	900	13208	370796	0.0	11.5	573258	909926	VAR	VAR	
	1115	1107	371903	0.0	11.5	573258	914354	10	VAR	
890706	1130	27858	399761	0.0	11.5	573258	1025786	10	VAR	
	1400	0	399761	0.0	11.5	573258	1025786	10	VAR	
890707	745	10440	410201	0.0	11.5	573258	1067546	10	VAR	
890707	.	.	.	.	.	.	.	.	.	FISSURATION 03
	1300	0	410201	0.0	11.5	573258	1067546	10	VAR	
890708	600	10747	420948	0.0	11.5	573258	1110534	10	VAR	
	1000	0	420948	0.0	11.5	573258	1110534	10	VAR	
	1400	2378	423326	0.0	11.5	573258	1120046	10	VAR	
890710	820	21894	445220	0.0	11.5	573258	1207622	10	VAR	
890710	.	.	.	.	.	.	.	.	.	FISSURATION 03
	1645	0	445220	0.0	11.5	573258	1207622	10	VAR	
	1715	246	445466	0.0	11.5	573258	1208606	10	VAR	
890711	830	0	445466	0.0	11.5	573258	1208606	10	VAR	
890712	645	13306	458772	0.0	11.5	573258	1261830	10	VAR	
	915	0	458772	0.0	11.5	573258	1261830	10	VAR	
890713	800	13639	472411	0.0	11.5	573258	1316386	10	VAR	
890713	.	.	.	.	.	.	.	.	.	FISSURATION 03
	1030	0	472411	0.0	11.5	573258	1316386	10	VAR	
890716	600	40387	512798	0.0	11.5	573258	1477934	10	VAR	
	1030	0	512798	0.0	11.5	573258	1477934	10	VAR	
890718	600	24903	537701	0.0	11.5	573258	1577546	10	VAR	
	915	0	537701	0.0	11.5	573258	1577546	10	VAR	
890719	800	13316	551017	0.0	11.5	573258	1630810	10	VAR	
	1630	0	551017	0.0	11.5	573258	1630810	10	VAR	
890720	800	9303	560320	0.0	11.5	573258	1668022	10	VAR	
890720	.	.	.	.	.	.	.	.	.	FISSURATION 03
890721	1045	0	560320	0.0	11.5	573258	1668022	9.5	VAR	
890722	2000	17904	578224	0.0	11.5	573258	1739638	9.5	VAR	
890723	1100	0	578224	0.0	11.5	573258	1739638	9.5	VAR	
890724	815	11702	589926	0.0	11.5	573258	1786446	9.5	VAR	
890725	900	0	589926	0.0	11.5	573258	1786446	10	VAR	
	1100	1032	590958	0.0	11.5	573258	1790574	10	VAR	
890727	.	.	.	.	.	.	.	.	.	FIN PHASE 5 - DEBUT PHASE 6
890727	.	.	.	.	.	.	.	.	.	RENFORCEMENT PLANCHE 03
890731	1600	0	590958	0.0	11.5	573258	1790574	10	VAR	
890801	1610	14228	605186	0.0	11.5	573258	1847486	10	VAR	
890802	1600	0	605186	0.0	11.5	573258	1847486	10	VAR	
	1700	610	605796	0.0	11.5	573258	1849926	10	VAR	
890803	945	0	605796	0.0	11.5	573258	1849926	VAR	VAR	
	1045	625	606421	0.0	11.5	573258	1852426	10	VAR	
890804	800	11321	617742	0.0	11.5	573258	1897710	10	VAR	
	900	600	618342	0.0	11.5	573258	1900110	VAR	VAR	
	1100	0	618342	0.0	11.5	573258	1900110	10	VAR	
890805	1020	13849	632191	0.0	11.5	573258	1955506	10	VAR	
	1100	0	632191	0.0	11.5	573258	1955506	10	VAR	
890807	800	22713	654904	0.0	11.5	573258	2046358	10	VAR	
	1300	0	654904	0.0	11.5	573258	2046358	10	VAR	
890808	810	11116	666020	0.0	11.5	573258	2090822	10	VAR	
	1300	0	666020	0.0	11.5	573258	2090822	10	VAR	
890809	950	11824	677844	0.0	11.5	573258	2138118	10	VAR	
	1015	0	677844	0.0	11.5	573258	2138118	10	VAR	
890811	1530	30946	708790	0.0	11.5	573258	2261902	10	VAR	
890816	1030	0	708790	0.0	11.5	573258	2261902	10	VAR	
890817	1900	18944	727734	0.0	11.5	573258	2337678	10	VAR	
890818	1130	0	727734	0.0	11.5	573258	2337678	10	VAR	
890819	1030	13075	740809	0.0	11.5	573258	2389978	10	VAR	
	2000	5519	746328	0.0	11.5	573258	2412054	10	VAR	
890820	930	0	746328	0.0	11.5	573258	2412054	10	VAR	
890821	500	11758	758086	0.0	11.5	573258	2459086	10	VAR	
	1500	0	758086	0.0	11.5	573258	2459086	10	VAR	
890822	815	10349	768435	0.0	11.5	573258	2500482	10	VAR	
890824	1615	0	768435	0.0	11.5	573258	2500482	10	VAR	
890825	1000	10655	779090	0.0	11.5	573258	2543102	10	VAR	
	1500	0	779090	0.0	11.5	573258	2543102	10	VAR	
	1610	622	779712	0.0	11.5	573258	2545590	10	VAR	
890829	1630	0	779712	0.0	11.5	573258	2545590	10	VAR	
	2230	3488	783200	0.0	11.5	573258	2559542	10	VAR	

890830	1130	0	783200	0.0	11.5	573258	2559542	10	VAR	
	1915	4430	787630	0.0	11.5	573258	2577262	10	VAR	
890831	815	0	787630	0.0	11.5	573258	2577262	10	VAR	
890901	800	13542	801172	0.0	11.5	573258	2631430	10	VAR	
	1100	0	801172	0.0	11.5	573258	2631430	10	VAR	
890902	910	12724	813896	0.0	11.5	573258	2682326	10	MANU	
	1010	59	813955	0.0	11.5	573258	2682562	10	MANU	
	1930	5032	818987	0.0	11.5	573258	2702690	10	MANU	
890903	850	8009	826996	0.0	11.5	573258	2734726	10	MANU	
	915	0	826996	0.0	11.5	573258	2734726	10	MANU	
	1900	5829	832825	0.0	11.5	573258	2758042	10	MANU	
890905	1630	0	832825	0.0	11.5	573258	2758042	10	MANU	
	1700	337	833162	0.0	11.5	573258	2759390	10	MANU	
890906	835	0	833162	0.0	11.5	573258	2759390	10	MANU	
890907	1530	18031	851193	0.0	11.5	573258	2831514	10	MANU	
	1630	0	851193	0.0	11.5	573258	2831514	10	MANU	
890908	800	9409	860602	0.0	11.5	573258	2869150	10	MANU	
	1500	0	860602	0.0	11.5	573258	2869150	10	MANU	
890909	2230	19084	879686	0.0	11.5	573258	2945486	10	MANU	
890910	900	0	879686	0.0	11.5	573258	2945486	10	MANU	
890914	830	54904	934590	0.0	11.5	573258	3165102	10	MANU	
	1500	0	934590	0.0	11.5	573258	3165102	10	MANU	
890915	815	10986	945576	0.0	11.5	573258	3209046	10	MANU	
	930	0	945576	0.0	11.5	573258	3209046	10	MANU	
	1645	3495	949071	0.0	11.5	573258	3223026	10	MANU	
890918	1000	0	949071	0.0	11.5	573258	3223026	10	MANU	
890919	1030	14525	963596	0.0	11.5	573258	3281126	10	MANU	
	1130	0	963596	0.0	11.5	573258	3281126	10	MANU	
890920	1645	12932	976528	0.0	11.5	573258	3332854	10	MANU	
890921	900	0	976528	0.0	11.5	573258	3332854	10	MANU	
	945	134	976662	0.0	11.5	573258	3333390	VAR	MANU	
	1500	0	976662	0.0	11.5	573258	3333390	VAR	MANU	
	1700	1017	977679	0.0	11.5	573258	3337458	VAR	MANU	
890922	1010	0	977679	0.0	11.5	573258	3337458	10	MANU	
	1600	2731	980410	0.0	11.5	573258	3348382	10	MANU	
890925	1130	0	980410	0.0	11.5	573258	3348382	10	MANU	
890926	1100	13886	994296	0.0	11.5	573258	3403926	10	MANU	
	1400	0	994296	0.0	11.5	573258	3403926	10	MANU	
	2330	5400	999696	0.0	11.5	573258	3425526	10	MANU	
890928	800	0	999696	0.0	11.5	573258	3425526	10	MANU	
	1210	1909	1001605	0.0	11.5	573258	3433162	VAR	MANU	FIN PHASE 6
891005	1015	0	1001605	0.0	13.0	573258	3433162	10	MANU	DEBUT PHASE 7
	2245	6260	1007865	0.0	13.0	573258	3458202	10	MANU	
891006	1100	0	1007865	0.0	13.0	573258	3458202	10	MANU	
891011	845	69917	1077782	0.0	13.0	573258	3737870	10	MANU	
	1000	0	1077782	0.0	13.0	573258	3737870	10	MANU	
891012	1630	17553	1095335	0.0	13.0	573258	3808082	10	MANU	
891016	1630	0	1095335	0.0	13.0	573258	3808082	10	MANU	
891017	800	9068	1104403	0.0	13.0	573258	3844354	10	MANU	
891030	800	2327	1106730	0.0	VAR	573258	3853662	VAR	MANU	
	1015	0	1106730	0.0	VAR	573258	3853662	VAR	MANU	
	1150	858	1107588	0.0	VAR	573258	3857094	10	MANU	
891030	-	-	-	-	-	-	-	-	-	FISSURATION 02
891102	850	0	1107588	0.0	VAR	573258	3857094	10	MANU	
	1645	264	1107852	0.0	VAR	573258	3858150	VAR	MANU	
891103	830	0	1107852	0.0	VAR	573258	3858150	VAR	MANU	
	1000	469	1108321	0.0	VAR	573258	3860026	VAR	MANU	
	1300	0	1108321	0.0	VAR	573258	3860026	10	MANU	
	1515	1093	1109414	0.0	13.0	573258	3864398	10	MANU	
891105	730	24412	1133826	0.0	13.0	573258	3962046	10	MANU	
	1115	0	1133826	0.0	13.0	573258	3962046	10	MANU	
891105	2000	5030	1138856	0.0	11.5	573258	3982166	10	MANU	FIN PHASE 7 ET DE L'EXPERIENCE

TOTAL DES TOURS EFFECTUES	1138856
TOTAL DES CHARGES POUR R=16 METRES	573258
TOTAL DES CHARGES POUR R=19 METRES	3982166
TOTAL DES CHARGES APPLIQUEES	4555424

Annex C

CLIMATIC DATA

Figure C. 1

WIND SPEED

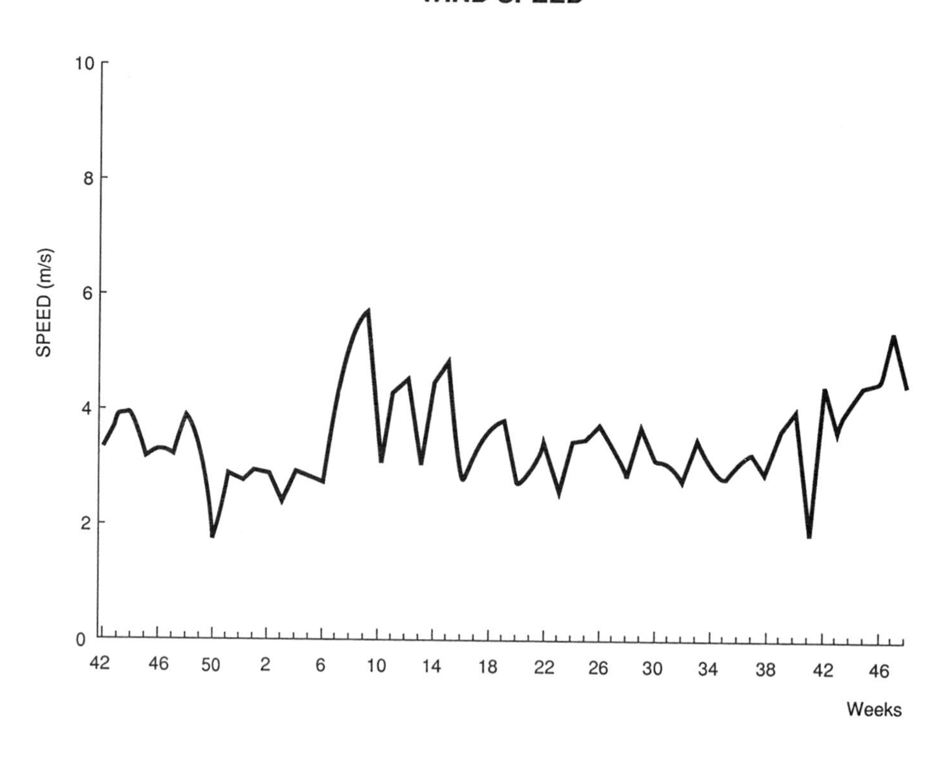

Figure C. 2

RELATIVE HUMIDITY

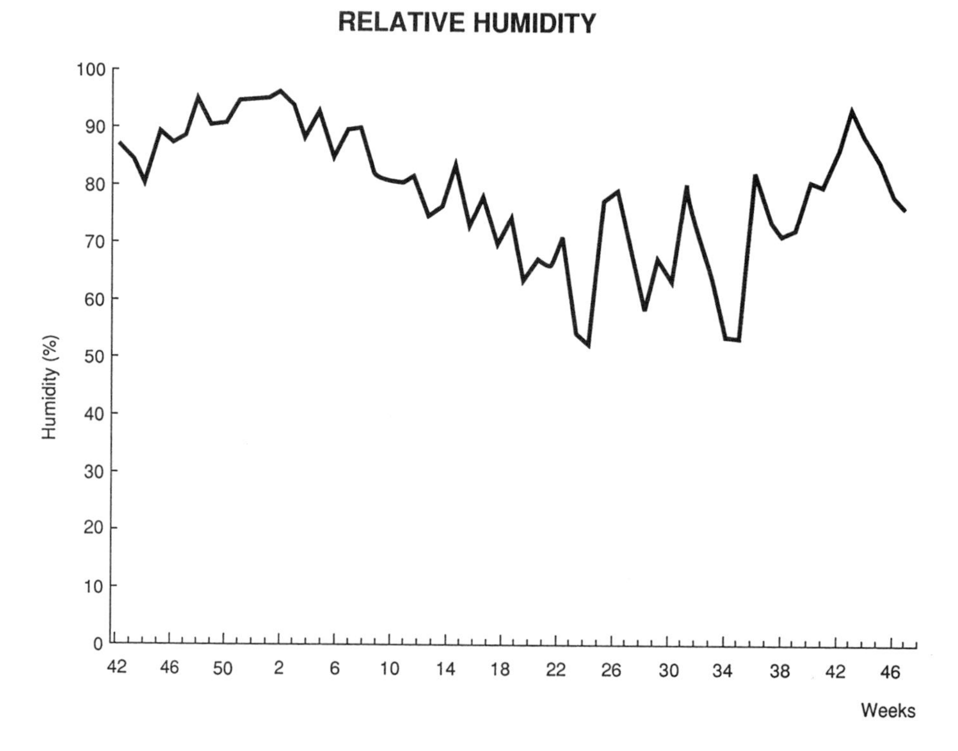

Figure C. 3

SOIL TEMPERATURE

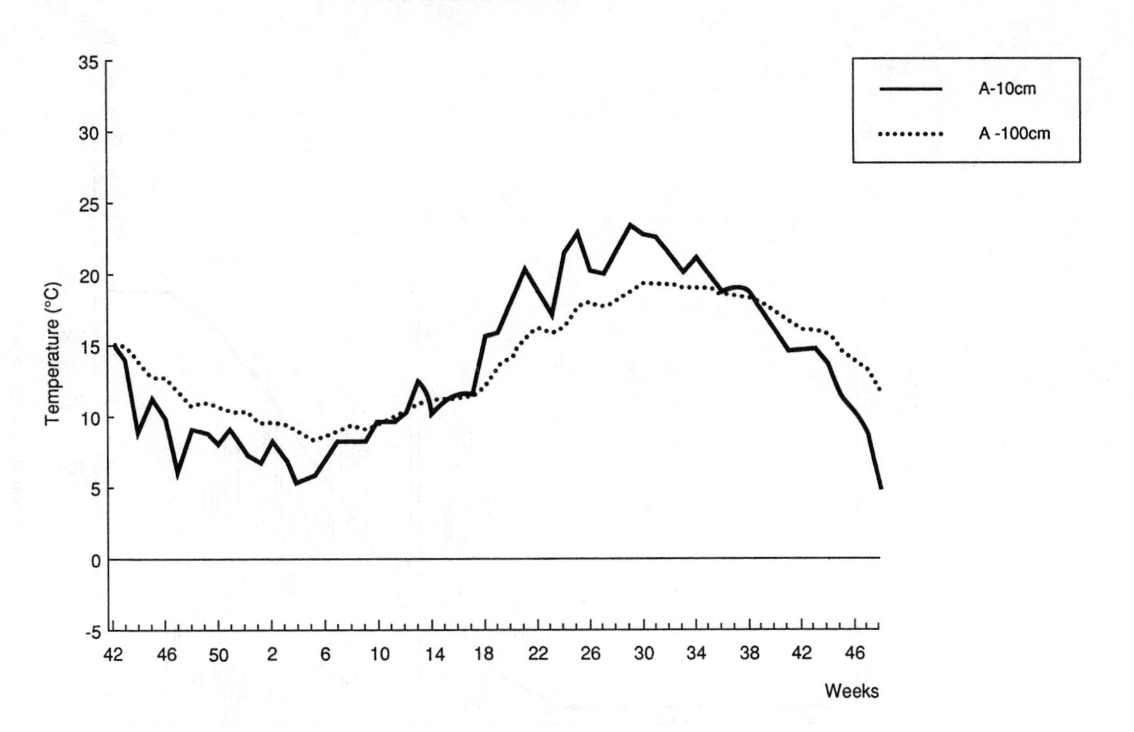

Figure C. 4

SUNSHINE

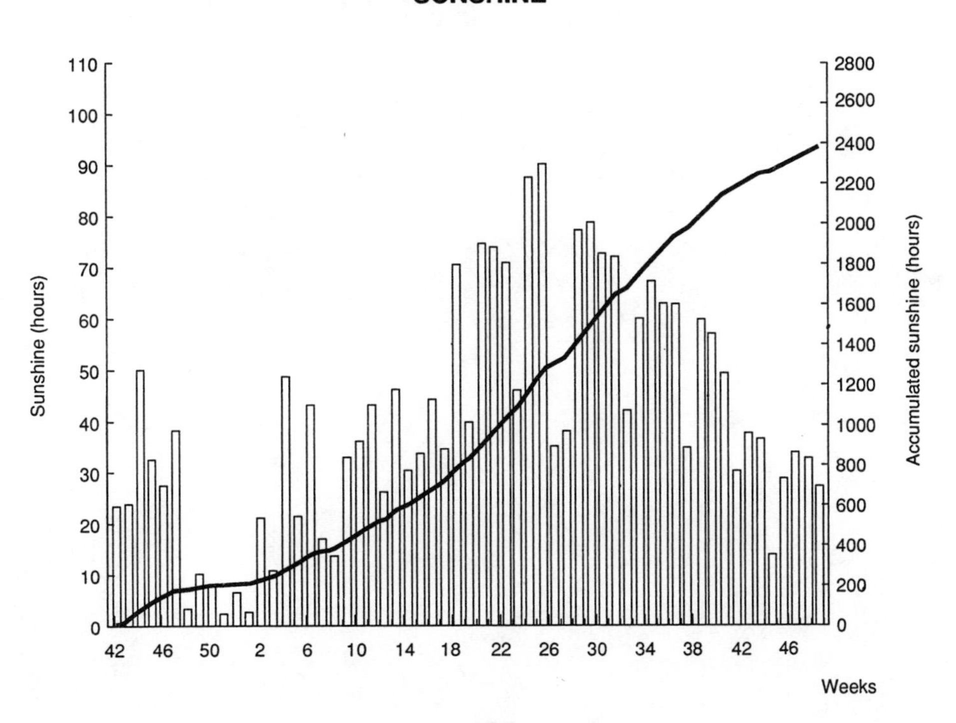

Figure C. 5

EVAPORATION

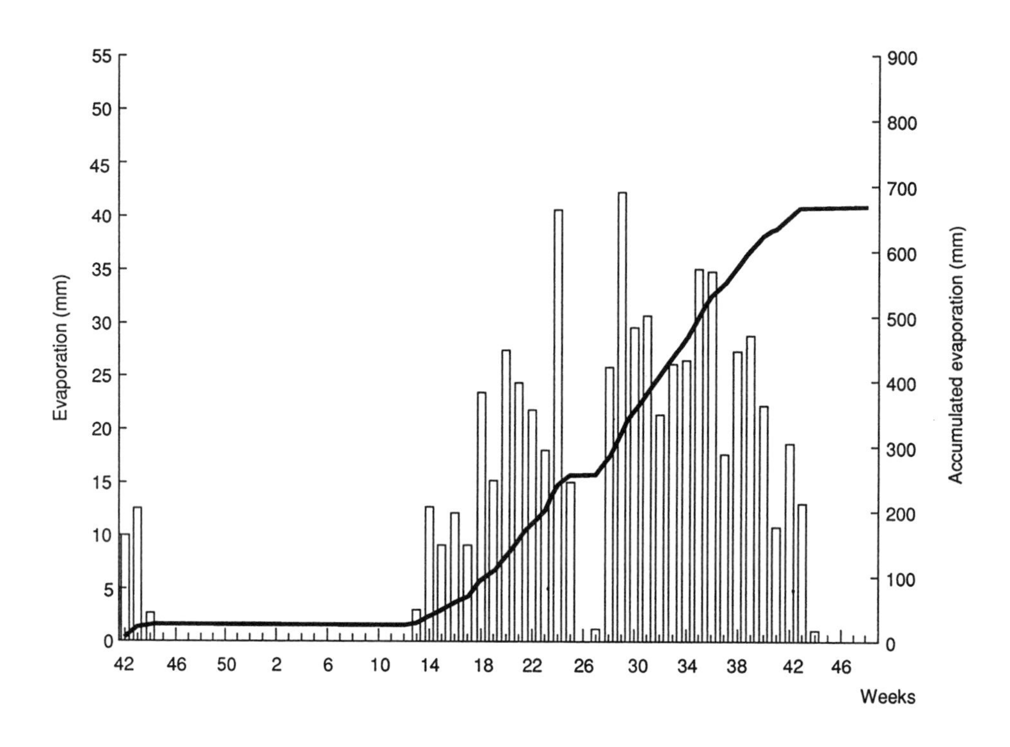

Annex D

DEVELOPMENT OF CRACKING ON THE SURFACE

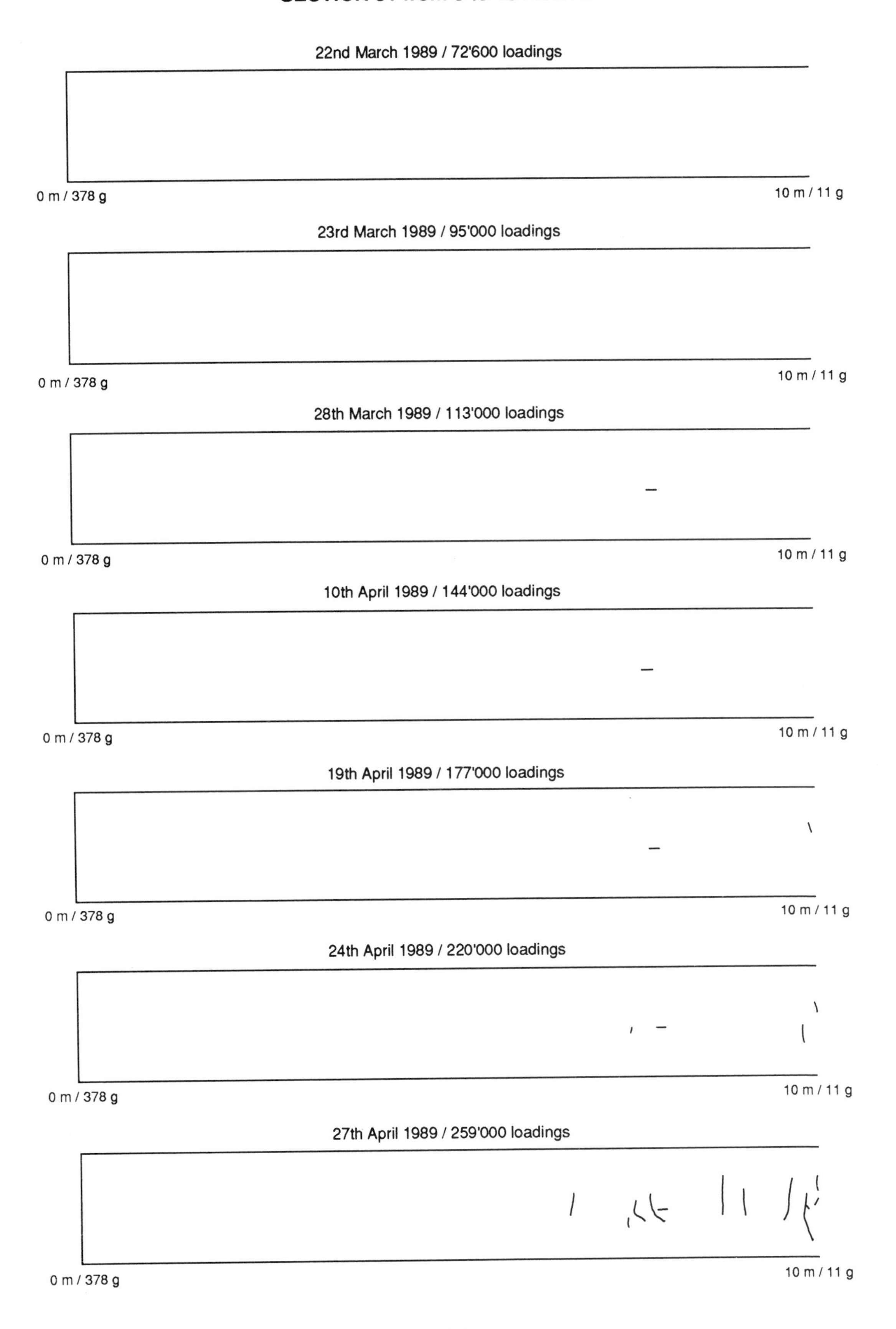
SECTION 01 from 0 to 10 metres
22nd March 1989 / 72'600 loadings
0 m / 378 g
10 m / 11 g
23rd March 1989 / 95'000 loadings
0 m / 378 g
10 m / 11 g
28th March 1989 / 113'000 loadings
0 m / 378 g
10 m / 11 g
10th April 1989 / 144'000 loadings
0 m / 378 g
10 m / 11 g
19th April 1989 / 177'000 loadings
0 m / 378 g
10 m / 11 g
24th April 1989 / 220'000 loadings
0 m / 378 g
10 m / 11 g
27th April 1989 / 259'000 loadings
0 m / 378 g
10 m / 11 g

SECTION 01 from 10 to 20 metres

22nd March 1989 / 72'600 loadings

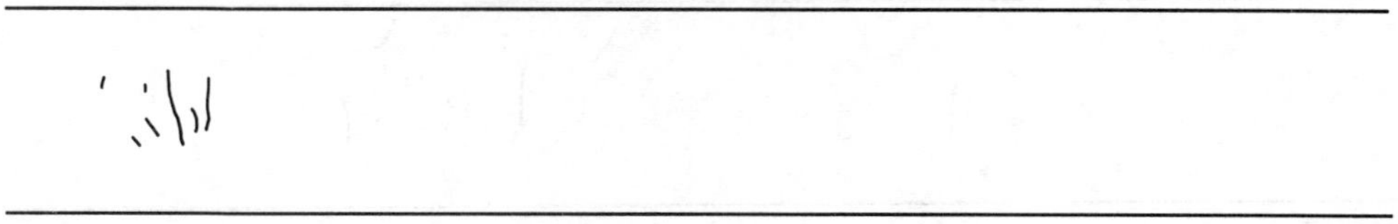

10 m / 11 g

20 m / 45 g

23rd March 1989 / 95'000 loadings

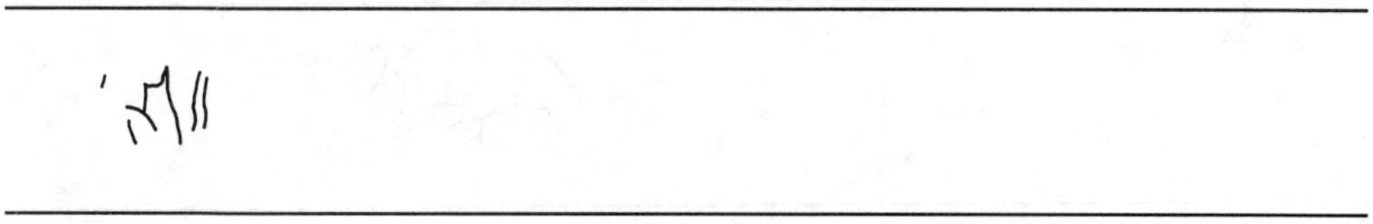

10 m / 11g

20 m / 45 g

28th March 1989 / 113'000 loadings

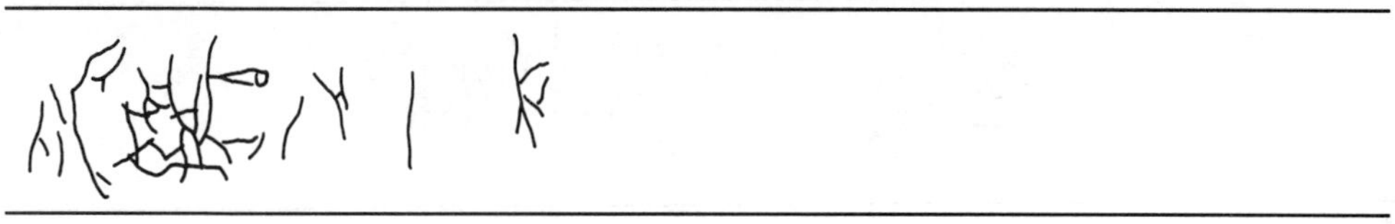

10 m / 11 g

20 m / 45 g

10th April 1989 / 144'000 loadings

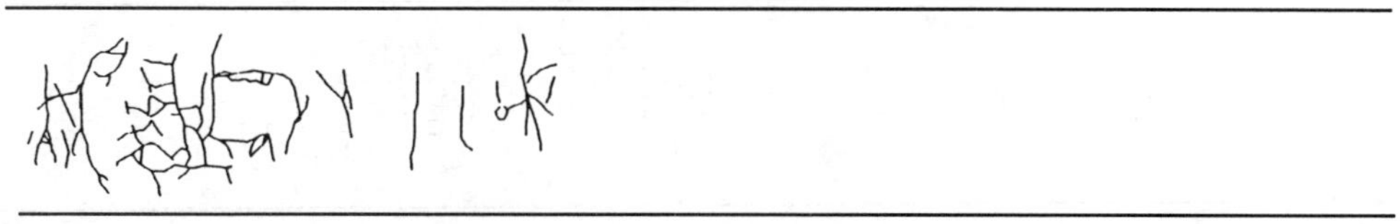

10 m / 11 g

20 m / 45 g

19th April 1989 / 177'000 loadings

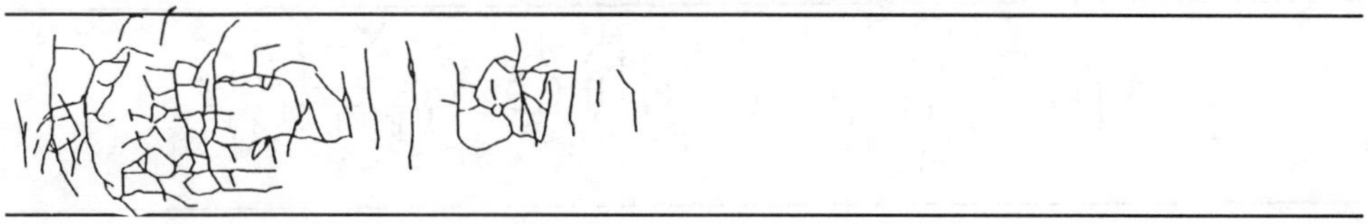

10 m / 11 g

20 m / 45 g

24th April 1989 / 220'000 loadings

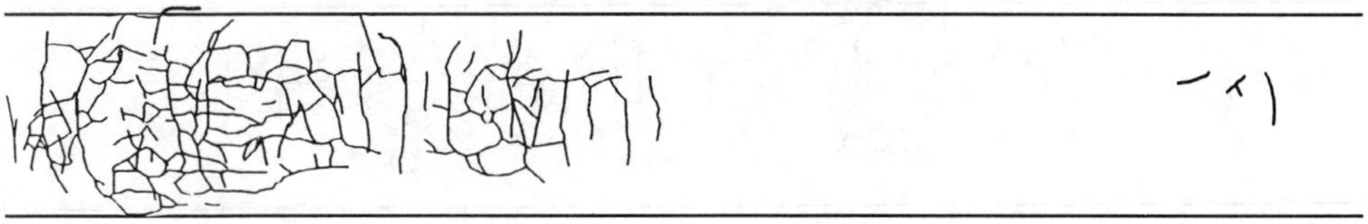

10 m / 11 g

20 m / 45 g

27th April 1989 / 259'000 loadings

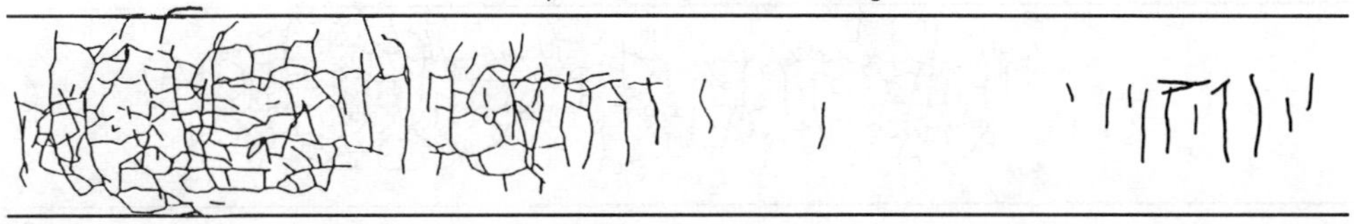

10 m / 11 g

20 m / 45 g

SECTION 01 from 20 to 30 metres

22nd March 1989 / 72'600 loadings

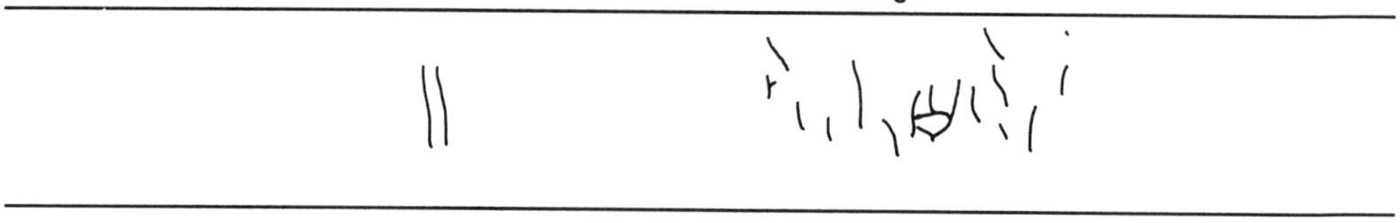

20 m / 45 g

30 m / 78 g

23rd March 1989 / 95'000 loadings

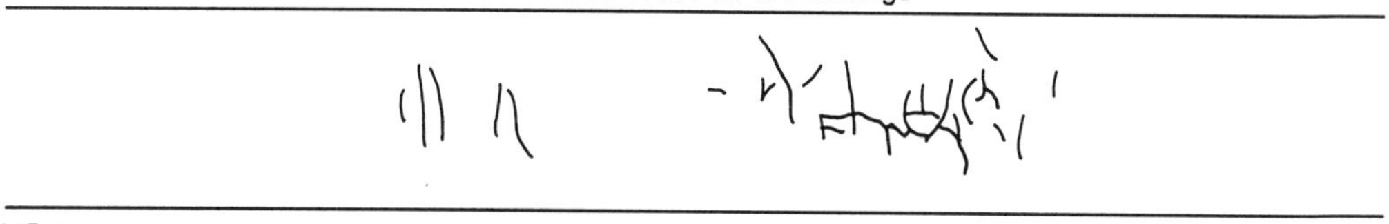

20 m / 45 g

30 m / 78 g

28th March 1989 / 113'000 loadings

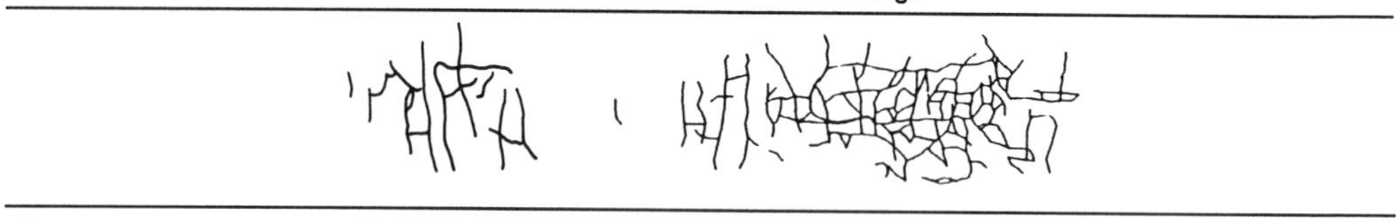

20 m / 45 g

30 m / 78 g

10th April 1989 / 144'000 loadings

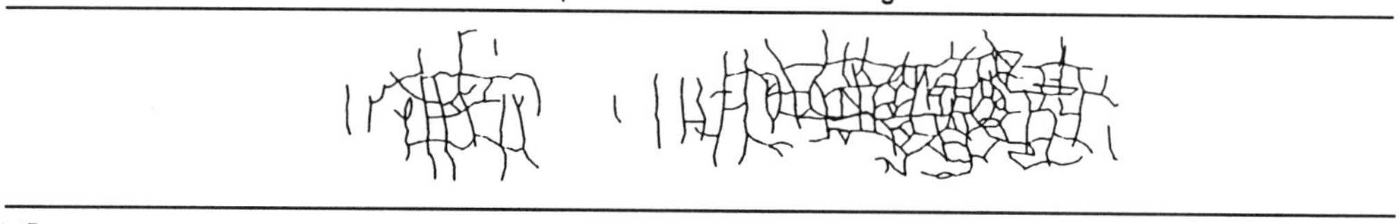

20 m / 45 g

30 m / 78 g

19th April 1989 / 177'000 loadings

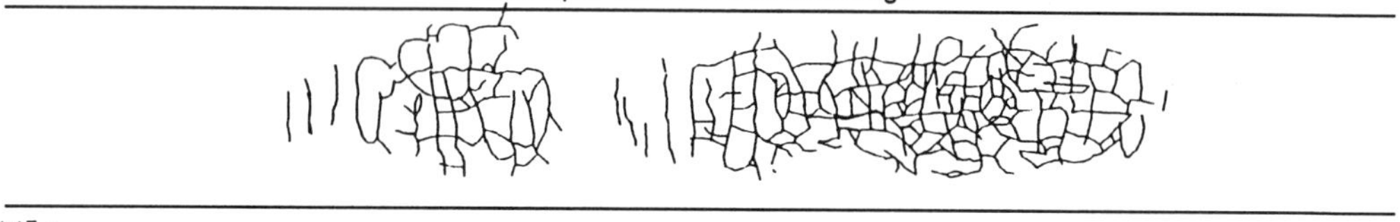

20 m / 45 g

30 m / 78 g

24th April 1989 / 220'000 loadings

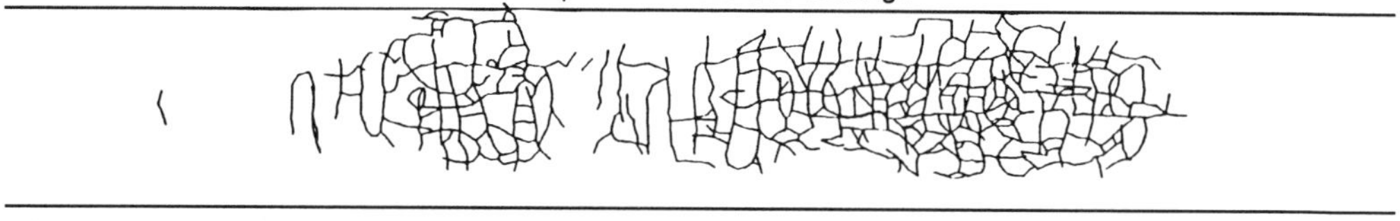

20 m / 45 g

30 m / 78 g

27th April 1989 / 259'000 loadings

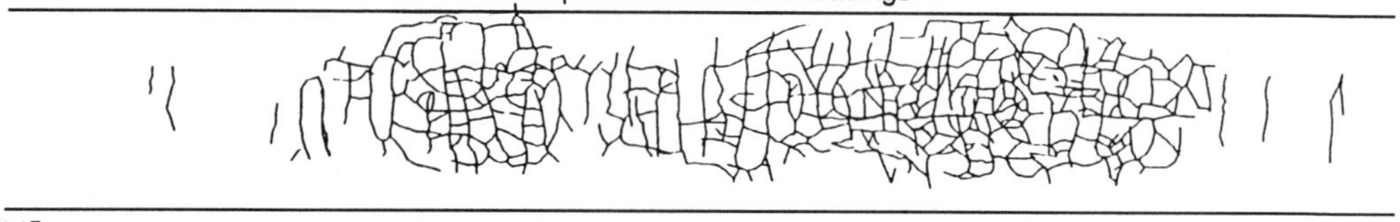

20 m / 45 g

30 m / 78 g

SECTION 01 from 30 to 40 metres

22nd March 1989 / 72'600 loadings

30 m / 78 g

40 m / 111 g

23rd March 1989 / 95'000 loadings

30 m / 78 g

40 m / 111 g

28th March 1989 / 113'000 loadings

30 m / 78 g

40 m / 111 g

10th April 1989 / 144'000 loadings

30 m / 78 g

40 m / 111 g

19th April 1989 / 177'000 loadings

30 m / 78 g

40 m / 111 g

24th April 1989 / 220'000 loadings

30 m / 78 g

40 m / 111 g

27th April 1989 / 259'000 loadings

30 m / 78 g

40 m / 111 g

SECTION 02 from 0 to 40 metres

31st October 1989 / 3'857'000 loadings

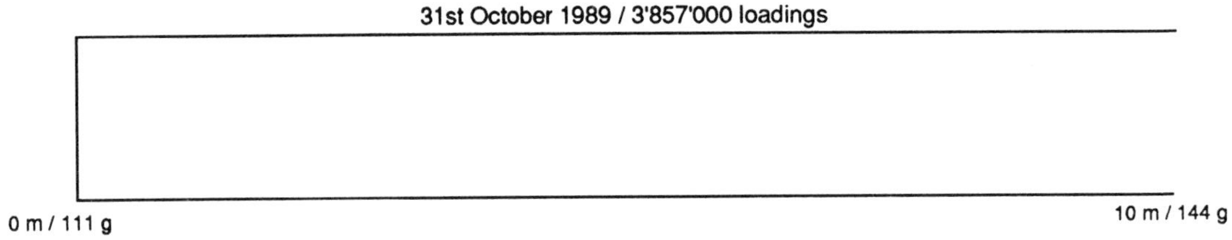

0 m / 111 g

10 m / 144 g

31st October 1989 / 3'857'000 loadings

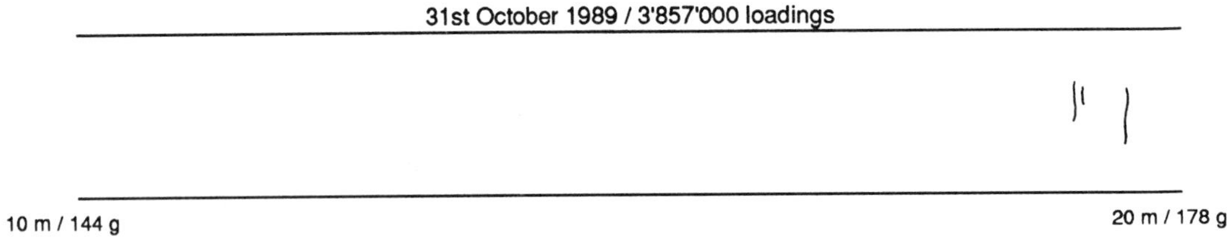

10 m / 144 g

20 m / 178 g

31st October 1989 / 3'857'000 loadings

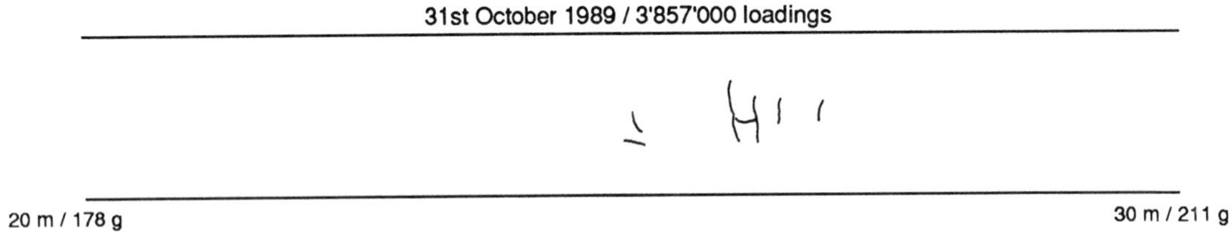

20 m / 178 g

30 m / 211 g

31st October 1989 / 3'857'000 loadings

30 m / 211 g

40 m / 378g

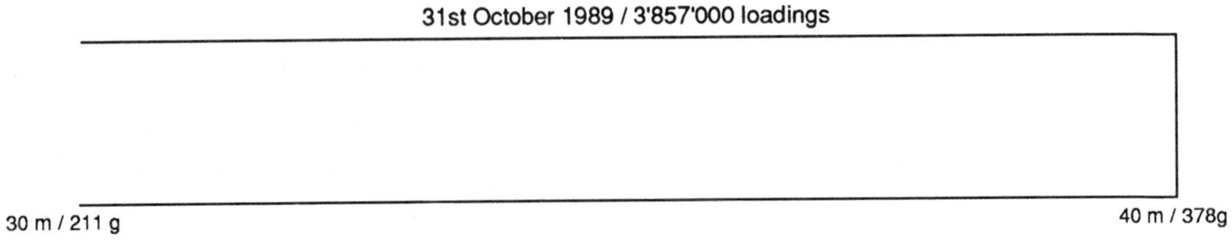

SECTION 03 from 0 to 10 metres

23rd June 1989 / 560'000 loadings

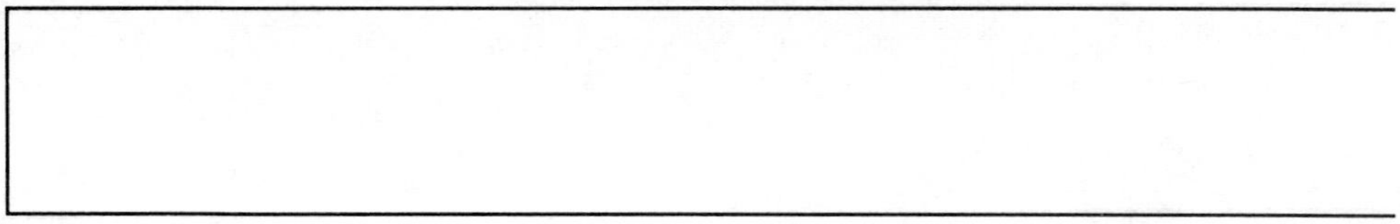

0 m / 244 g — 10 m / 278 g

3rd July 1989 / 857'000 loadings

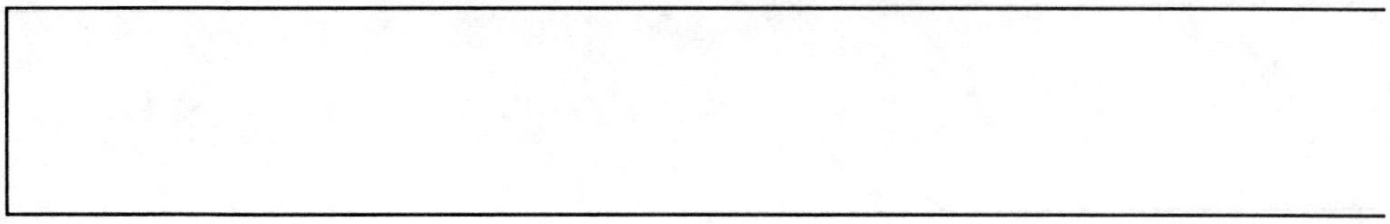

0 m / 244 g — 10 m / 278 g

7th July 1989 / 1'068'000 loadings

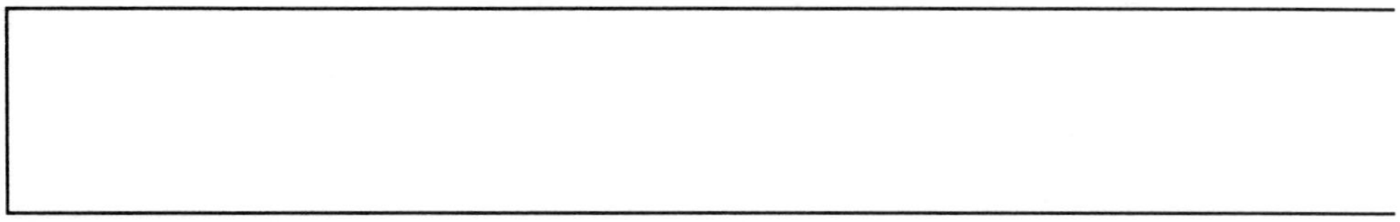

0 m / 244 g — 10 m / 278 g

10th July 1989 / 1'208'000 loadings

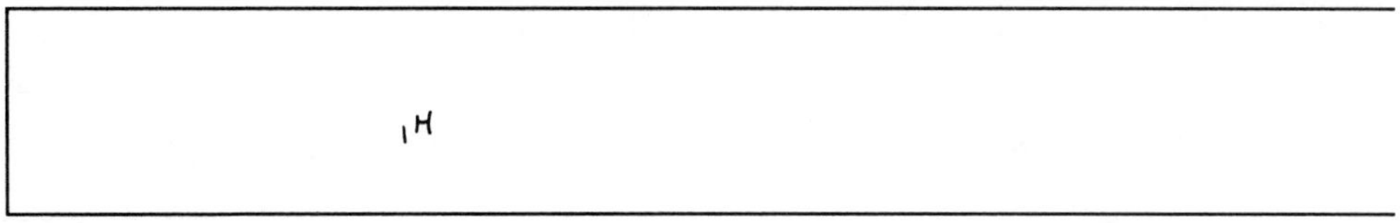

0 m / 244 g — 10 m / 278 g

13th July 1989 / 1'316'000 loadings

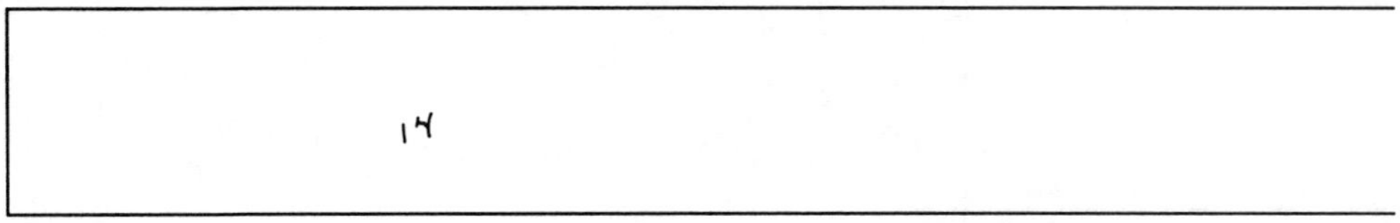

0 m / 244 g — 10 m / 278 g

21st July 1989 / 1'668'000 loadings

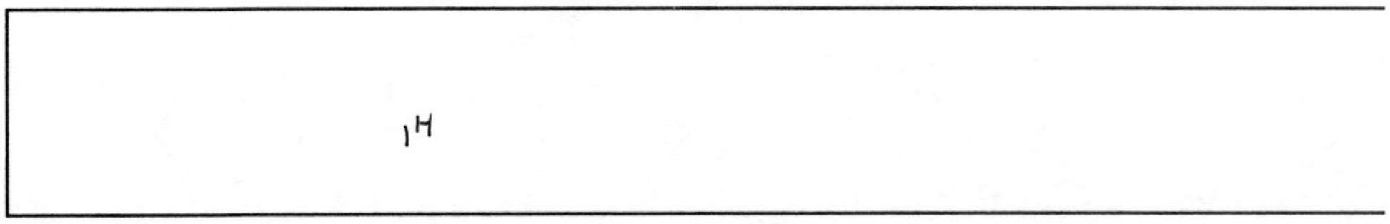

0 m / 244 g — 10 m / 278 g

SECTION 03 from 10 to 20 metres

23rd June 1989 / 560'000 loadings

10 m / 278 g

20 m / 311 g

3rd July 1989 / 857'000 loadings

10 m / 278 g

20 m / 311 g

7th July 1989 / 1'068'000 loadings

10 m / 278 g

20 m / 311 g

10th July 1989 / 1'208'000 loadings

10 m / 278 g

20 m / 311 g

13th July 1989 / 1'316'000 loadings

10 m / 278 g

20 m / 311 g

21st July 1989 / 1'668'000 loadings

10 m / 278 g

20 m / 311 g

SECTION 03 from 20 to 30 metres

23rd June 1989 / 560'000 loadings

20 m / 311g

30 m / 345 g

3rd July 1989 / 857'000 loadings

20 m / 311 g

30 m / 345 g

7th July 1989 / 1'068'000 loadings

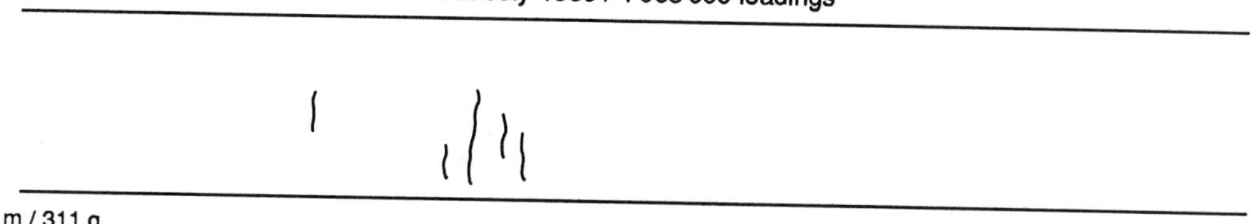

20 m / 311 g

30 m / 345 g

10th July 1989 / 1'208'000 loadings

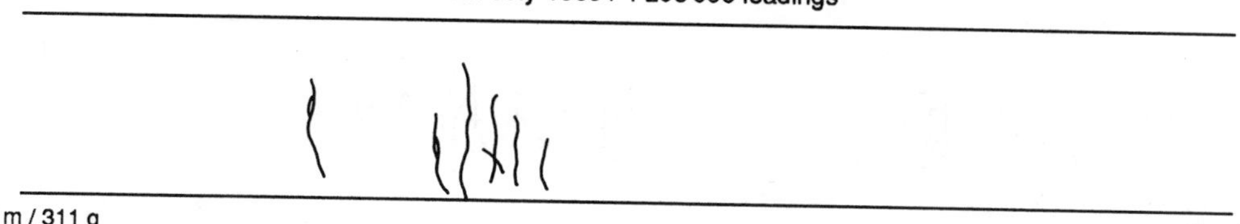

20 m / 311 g

30 m / 345 g

13th July 1989 / 1'316'000 loadings

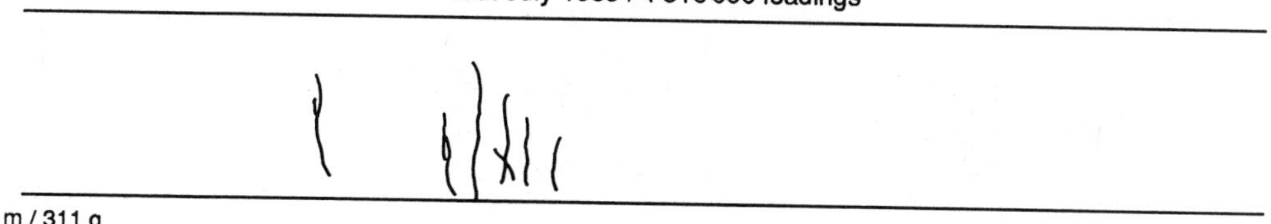

20 m / 311 g

30 m / 345 g

21st July 1989 / 1'668'000 loadings

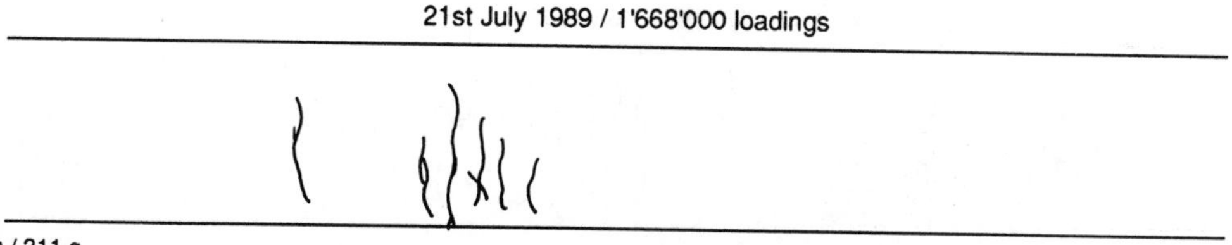

20 m / 311 g

30 m / 345 g

SECTION 03 from 30 to 40 metres

23rd June 1989 / 560'000 loadings

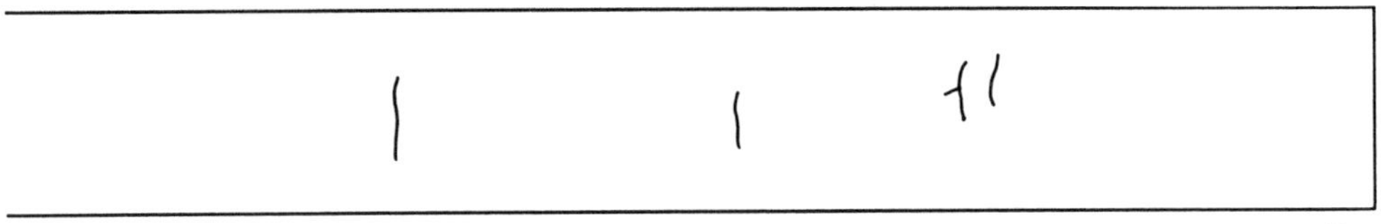

30 m / 345 g

40 m / 378 g

3rd July 1989 / 857'000 loadings

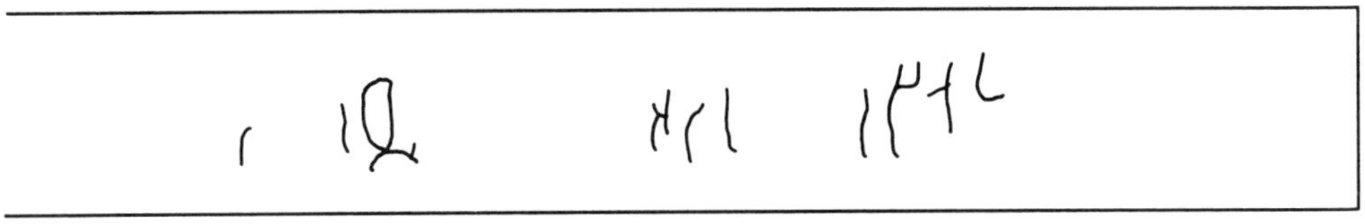

30 m / 345 g

40 m / 378 g

7th July 1989 / 1'068'000 loadings

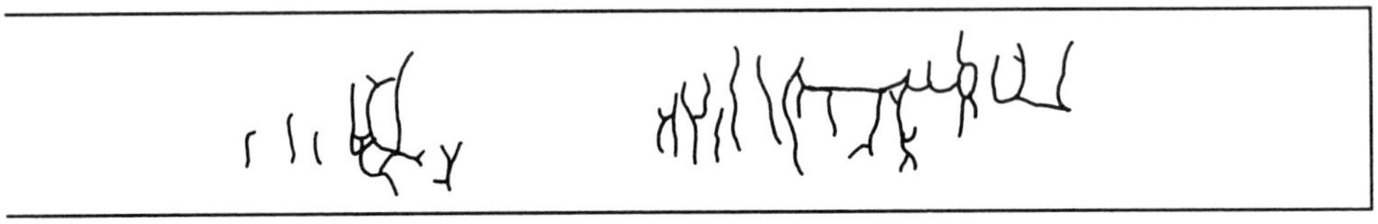

30 m / 345 g

40 m / 378 g

10th July 1989 / 1'208'000 loadings

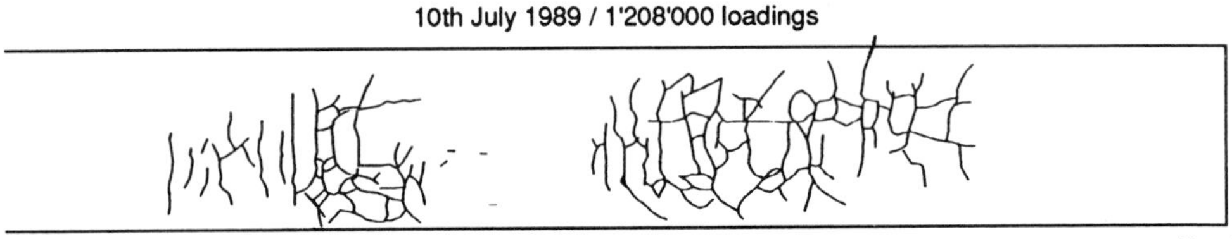

30 m / 345 g

40 m / 378g

13th July 1989 / 1'316'000 loadings

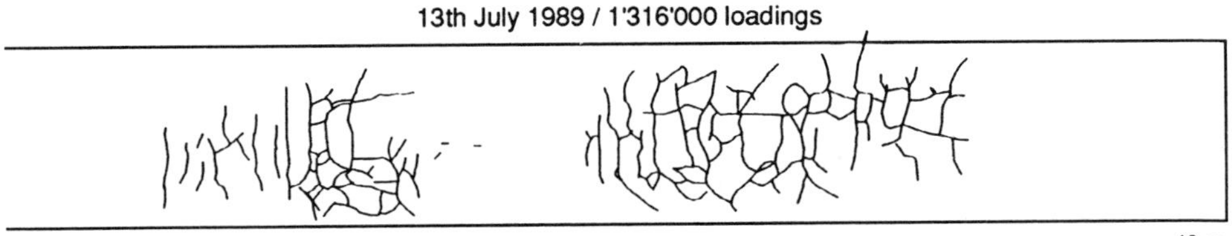

30 m / 345 g

40 m / 378 g

21st July 1989 / 1'668'000 loadings

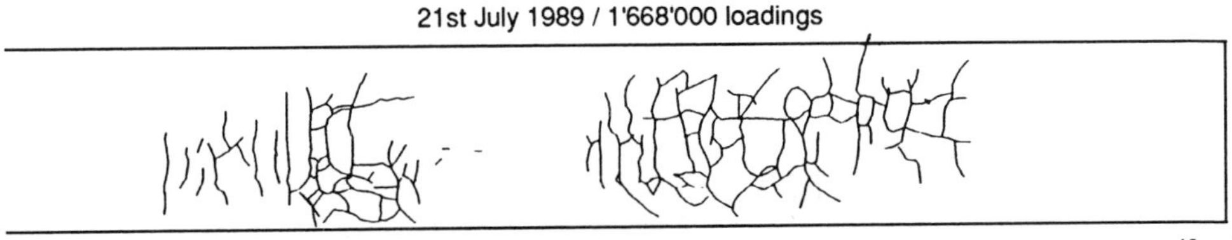

30 m / 345 g

40 m / 378 g

SECTION 11 from 0 to 11.2 metres

28th March 1989 / 103'000 loadings

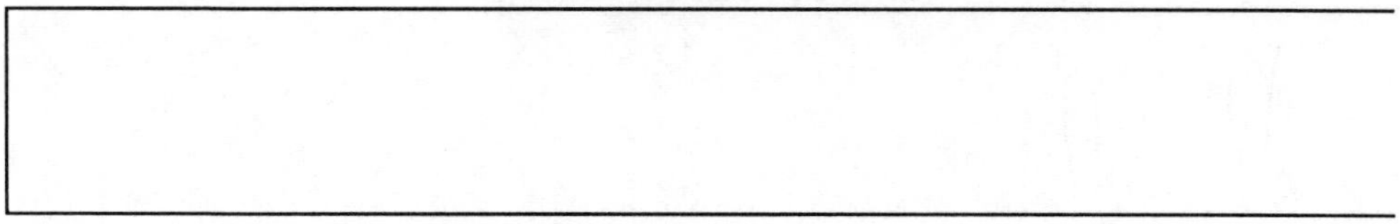

0 m / 378 g 11.2 m / 22 g

10th April 1989 / 134'000 loadings

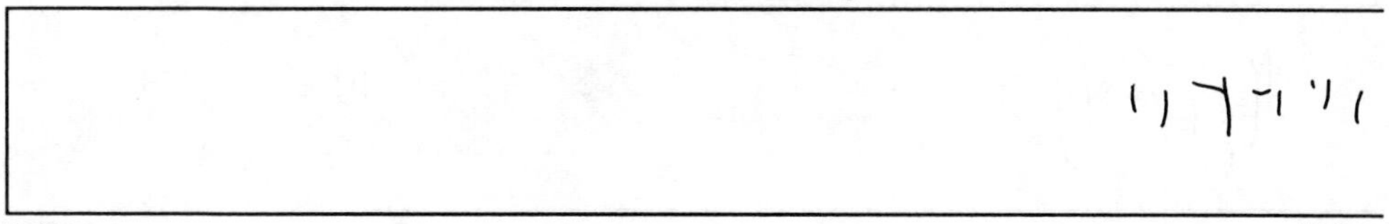

0 m / 378 g 11.2 m / 22 g

19th April 1989 / 167'000 loadings

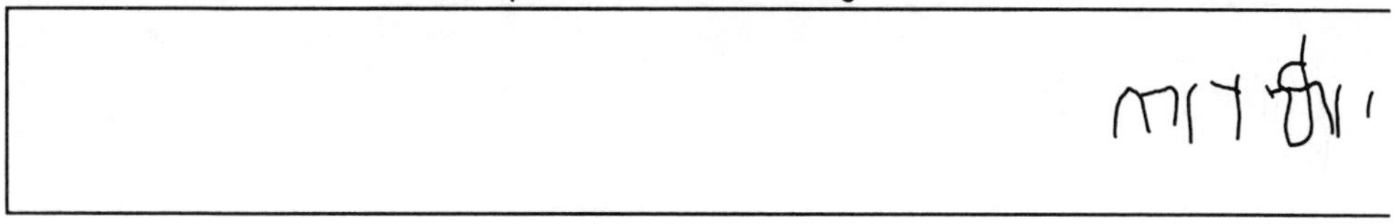

0 m / 378 g 11.2 m / 22 g

24th April 1989 / 210'000 loadings

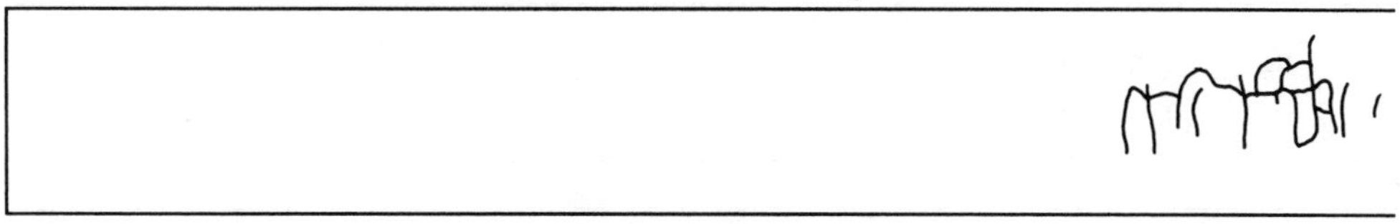

0 m / 378 g 11.2 m / 22 g

27th April 1989 / 248'000 loadings

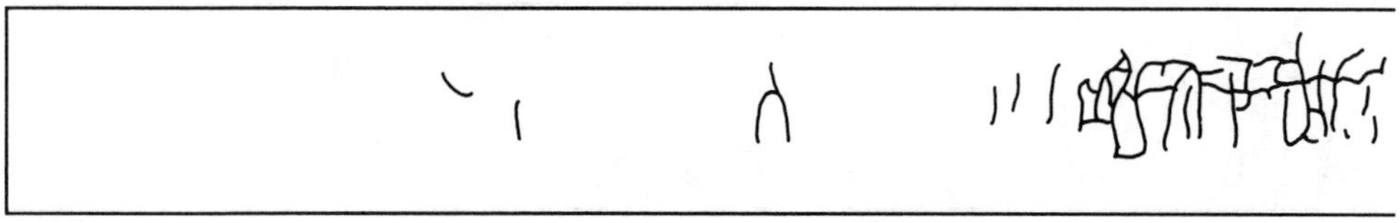

0 m / 378 g 11.2 m / 22 g

12th May 1989 / 374'000 loadings

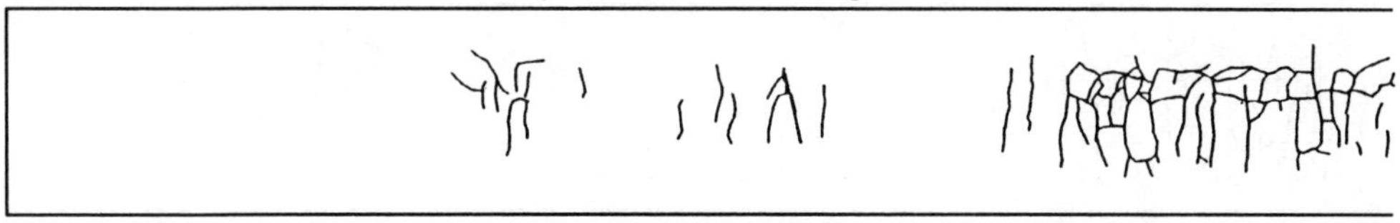

0 m / 378 g 11.2 m / 22 g

19th May1989 / 473'000 loadings

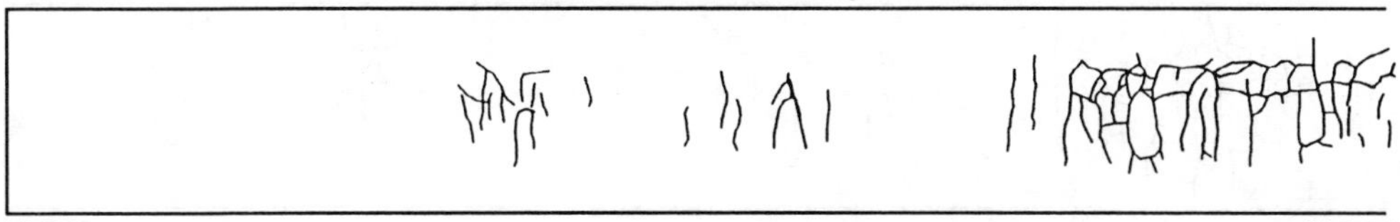

0 m / 378 g 11.2 m / 22 g

22nd May 1989 / 560'000 loadings

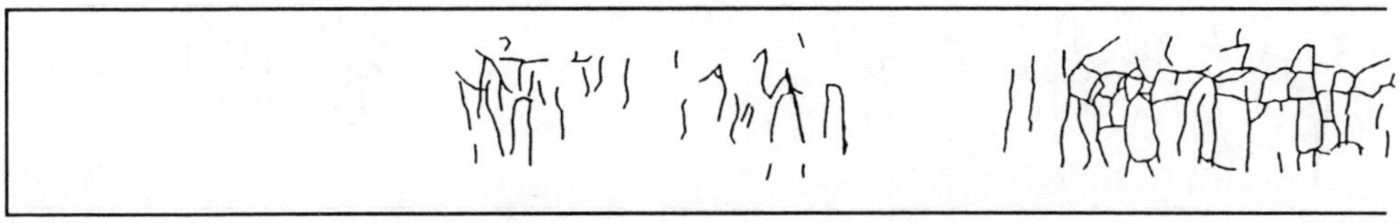

0 m / 378 g 11.2 m / 22 g

SECTION 11 from 11.2 to 22.3 metres

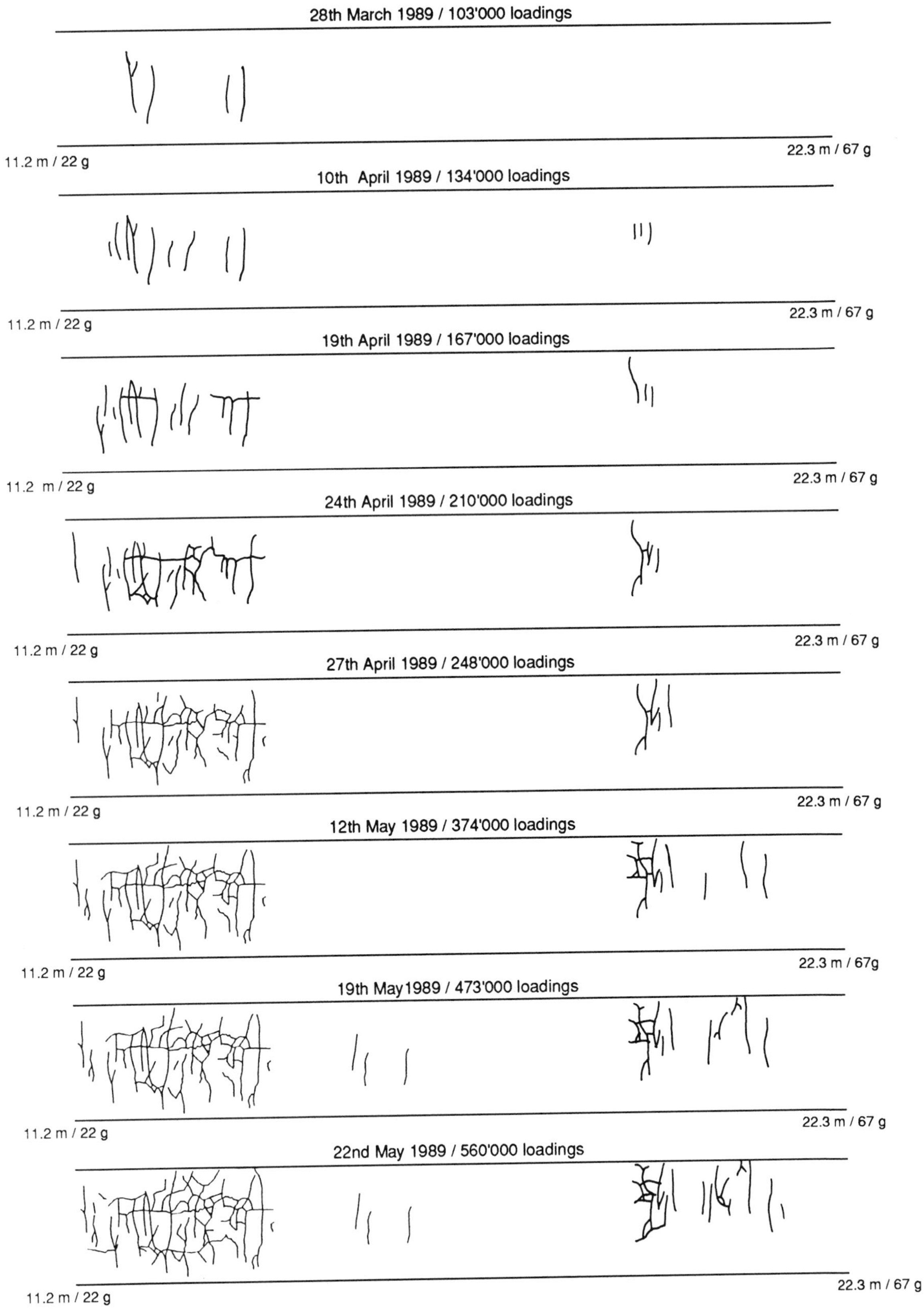

28th March 1989 / 103'000 loadings

11.2 m / 22 g — 22.3 m / 67 g

10th April 1989 / 134'000 loadings

11.2 m / 22 g — 22.3 m / 67 g

19th April 1989 / 167'000 loadings

11.2 m / 22 g — 22.3 m / 67 g

24th April 1989 / 210'000 loadings

11.2 m / 22 g — 22.3 m / 67 g

27th April 1989 / 248'000 loadings

11.2 m / 22 g — 22.3 m / 67 g

12th May 1989 / 374'000 loadings

11.2 m / 22 g — 22.3 m / 67g

19th May1989 / 473'000 loadings

11.2 m / 22 g — 22.3 m / 67 g

22nd May 1989 / 560'000 loadings

11.2 m / 22 g — 22.3 m / 67 g

SECTION 11 from 22.3 to 33.5 metres

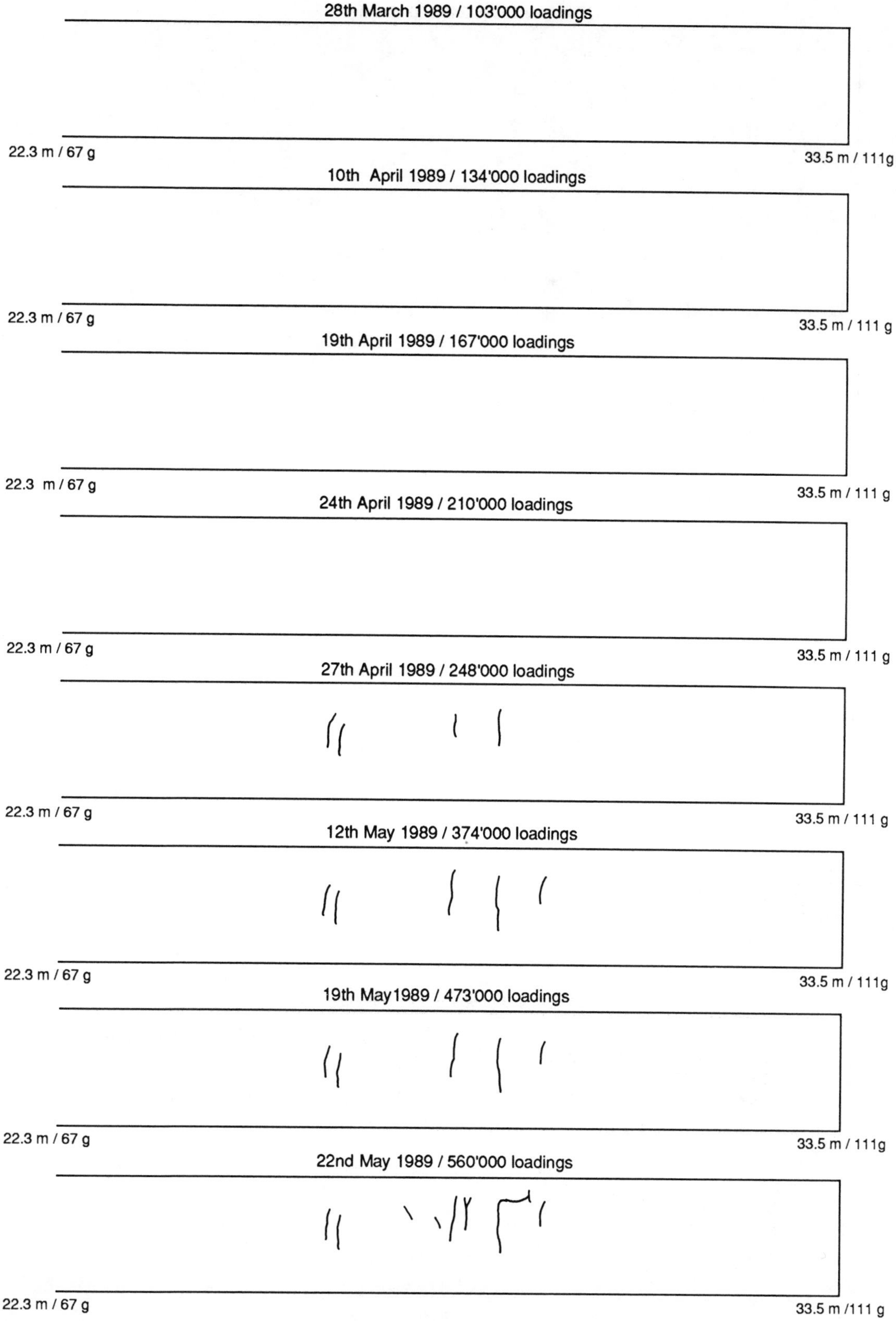

28th March 1989 / 103'000 loadings

22.3 m / 67 g

33.5 m / 111g

10th April 1989 / 134'000 loadings

22.3 m / 67 g

33.5 m / 111 g

19th April 1989 / 167'000 loadings

22.3 m / 67 g

33.5 m / 111 g

24th April 1989 / 210'000 loadings

22.3 m / 67 g

33.5 m / 111 g

27th April 1989 / 248'000 loadings

22.3 m / 67 g

33.5 m / 111 g

12th May 1989 / 374'000 loadings

22.3 m / 67 g

33.5 m / 111g

19th May1989 / 473'000 loadings

22.3 m / 67 g

33.5 m / 111g

22nd May 1989 / 560'000 loadings

22.3 m / 67 g

33.5 m /111 g

SECTION 13 from 0 to 11.2 metres

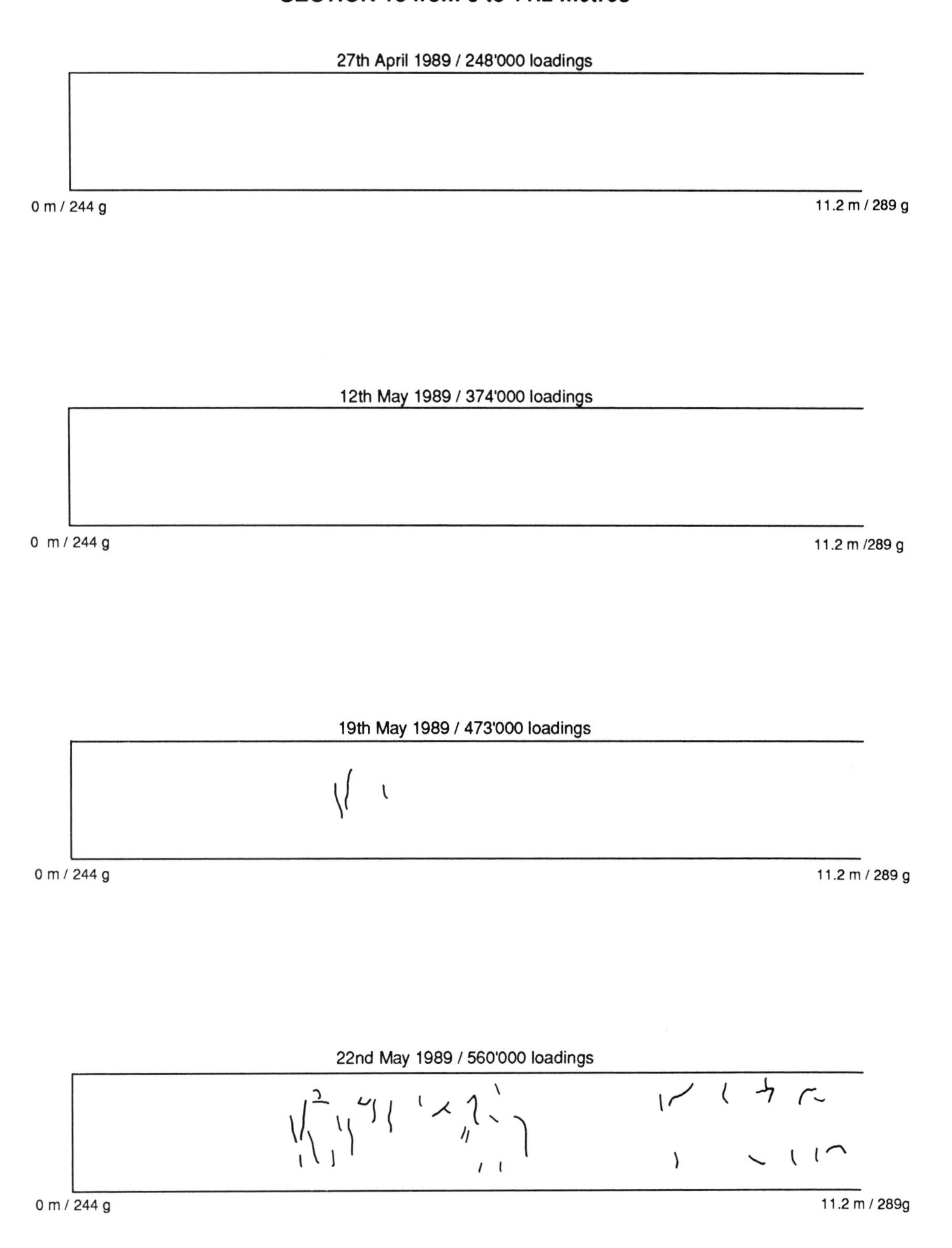

SECTION 13 from 11.2 to 22.3 metres

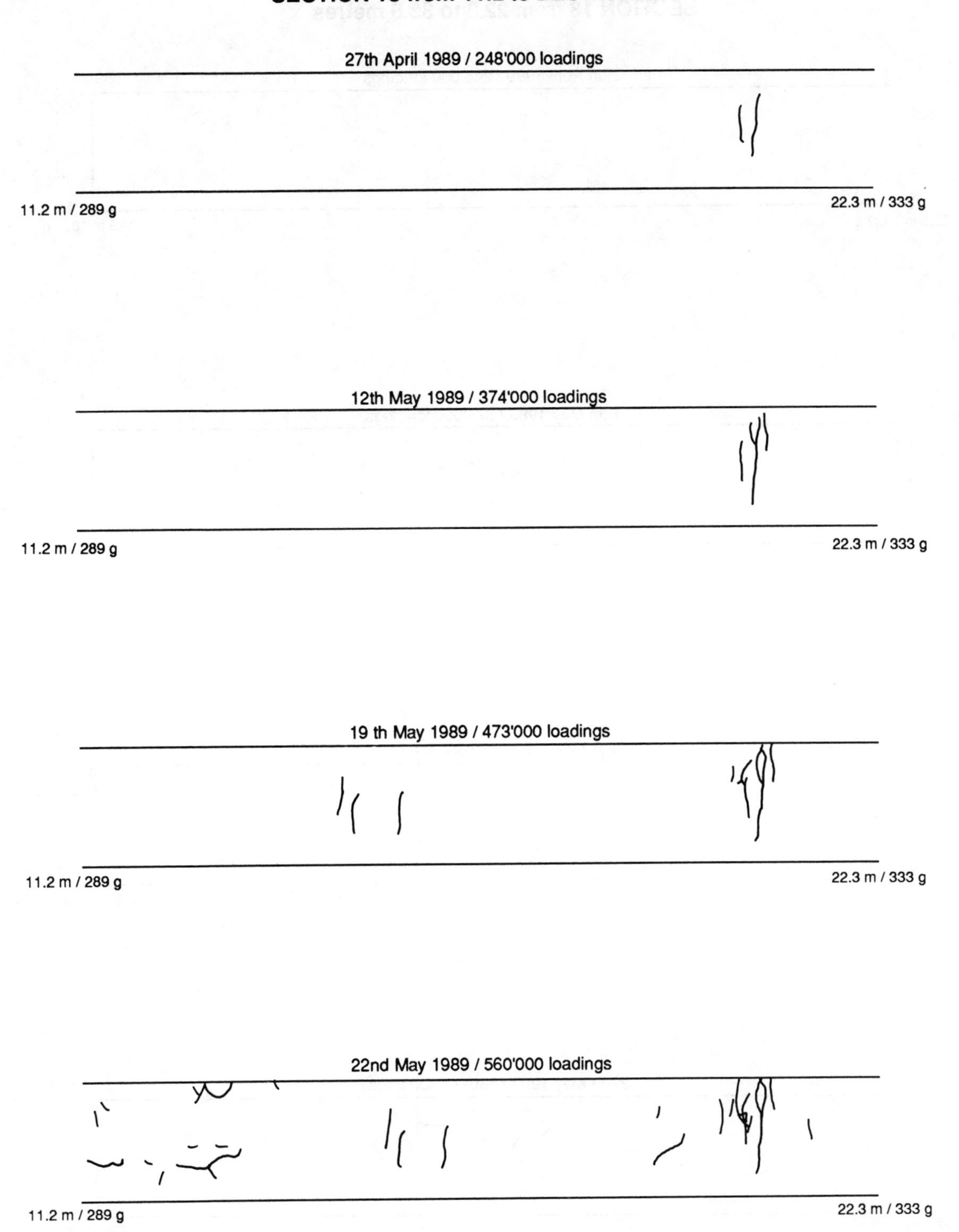

SECTION 13 from 22.3 to 33.5 metres

27th April 1989 / 248'000 loadings

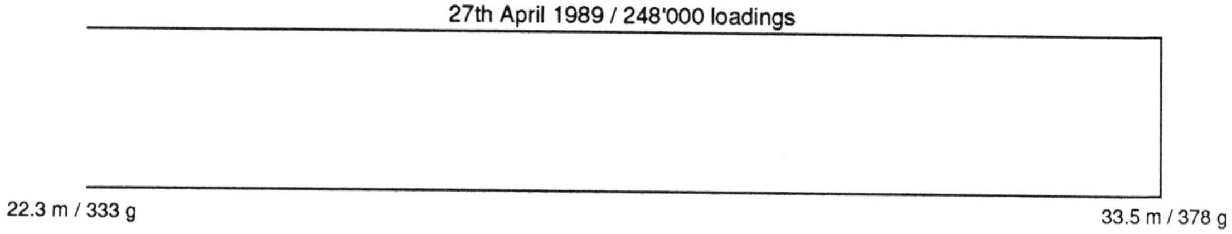

22.3 m / 333 g

33.5 m / 378 g

12th May 1989 / 374'000 loadings

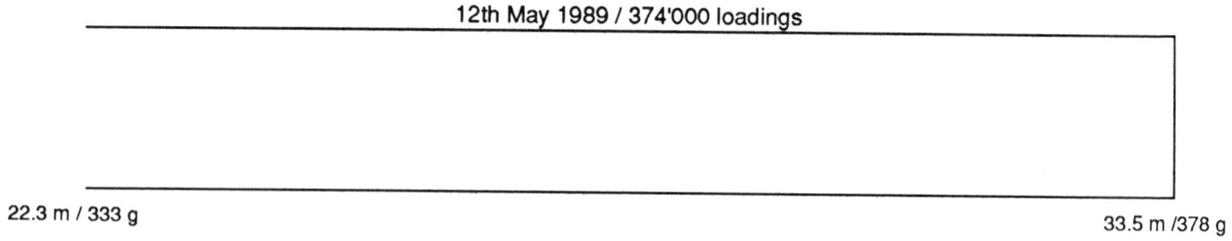

22.3 m / 333 g

33.5 m /378 g

19th May 1989 / 473'000 loadings

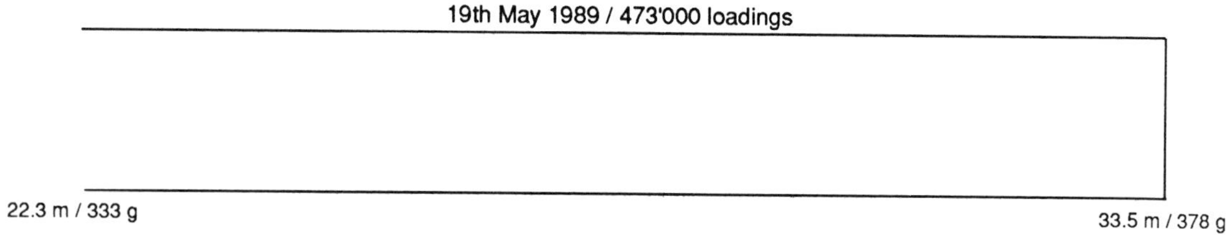

22.3 m / 333 g

33.5 m / 378 g

22nd May 1989 / 560'000 loadings

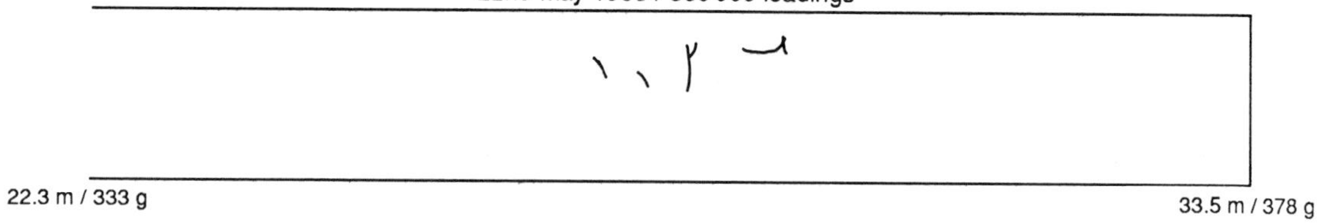

22.3 m / 333 g

33.5 m / 378 g

Annex E

STRAIN MEASUREMENTS CONDUCTED BY THE DUTCH AND FINNISH TEAMS

E.1. INTERPRETATION OF DUTCH STRAIN MEASUREMENTS

E.1.1. Introduction

During construction of the FORCE test track, a dutch team placed ten strain gauges in sections 01 and 02 (R = 19 m) for the measurement of radial strains at the bottom of the bituminous concrete (BC) layer. The type of strain gauge and its installation are described in subsection E.1.2.

A global interpretation of the different measurements carried out with the Dutch gauges is presented in subsection E.1.3. The measurements involved:

a) those during the "point zero" inventory. These can be divided into two groups:

   i) Strain measurements under the moving wheels

   ii) Strain measurements carried out during Falling Weight Deflection (FWD) measurements; besides deflections, bituminous strains were also recorded under the falling weight.

b) those during accelerated loading of the test pavements.

Concluding remarks are given in subsection E.1.4.

E.1.2. Installation of Dutch strain gauges

The Delft University of Technology uses TML embedment strain gauges (type KM-100-HAS) for measurement of bituminous concrete (BC) strain. The gauge consists of a low modulus waterproof tube which has a small beam on which strain gauges are glued into a full-bridge configuration with temperature compensation. The length of the strain gauge is 120 mm, the diameter is 20 mm. Because of the low modulus of 1 000 MN/m^2 and the high temperature resistance until 180°C, this type of gauge is ideally suited for measuring strains in BC pavement structures.

Each of the FORCE sections 01 and 02 (R = 19 m) was equipped with five of such strain gauges. All gauges were placed at the surface of the granular base course for measuring radial asphalt strains at the bottom of the bituminous layer under the centreline of the wheel load ("position 6"). Much attention was paid to a good fixation of the strain gauges on the granular base, so that the gauges are not displaced when laying down and compacting the BC layer. The cable of each strain gauge is protected by digging it into the granular base course. Much attention was also paid to the determination of the vertical position in the BC layer. Therefore, levelling measurements were carried out at three stages during construction of the test pavement namely on top of the granular base just beside the strain gauges already placed, on top of the strain gauge before construction of the BC layer and after construction of the BC course on top of it just above the strain gauges. In this way, the exact vertical position of the gauges can be determined, as well as the exact layer thickness in-situ at the position of the gauges. After completion of the test, BC cores were taken from the test pavement at the position of the Dutch strain gauges for determining exact layer thickness in-situ. These thicknesses were equal to the thicknesses derived from the levelling measurements.

In order to measure BC temperature, Dutch thermocouples were incorporated during construction at different levels in the bituminous layer close to the strain gauges.

E.1.3. Interpretation of strain measurements

Measurement of Strain Caused by the Moving Wheels of the LCPC Test Machine

Results of BC strain measurements described here were carried out on 9th, 10th and 13th March 1989. At these dates a number of about 50 000 moving wheel loads had already been applied. Only results of section 02 (120 mm bituminous concrete on 300 mm granular base) are considered. In Figure E.1. the measured peak values that have been recorded for one radial strain gauge are given for 11 different lateral positions of a dual wheel load of 57,5 kN (half axle). For each lateral position, three points are given in the figure. Each point corresponds to a measurement of the strain gauge at a certain date. The speed of the moving wheels was set at 72 km/h, and for the purpose of comparison, BC strains were normalized to a reference temperature of 15°C. This temperature normalization method is described in (1).

The drawn line in Figure E.1 shows the result of calculations of the radial BC strain at the position of the gauge for different lateral positions of the wheel load. These calculations were performed with the program BISAR. The exact place where BC strain was calculated was derived from the levelling measurements as described in section E.1.2. The calculations were done for different values of BC stiffness. For the elastic stiffnesses of granular base course and subgrade, values are used that were derived from the interpretation of FWD-measurements (see below). Using a BC stiffness of 9 000 MN/m^2 obtained from four point bending tests (2) with a loading frequency of 30 Hz shows a good agreement between measured and calculated BC strain as can be seen from Figure E.1. The same good agreement has been found for the other four BC strain gauges in section 02.

Measurement of Strain Caused by the Impact of the Falling Weight Deflectometer

On 24th February 1989, FWD-measurements were carried out just above the five Dutch strain gauges of section 02. Besides deflections, BC strains caused by the impact loading of a Falling Weight Deflectometer were measured. Two load levels were used, namely 60 and 75 kN. A total number of ten measurements were performed: two load levels on five strain gauges. Temperature measurements were carried out by reading the Dutch thermocouples of section 02. During the measurements mean BC temperature was 8°C. A number of 34 050 moving wheels loads had already been applied by 24th February 1989.

Figure E.1

COMPARISON OF MEASURED AND CALCULATED STRAINS IN BITUMINOUS CONCRETE
(SECTION 02)

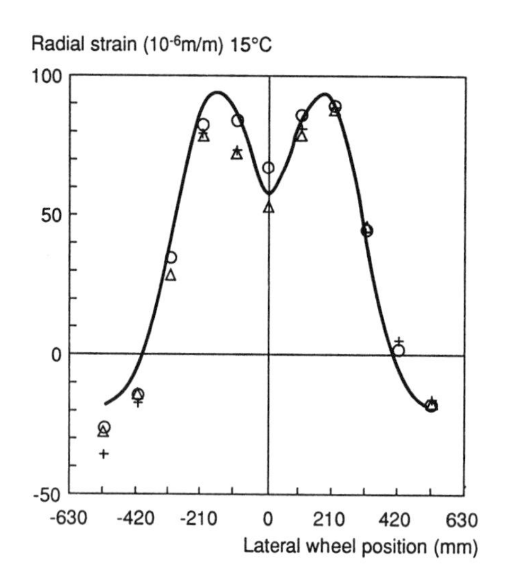

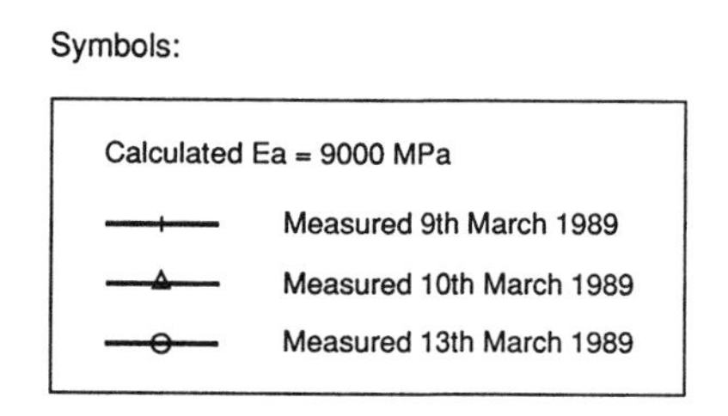

Figure E.2

FWD INTERPRETATION:MEASURED AND CALCULATED STRAINS IN BITUMINOUS CONCRETE
(10^{-6}m/m)
(SECTION 02)

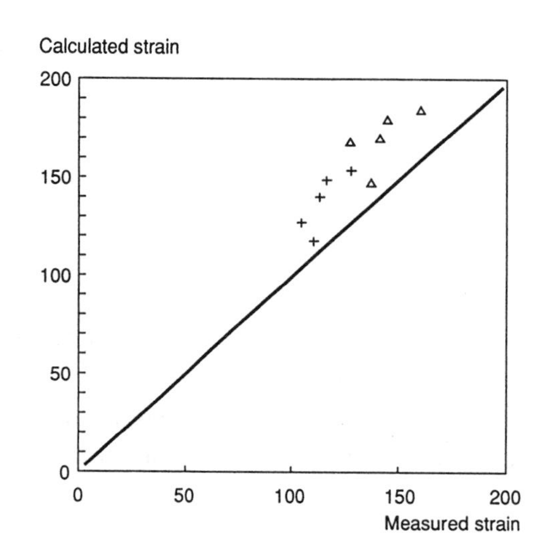

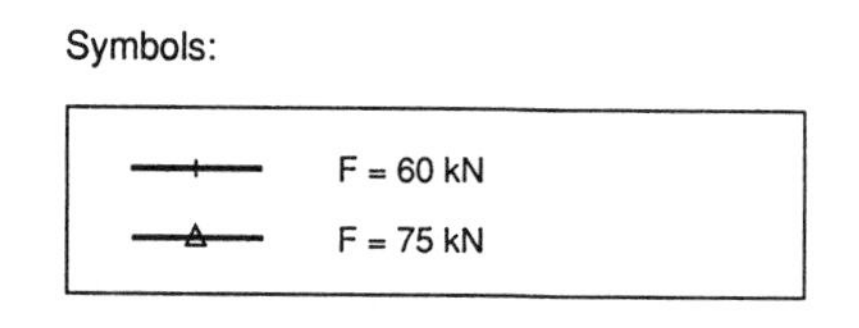

With a back-calculation program of the Delft University of Technology, the measured deflection curves were interpreted. The result of this interpretation is the stiffness of each distinguished layer of the test pavement. BC stiffness of 12 500 - 13 000MN/m^2 was derived from this interpretation, which is quite consistent with the results of four point bending tests conducted in the laboratory on BC specimens coming from the FORCE test site (2). With these results a BC stiffness of about 13 000MN/m^2 follows for a temperature of 8°C and a loading frequency of 20 Hz.

With the derived layer stiffnesses, radial BC strains at the position of the Dutch strain gauges were calculated with the BISAR program, using the FWD load conditions. The calculated asphalt strains were compared with the measured strains. The result of this comparison is given in Figure E.2 which shows the relation between calculated and measured BC strain for the two load levels of 60 and 75 kN. From Figure E.2 it can be seen that a reasonable agreement has been attained between measured and calculated BC strains.

Strain Measurements During Accelerated Loading of the Test Pavements

At several intervals during accelerated loading of the FORCE test pavements, BC strains were recorded from the Dutch strain gauges. A graphical representation of these measurements is given in Figure E.3, which shows the recorded peak values of two Dutch radial Bc strain gauges in section 02 as function of the number of applied load repetitions by the LCPC machine. In Figure E.3 results of measurements are shown for two lateral positions ("tracks") of the wheel configuration of +21 cm and -21 cm out of the central position. The measured BC strains were normalized to a reference temperature of 15°C.

From Figure E.3 it can be seen that there is a relative strong increase of BC strain in the beginning of the test. Such behaviour is in line with the results of the four point bending tests (constant strain). These tests generally show a relative strong decrease of BC stiffness in the beginning of the test. From Figure E.3 it can also be seen that even after 3.5 million load cycles no relevant further increase of BC strain occurred. This indicates that no relevant structural fatigue cracks occurred in section 02. This is consistent with the results of the visual condition surveys of section 02. These surveys were carried out at regular intervals and showed no relevant cracking at the surface of the bituminous layer of section 02 at the end of the test.

E.1.4. Concluding remarks

With respect to the Dutch BC strain measurements carried out during the FORCE experiment, the following conclusions can be drawn:

a) BC strain measurements in pavement structures under moving wheel loads supply valuable information with respect to the mechanical behaviour of pavement structures, provided that sufficient attention is paid to the choice of the type of strain gauge, the way in which they are placed at position and the determination of vertical and horizontal position of the strain gauge.

b) With results of such BC strain measurements, among others, calculation models for pavement structures can be validated as well as interpretation models for FWD-measurements. Furthermore, measured BC strain is a descriptive parameter for structural behaviour of test pavements as a function of the number of applied load repetitions.

Figure E.3

MEASURED STRAINS IN BITUMINOUS CONCRETE AS A FUNCTION OF LOAD REPETITIONS
(SECTION 02)

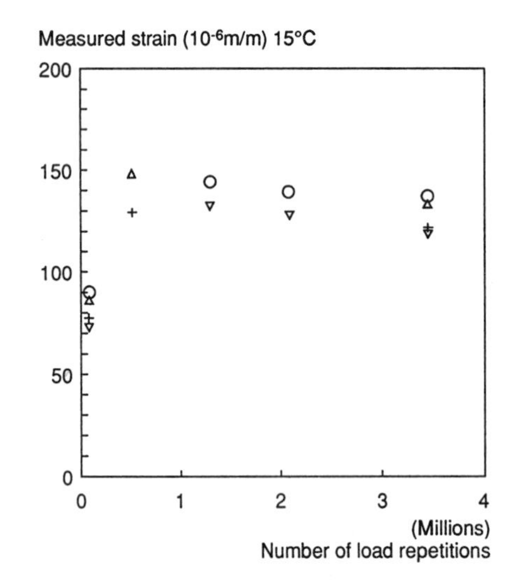

E.2. THE FINNISH STRAIN MEASUREMENTS

E.2.1. Introduction

The Road and Traffic Laboratory of the Technical Research Center of Finland (VTT) made measurements with strain gauges in bituminous materials at the LCPC Test Track as part of the common OECD FORCE test.

The work can be divided into the following phases:

a) Forty strain gauges and six temperature gauges were installed in November-December 1988.

b) The "point zero" inventory measurements were made in February 1989 before applying repeated moving axle loads. Different speeds, lateral positions and axle loads were assessed.

c) Response measurements were made in May 1989 at various speeds and lateral positions.

d) Thirty new surface gauges were installed in October 1989. Different speeds, tyre inflation pressures and axle loads were considered.

E.2.2. Installation of Finnish strain gauges

VTT started to develop gauges for strain measurements in bituminous layers in the early 1980s. The measurement system consists of strain gauges glued to laboratory-made six-inch core samples which fit into a hole in the pavement with a tolerance of less than one millimeter. The samples were glued to the bituminous pavement. The gauges act as an integral part of the bituminous layer and have no strengthening effect because they are made up of the same material and the thickness of the glue is very thin. The gauges have no elastic component and it is thus also possible to monitor plastic deformation and relaxation (up to 30 mins).

The installation of the gauges demands meticulous work. The principle is presented in Figure E.4.

The same technology can be used for longitudinal and transversal gauges, at the bottom and on the surface (directly on the pavement) and at different depths in bituminous layers, as well as for vertical gauges. VTT used the same type of gauges with success in the common OECD Test at Nardo in Italy in 1984.

Figure E.4

PRINCIPLE OF VTT GAUGES

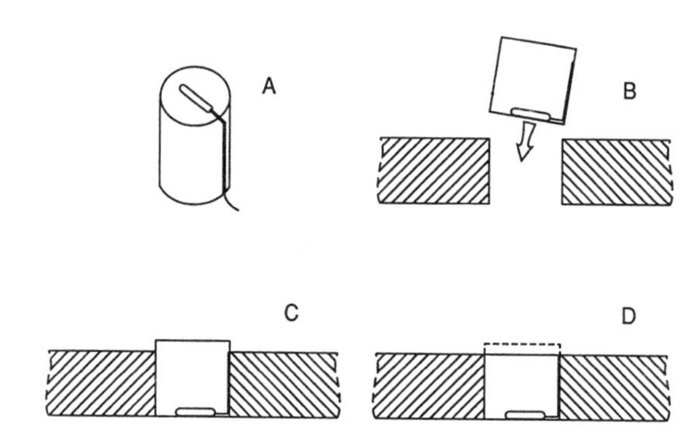

Figure E.5

TYPICAL SIGNAL FROM A LONGITUDINAL GAUGE

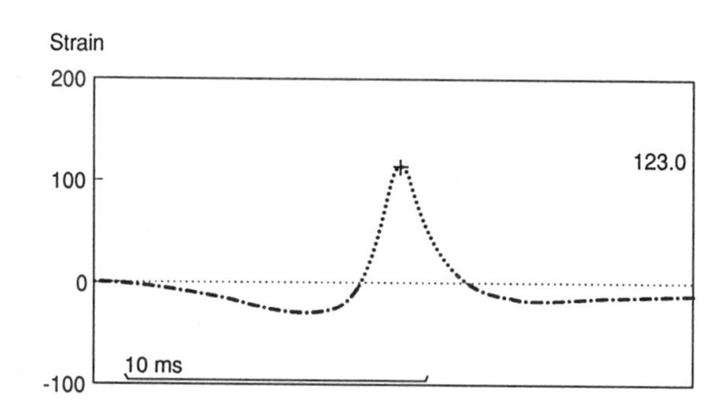

VTT installed four longitudinal and transversal gauges at the bottom of the bituminous layers in both structures I and II and four longitudinal and transversal gauges at the surface of each structure in the beginning of the test. Thirty longitudinal, diagonal and transversal gauges were fixed at the surface in October 1989. A sophisticated microcomputer based system collects, handles and stores the signals and calculates automatically the peak values as a function of lateral wheel positions.

E.2.3. Results

A typical signal from a longitudinal gauge is shown in Figure E.5. taken from a computer display. There is always compression first (negative values), then tension and thereafter compression. After the passage of an axle the strain level will be always about zero (no permanent deformation). The shape of the signal is not symmetric but relaxation can be found because of the viscoelastic nature of bituminous materials. In the case of transversal gauges there is no compression but only tension, and the tension decreases slowly to zero (relaxation). Because the temperature is only 10°C the relaxation is reasonably fast.

VTT had no experience on fatigue properties of the gauges before the Nantes test. Seven out of eight gauges survived up to the end of the structure I (270 000 loadings). during the overlay the observed further. Six from eight gauges in structure II worked up to the same time and three transversal at least to one million loadings. Corrosion was found in gauges; it was heard later naturally higher but they can be easily replaced by new gauges.

E.2.4. Concluding remarks

The data obtained has not yet been treated. More complete results will be published later.

REFERENCES

1. BOSCH, HG van den. Interpretation Dutch strain measurements, first phase. Project FORCE (draft). Delft University of Technology, Faculty of Civil Engineering, Road and Railroad Research Laboratory. Delft, November 1989.

2. GURP, CAPM van and ELZENAAR, J. Fatigue tests on asphalt mix. Project FORCE. Interim report. Delft University of Technology, Faculty of Civil Engineering, Road and Railroad Research Laboratory. Delft, September 1989.

Annex F

LIST OF PARTICIPANTS

R. ADDIS	TRRL, Old Wokingham Road, Crowthorne, Berks RG11 6AU, United Kingdom
R. ALKIO	Technical Research Center, Road and Traffic Laboratory (VTT), Lamponiehenkuja 2A, 02150 Espoo, Finland
Y. ANZAKI	Road Department, Public Works Research Institute, Asaki I-Banchi Toyosato-machi, J-Tsukuba-shi Ibaraki-ken 305, Japan
M. APPARICIO	CEDEX, Autovia de Colmenar Viejo, km 18.200, El Goloso, 28049 Madrid, Spain
H. AUGUSTIN	Bundesversuch- und Forschungsanstalt Arsenal, Postfach 8, 1031 Vienna, Austria
P. AUTRET	LCPC, Centre de Nantes, BP 19, 44340 Bouguenais, France
G. BATTIATO	RO.DE.CO. s.a.s., Via F. Rosselli 30, 27058 Voghera/Pv, Italy
A. de BOISSOUDY	LCPC, Centre de Nantes, BP 19, 44340 Bouguenais, France
H.G. VAN DEN BOSCH	Delft University of Technology, PO Box 5048, 2600 GA Delft, Netherlands
H. BREM	IVT-ETH, Hoenggerberg, 8093 ZURICH, Switzerland
P. BUCHELI	LAVOC-DGC-EPFL, 1015 Lausanne, Switzerland
H. BUSECK	Bundesanstalt für Strassenwesen, Brüderstrasse 53, Postfach 1001 50, 5060 Bergisch Gladbach, Germany
G. CAMOMILLA	Autostrade s.p.a., Via A. Bergamini 50, 00159 Rome, Italy
Ch. CHURILLA	Federal Highway Administration, HNR 20, 400 7th Street SW, Washington DC 20590, United States
F. COMASHI	RO.DE.CO s.a.s., Via F. Rosselli 30, 27058 Voghera/PV, Italy
D. CORNELIUS	TRRL, Old Wokingham Road, Crowthorne, Berks RG11 6AU, United Kingdom
W. CORTENRAAD	Dienst Weg, En Waterbouwkunde, Postbus 5044, 2600 GA Delft, Netherlands

J.F. COSTE	LCPC, 58 Boulevard Lefebvre, 75732 Paris Cedex 15, France
A.G. DUMONT	LAVOC-DGC-EPFL, 1015 Lausanne, Switzerland
B. ECKMAN	ESSO S.A.F. Centre de Recherches, BP 198, 76136 Mt St Aignan, France
M. FUCHS	Bundesversuchs- und Forschungsanstlat Arsenal, Postfach 8, 1031 Vienna, Austria
A. GARCIA FERNANDEZ	CEDEX, S. de Fisicas, c. Gral Varela 25, 28020 Madrid, Spain
J.M. GOLDEN	An Foras Forbartha, Pottery Road, Deansgrange, IR.Co. Dublin, Ireland
M.D. GORRIGAN	OECD - Road Transport Research Programme, 2 André Pascal, 75775 Paris Cedex 16, France
J.C. GRAMSAMMER	LCPC, Centre de Nantes, BP 19, 44340 Bouguenais, France
A.R. HALLIDAY	TRRL, Old Wokingham Road, Crowthorne, Berks RG11 6AU, United Kingdom
R. HENNY	Delft University of Technology, PO Box 5048, 2600 GA Delft, Netherlands
W. HERMANN	IVT-ETH, Hoenggerberg, 8093 ZURICH, Switzerland
J. HILPERT-HAUSER	IVT-ETH, Hoenggerberg, 8093 ZURICH, Switzerland
T. HOFBAUER	Bundesversuch- und Forschungsanstalt Arsenal, Postfach 8, 1031 Vienna, Austria
F. HOELLHUBER	Universitaet für Bodenkultur, Gregor Mendel-Strasse 33, 1180 Vienna, Austria
R. HOLSTER	Delft University of Technology, PO Box 5048, 2600 GA Delft, Netherlands
M. HORAT	IVT-ETH, Hoenggerberg, 8093 ZURICH, Switzerland
B. HORN	OECD - Road Transport Research Programme, 2 rue André Pascal, 75775 Paris Cedex 16, France

M. HUHTALA	Technical Research Center, Road and Traffic Laboratory (VTT), Lamponiehenkuja 2A, 02150 Espoo, Finland
H.M. JEPPESEN	Technical University of Denmark, Building 115, 2800 Lyngby, Denmark
P. KADAR	Australian Road Research Board, PO Box 156, Nunawading, Victoria 3131, Australia
E. KANKARE	Technical Research Center, Road and Traffic Laboratory (VTT), Lamponiehenkuja 2A, 02150 Espoo, Finland
W.J. KENIS	Federal Highway Administration, Turner-Fairbank Highway Research Center, 6300 Georgetown Pike, McLean, Va 22101, United States
J.P. KERZREHO	LCPC, Centre de Nantes, BP 19, 44340 Bouguenais, France
W. KNOBEL	Office fédéral des routes, Monbijoustrasse 40, 3003 Bern, Switzerland
A. LACLETA MUNOZ	Ministerio de Obras Publicas, P. Castellana 67, 28071 Madrid, Spain
R. LAMALLE	LCPC, Centre de Nantes, BP 19, 44340 Bouguenais, France
G. LEROY	LCPC, Centre de Nantes, BP 19, 44340 Bouguenais, France
J. LITZKA	Universitaet für Bodenkultur, Gregor Mendel-Strasse 33, 1180 Vienna, Austria
B. LORD	Federal Highway Administration, Turner-Fairbank Highway Research Center, 6300 Georgetown Pike, McLean, Va 22101, United States
M. LOUET	LCPC, Centre de Nantes, BP 19, 44340 Bouguenais, France
M. MALGARINI	Autostrade s.p.a., Via A. Gergamini 50, 00159 Rome, Italy
J. McLEAN	Australian Road Research Board, PO Box 156, Nunawading, Victoria 3131, Australia
J.P. NERFIE	LCPC, Centre de Nantes, BP 19, 44340 Bouguenais, France

N. VAN NESS — Federal Highway Administration, HHO-10, 400 7th Street SW, Washington DC 20590, United States

J. PIHLAJAMAKI — Technical Research Center, Road and Traffic Laboratory (VTT), Lamponiehenkuja 2A, 02150 Espoo, Finland

M. RATH — Bundesanstalt für Strassenwesen, Brüderstrasse 53, Postfach 1001 50, 5060 Bergisch Gladbach, Germany

R. ROBINSON — TRRL, Old Wokingham Road, Crowthorne, Berks RG11 6AU, United Kingdom

C. ROHR — LAVOC-DGC-EPFL, 1015 Lausanne, Switzerland

R. ROMERO — CEDEX, Autovia de Colmenar Viejo, km 18,200, El Goloso, 28049 Madrid, Spain

L.E.B. SAATHOF — Dienst Weg, En Waterbouwkunde, Postbus 5044, 2600 GA Delft, Netherlands

A. SALHI — LAVOC-DGC-EPFL, 1015 Lausanne, Switzerland

I. SCAZZIGA — IVT-ETH, Hoenggerberg, 8093 ZURICH, Switzerland

B. SIMONSSON — Swedish Road and Traffic Research Institute (VTT), 58101 Linkoping, Sweden

V. SUONIO + — Road and Waterways Administration (RWA), Opastinsilta 12 A, Postbox 33, 00521 Helsinki, Finland

G. SWEERE — Delft University of Technology, PO Box 5048, 2600 GA Delft, Netherlands

J. TAMARI RODRIGUEZ — CEDEX, Autovia de Colmenar Viejo, km 18.200, El Goloso, 28049 Madrid, Spain

R. ULLIDTZ — 13 bd Mal Foch, 06600 Antibes, France

J. VERSTRAETEN — CRR, 42 bd de la Woluwe, 1200 Brussels, Belgium

A. VINUALES PALACIOS — CEDEX, Autovia de Colmenar Viejo, km 18.200, El Goloso, 28049 Madrid, Spain

C. VOGELZANG	Delft University of Technology, PO Box 5048, 2600 GA Delft, Netherlands
L.J. WERRING	Commission of the European Communities, 34 rue Belliard, 1040 Brussels, Belgium
R.A. WITHMARSH	TRRL, Old Wokingham Road, Crowthorne, Berks RG11 6AU, United Kingdom

ALSO AVAILABLE

Road Transport Research

Curtailing Usage of De-icing Agents in Winter Maintenance (1989)
(77 89 04 1) ISBN 92-64-13280-5 FF110 £13.50 US$24.00 DM46

Durability of Concrete Road Bridges (1989)
(77 89 01 1) ISBN 92-64-13199-X FF110 £13.50 US$23.50 DM46

Heavy Trucks, Climate and Pavement Damage (1988)
(77 88 04 1) ISBN 92-64-13150-7 FF140 £16.50 US$31.00 DM60

Pavement Management Systems (1987)
(77 87 01 1) ISBN 92-64-12907-3 FF80 £8.00 US$16.00 DM36

Road Monitoring for Maintenance Management. Volume 1 – Manual for Developing Countries. Volume 2 – Damage Catalogue for Developing Countries. (1990)
(77 89 05 1) ISBN 92-64-13309-7 FF140 £16.00 US$22.95 DM50

Prices charged at the OECD Bookshop.

THE OECD CATALOGUE OF PUBLICATIONS and supplements will be sent free of charge on request addressed either to OECD Publications Service, 2, rue André-Pascal, 75775 PARIS CEDEX 16, France, or to the OECD Distributor in your country.

WHERE TO OBTAIN OECD PUBLICATIONS – OÙ OBTENIR LES PUBLICATIONS DE L'OCDE

Argentina – Argentine
CARLOS HIRSCH S.R.L.
Galería Güemes, Florida 165, 4° Piso
1333 Buenos Aires Tel. 30.7122, 331.1787 y 331.2391
Telegram: Hirsch-Baires
Telex: 21112 UAPE-AR. Ref. s/2901
Telefax:(1)331-1787

Australia – Australie
D.A. Book (Aust.) Pty. Ltd.
648 Whitehorse Road, P.O.B 163
Mitcham, Victoria 3132 Tel. (03)873.4411
Telex: AA37911 DA BOOK
Telefax: (03)873.5679

Austria – Autriche
OECD Publications and Information Centre
Schedestrasse 7
DW-5300 Bonn 1 (Germany) Tel. (49.228)21.60.45
Telefax: (49.228)26.11.04

Gerold & Co.
Graben 31
Wien I Tel. (0222)533.50.14

Belgium – Belgique
Jean De Lannoy
Avenue du Roi 202
B-1060 Bruxelles Tel. (02)538.51.69/538.08.41
Telex: 63220 Telefax: (02) 538.08.41

Canada
Renouf Publishing Company Ltd.
1294 Algoma Road
Ottawa, ON K1B 3W8 Tel. (613)741.4333
Telex: 053-4783 Telefax: (613)741.5439
Stores:
61 Sparks Street
Ottawa, ON K1P 5R1 Tel. (613)238.8985
211 Yonge Street
Toronto, ON M5B 1M4 Tel. (416)363.3171

Federal Publications
165 University Avenue
Toronto, ON M5H 3B8 Tel. (416)581.1552
Telefax: (416)581.1743
Les Publications Fédérales
1185 rue de l'Université
Montréal, PQ H3B 3A7 Tel.(514)954-1633

Les Éditions La Liberté Inc.
3020 Chemin Sainte-Foy
Sainte-Foy, PQ G1X 3V6 Tel. (418)658.3763
Telefax: (418)658.3763

Denmark – Danemark
Munksgaard Export and Subscription Service
35, Nørre Søgade, P.O. Box 2148
DK-1016 København K Tel. (45 33)12.85.70
Telex: 19431 MUNKS DK Telefax: (45 33)12.93.87

Finland – Finlande
Akateeminen Kirjakauppa
Keskuskatu 1, P.O. Box 128
00100 Helsinki Tel. (358 0)12141
Telex: 125080 Telefax: (358 0)121.4441

France
OECD/OCDE
Mail Orders/Commandes par correspondance:
2, rue André-Pascal
75775 Paris Cédex 16 Tel. (33-1)45.24.82.00
Bookshop/Librairie:
33, rue Octave-Feuillet
75016 Paris Tel. (33-1)45.24.81.67
(33-1)45.24.81.81
Telex: 620 160 OCDE
Telefax: (33-1)45.24.85.00 (33-1)45.24.81.76

Librairie de l'Université
12a, rue Nazareth
13100 Aix-en-Provence Tel. 42.26.18.08
Telefax : 42.26.63.26

Germany – Allemagne
OECD Publications and Information Centre
Schedestrasse 7
DW-5300 Bonn 1 Tel. (0228)21.60.45
Telefax: (0228)26.11.04

Greece – Grèce
Librairie Kauffmann
28 rue du Stade
105 64 Athens Tel. 322.21.60
Telex: 218187 LIKA Gr

Hong Kong
Swindon Book Co. Ltd.
13 - 15 Lock Road
Kowloon, Hong Kong Tel. 366.80.31
Telex: 50 441 SWIN HX Telefax: 739.49.75

Iceland – Islande
Mál Mog Menning
Laugavegi 18, Pósthólf 392
121 Reykjavik Tel. 15199/24240

India – Inde
Oxford Book and Stationery Co.
Scindia House
New Delhi 110001 Tel. 331.5896/5308
Telex: 31 61990 AM IN
Telefax: (11)332.5993
17 Park Street
Calcutta 700016 Tel. 240832

Indonesia – Indonésie
Pdii-Lipi
P.O. Box 269/JKSMG/88
Jakarta 12790 Tel. 583467
Telex: 62 875

Ireland – Irlande
TDC Publishers – Library Suppliers
12 North Frederick Street
Dublin 1 Tel. 744835/749677
Telex: 33530 TDCP EI Telefax: 748416

Italy – Italie
Libreria Commissionaria Sansoni
Via Benedetto Fortini, 120/10
Casella Post. 552
50125 Firenze Tel. (055)64.54.15
Telex: 570466 Telefax: (055)64.12.57
Via Bartolini 29
20155 Milano Tel. 36.50.83
La diffusione delle pubblicazioni OCSE viene assicurata dalle principali librerie ed anche da:

Editrice e Libreria Herder
Piazza Montecitorio 120
00186 Roma Tel. 679.46.28
Telex: NATEL I 621427

Libreria Hoepli
Via Hoepli 5
20121 Milano Tel. 86.54.46
Telex: 31.33.95 Telefax: (02)805.28.86

Libreria Scientifica
Dott. Lucio de Biasio 'Aeiou'
Via Meravigli 16
20123 Milano Tel. 805.68.98
Telefax: 800175

Japan – Japon
OECD Publications and Information Centre
Landic Akasaka Building
2-3-4 Akasaka, Minato-ku
Tokyo 107 Tel. (81.3)3586.2016
Telefax: (81.3)3584.7929

Korea – Corée
Kyobo Book Centre Co. Ltd.
P.O. Box 1658, Kwang Hwa Moon
Seoul Tel. (REP)730.78.91
Telefax: 735.0030

Malaysia/Singapore – Malaisie/Singapour
Co-operative Bookshop Ltd.
University of Malaya
P.O. Box 1127, Jalan Pantai Baru
59700 Kuala Lumpur
Malaysia Tel. 756.5000/756.5425
Telefax: 757.3661

Information Publications Pte. Ltd.
Pei-Fu Industrial Building
24 New Industrial Road No. 02-06
Singapore 1953 Tel. 283.1786/283.1798
Telefax: 284.8875

Netherlands – Pays-Bas
SDU Uitgeverij
Christoffel Plantijnstraat 2
Postbus 20014
2500 EA's-Gravenhage Tel. (070 3)78.99.11
Voor bestellingen: Tel. (070 3)78.98.80
Telex: 32486 stdru Telefax: (070 3)47.63.51

New Zealand – Nouvelle-Zélande
GP Publications Ltd.
Customer Services
33 The Esplanade - P.O. Box 38-900
Petone, Wellington
Tel. (04)685-555 Telefax: (04)685-333

Norway – Norvège
Narvesen Info Center - NIC
Bertrand Narvesens vei 2
P.O. Box 6125 Etterstad
0602 Oslo 6 Tel. (02)57.33.00
Telex: 79668 NIC N Telefax: (02)68.19.01

Pakistan
Mirza Book Agency
65 Shahrah Quaid-E-Azam
Lahore 3 Tel. 66839
Telex: 44886 UBL PK. Attn: MIRZA BK

Portugal
Livraria Portugal
Rua do Carmo 70-74
Apart. 2681
1117 Lisboa Codex Tel.: 347.49.82/3/4/5
Telefax: (01) 347.02.64

Singapore/Malaysia – Singapour/Malaisie
See Malaysia/Singapore" – Voir «Malaisie/Singapour»

Spain – Espagne
Mundi-Prensa Libros S.A.
Castelló 37, Apartado 1223
Madrid 28001 Tel. (91) 431.33.99
Telex: 49370 MPLI Telefax: 575.39.98

Libreria Internacional AEDOS
Consejo de Ciento 391
08009-Barcelona Tel. (93) 301.86.15
Telefax: (93) 317.01.41

Sri Lanka
Centre for Policy Research
c/o Mercantile Credit Ltd.
55, Janadhipathi Mawatha
Colombo 1 Tel. 438471-9, 440346
Telex: 21138 VAVALEX CE Telefax: 94.1.448900

Sweden – Suède
Fritzes Fackboksföretaget
Box 16356, S 103 27 STH
Regeringsgatan 12
DS Stockholm Tel. (08)23.89.00
Telex: 12387 Telefax: (08)20.50.21

Subscription Agency/Abonnements:
Wennergren-Williams AB
Nordenflychtsvagen 74
Box 30004
104 25 Stockholm Tel. (08)13.67.00
Telex: 19937 Telefax: (08)618.62.36

Switzerland – Suisse
OECD Publications and Information Centre
Schedestrasse 7
DW-5300 Bonn 1 (Germany) Tel. (49.228)21.60.45
Telefax: (49.228)26.11.04

Librairie Payot
6 rue Grenus
1211 Genève 11 Tel. (022)731.89.50
Telex: 28356
Subscription Agency – Service des Abonnements
Naville S.A.
7, rue Lévrier
1201 Genève Tél.: (022) 732.24.00
Telefax: (022) 738.48.03

Maditec S.A.
Chemin des Palettes 4
1020 Renens/Lausanne Tel. (021)635.08.65
Telefax: (021)635.07.80

United Nations Bookshop/Librairie des Nations-Unies
Palais des Nations
1211 Genève 10 Tel. (022)734.60.11 (ext. 48.72)
Telex: 289696 (Attn: Sales) Telefax: (022)733.98.79

Taiwan – Formose
Good Faith Worldwide Int'l. Co. Ltd.
9th Floor, No. 118, Sec. 2
Chung Hsiao E. Road
Taipei Tel. 391.7396/391.7397
Telefax: (02) 394.9176

Thailand – Thaïlande
Suksit Siam Co. Ltd.
1715 Rama IV Road, Samyan
Bangkok 5 Tel. 251.1630

Turkey – Turquie
Kültur Yayinlari Is-Türk Ltd. Sti.
Atatürk Bulvari No. 191/Kat. 21
Kavaklidere/Ankara Tel. 25.07.60
Dolmabahce Cad. No. 29
Besiktas/Istanbul Tel. 160.71.88
Telex: 43482B

United Kingdom – Royaume-Uni
HMSO
Gen. enquiries Tel. (071) 873 0011
Postal orders only:
P.O. Box 276, London SW8 5DT
Personal Callers HMSO Bookshop
49 High Holborn, London WC1V 6HB
Telex: 297138 Telefax: 071 873 8463
Branches at: Belfast, Birmingham, Bristol, Edinburgh, Manchester

United States – États-Unis
OECD Publications and Information Centre
2001 L Street N.W., Suite 700
Washington, D.C. 20036-4095 Tel. (202)785.6323
Telefax: (202)785.0350

Venezuela
Libreria del Este
Avda F. Miranda 52, Aptdo. 60337
Edificio Galipán
Caracas 106 Tel. 951.1705/951.2307/951.1297
Telegram: Libreste Caracas

Yugoslavia – Yougoslavie
Jugoslovenska Knjiga
Knez Mihajlova 2, P.O. Box 36
Beograd Tel.: (011)621.992
Telex: 12466 jk bgd Telefax: (011)625.970

Orders and inquiries from countries where Distributors have not yet been appointed should be sent to: OECD Publications Service, 2 rue André-Pascal, 75775 Paris Cedex 16, France.

Les commandes provenant de pays où l'OCDE n'a pas encore désigné de distributeur devraient être adressées à : OCDE, Service des Publications, 2, rue André-Pascal, 75775 Paris Cédex 16, France.

75490-1/91

OECD PUBLICATIONS, 2 rue André-Pascal, 75775 PARIS CEDEX 16
PRINTED IN FRANCE
(77 91 01 1) ISBN 92-64-13469-7 – No. 45459 1991